REAL ANALYSIS

– PART 2 –

Prof. Dr. Roselin Antony
Professor (Mathematics)
Department of Mathematics and Statistics
Faculty of Sciences
Sam Higginbottom University of
Agriculture, Technology and Sciences
Prayagraj (Allahabad), Uttar Pradesh, India

SCIENTIFIC PUBLISHERS

Published by

SCIENTIFIC PUBLISHERS (INDIA)
5 A, New Pali Road, P.O. Box 91
Jodhpur 342 001 (India)
E-mail: info@scientificpub.com
Website: www.scientificpubonline.com

ISBN : 978-93-89412-92-5 [H/B] :
eISBN 978-93-89412-94-9 (VOL 2)

ISBN: 978-93-89412-95-6 HB SET

ISBN : 978-93-89412-89-5 HB VOL 1

Visit the Scientific Publishers (India) website at
http://www.scientificpubonline.com
Printed in India

FOREWORD

Mathematics is a life-long love and it is both complex & beautiful. The complexity of mathematics is a reflection of the complexity of the relationships that exist in the universe. The beauty of mathematics is a reflection of the ability of the human mind to identify them in a unit-economical way. This book is a nice and recommended read for every mathematics lovers. The author's writing style is so light and clear and these makes all the content understandable without a heavy background of mathematics. This book is definitely not boring and it can be a great introduction to many students who are interested in Real Analysis of mathematics. I am pretty sure that they can really enjoy it.

This is part two of a two-volume book series on Real Analysis. This second part of the Real Analysis book introduces the basic set theory, the measurable functions, and related theorems earlier in the text, and contains many new and easier exercises. This book totally has eight units with detailed proofs of theorems and covers good number of examples with clear steps. Where part one of Real Analysis helped to establish the basics and form the reader's understanding, part two of Real Analysis expands that knowledge in a way that demands full immersion into the text.

Anyway, I think every calculus student should read this book more than once. This book is perfectly written and Calculus students would love it. This book is about all Real Analysis and it is perfectly written for all undergraduate, graduate and research students. I hope that this book will be more helpful for teachers, students and researchers of mathematics in India and worldwide. It is very understandable and enjoyable. Rereading this book really helps everyone understand Real Analysis in a better way and enrich their knowledge about Real Analysis.

I appreciate the author for her hard work and effort to make this book a successful one.

Most Rev. (Prof. Dr.) RAJENDRA B. LAL

Vice-Chancellor

Sam Higginbottom University of Agriculture, Technology and Sciences (SHUATS)

Prayagraj (Allahabad), UP, India

Date: 19th April, 2022

PREFACE

Advanced Calculus or Introductory Real Analysis courses are taken by a variety of students, serve a number of purposes, and are written at various levels of sophistication. The purposes of this book are to present familiar concepts from calculus at a more rigorous level, to provide students with a level of mathematical sophistication that will prepare them for graduate work in mathematical analysis, or for graduate work in several applied fields such as engineering or economics, and also to develop many of the topics that the authors feel all students of mathematics should know.

This book has been meticulously tailored to motivate students and inspire readers to explore the material, and to continue exploring even after they have finished the book. The definitions, theorems, and proofs contained within are presented with mathematical rigor, but conveyed in an accessible manner and with language and motivation meant for all levels of students.

Considering the role of this book as an important text of the subject, the proofs are considerably given in detailed manner. This may make some of the proofs longer than expected, since the essentials of the subject are a knowledge of the basic results and an ability to apply them.

Chapter 1 begins with the basic set theory, which helps the students to recall whatever they have studied in their undergraduate course. Chapter 2 concerned with the measurable functions and convergence theorems whereas Chapter 3 deals with the signed measures and Radon Nikodym theorem. Chapter 4 covers the concepts of functional analysis. Chapter 5 addresses L^p spaces and some important inequalities. Chapter 6 covers fundamental theorems of vector calculus. Chapter 7 describes Radon measures and deals with the Riesz representation theorem and Chapter 8 is devoted to elements of Fourier analysis and it discusses about Fourier series.

I am pleased to present this book *Real Analysis, Part 2* to Undergraduate, Postgraduate and Doctoral students of science, engineering and business discipline in University and Colleges. The topics have been dealt in a detailed manner, supported by illustrations for better comprehension. In many aspects, the topics and structure of this book will be highly meritorious and unique. This book will contribute significantly to academic teaching, scientific research, practical works and for competitive exams preparation.

This Real Analysis (Part 2) book is intended to provide students, professors, school teachers, technicians, scientists and engineers with a readily available reference to the essential mathematics formulae, tables and general information needed during their studies and work situation.

I have to start by thanking my awesome husband Prof. Dr. Antony Joseph Raj, Dean of College of Forestry in Sam Higginbottom University of Agriculture, Technology and Sciences (SHUATS), Prayragraj, India. He was so important to this book getting done from reading early drafts to giving me advice on the cover and encouragement, so I could work continuously on this book. Thank you so much, Dear! I also greatly appreciate and thank my daughters Rithika Marlene Antony and Runisha Smiline Antony for their patience and tolerance and always making me cheer up, to make both the parts of my Real Analysis books a successful one. At this moment, I would also like to remember my parents, whose prayers and blessings are always with me and who would have been happy to see both the parts of my Real Analysis books a successful one. Critical evaluation and suggestions for the improvement of the book are welcome and will be gratefully acknowledged.

19th April, 2022 **Prof. Dr. Roselin Antony**

For my Husband
Prof. Dr. Antony Joseph Raj

and

My Daughters
Rithika Marlene Antony
&
Runisha Smiline Antony

Real Analysis (Part - 2)

Contents

Unit	
1	**FAMILIES OF SETS**

1.1 Introduction

In this chapter, we will recall a few definitions and results of sets from the undergraduate mathematics.

1.2 Notations and Preliminaries

Let X be a given set. We assume that all the sets are the subsets of X.

For any set A, the complement of A, denoted by A^c, is the set of points not in A. It is written as

$$A^c = \{x \in A : x \notin A\}.$$

We denote the complement of B with respect to A by

$$A \setminus B = A \cap B^c.$$

The set of all subsets of X is the power set of X, and is denoted by $P(X)$.

The set $A\Delta B$ is called the symmetric difference of A and B and is the set of points that are in one of the sets but not in the other. Therefore,

$$A\Delta B = (A \setminus B) \cup (B \setminus A).$$

If I is an index set, a collection of subsets $\{A_i\}_{i \in I}$ is disjoint, if $A_i \cap A_j = \Phi$, whenever $i \neq j$.

A subset S of P(X) is said to be;

Closed under finite intersections if, whenever $\{A_1, A_2, \ldots\ldots, A_n\}$ is a finite collection of elements of S, then

$$\bigcap_{j=1}^{n} A_j \in S.$$

Closed under finite unions if, whenever $\{A_1, A_2, \ldots\ldots, A_n\}$ is a finite collection of elements of S, then

$$\bigcup_{j=1}^{n} A_j \in S.$$

Closed under countable intersections if, whenever (A_n) is a sequence of elements of S, then

$$\bigcap_{j=1}^{\infty} A_j \in S.$$

Closed under countable unions if, whenever (A_n) is a sequence of elements of S, then

$$\bigcup_{j=1}^{\infty} A_j \in S.$$

We say a function $f: R \to R$ is increasing if $x < y$ implies $f(x) \le f(y)$ and f is strictly increasing if $x < y$ implies $f(x) < f(y)$. We also say that $f: R \to R$ is decreasing if $x > y$ implies $f(x) \ge f(y)$ and f is strictly decreasing if $x > y$ implies $f(x) > f(y)$. A function is monotone if f is either increasing or decreasing.

Given a sequence $\{A_n\}$ of real numbers, then

$$\limsup_{n\to\infty} A_n = \inf_n \sup_{m\ge n} A_m = \bigcap_{n=1}^{\infty} \bigcup_{m=n}^{\infty} A_m,$$

$$\liminf_{n\to\infty} A_n = \sup_n \inf_{m\ge n} A_m = \bigcup_{n=1}^{\infty} \bigcap_{m=n}^{\infty} A_m.$$

1.3 Algebras and σ-algebras

Definition 1.3.1

Let X be a given set. An *algebra* is a collection $\mathcal{A}$ of subsets of X such that

i) $\phi \in \mathcal{A}$ and $X \in \mathcal{A}$

ii) if $A \in \mathcal{A}$, then $A^c \in \mathcal{A}$

iii) if $A_1, \ldots\ldots, A_n \in \mathcal{A}$, then $\bigcup_{i=1}^{n} A_i$ and $\bigcap_{i=1}^{n} A_i$ are in $\mathcal{A}$.

In addition, $\mathcal{A}$ is a σ-algebra (or a σ-field) if

iv) whenever $A_1, A_2, \ldots\ldots, A_n$ are in $\mathcal{A}$, then $\bigcup_{i=1}^{\infty} A_i$ and $\bigcap_{i=1}^{\infty} A_i$ are in $\mathcal{A}$.

The pair $(X, \mathcal{A})$ is called a *measurable space*. A set A is *measurable* if $A \in \mathcal{A}$.

Examples 1.3.2

(1) Let X be any nonempty set. Then, the power set of X, that is, $P(X)$ is the special σ-algebra on X. Also, $A=\{\phi, X\}$ is also a special σ-algebra on X.

(2) Let $X = \mathbb{R}$ and let $\mathcal{A} = \{A \subset \mathbb{R}: A \text{ is countable or } A^c \text{ is countable}\}$.

(3) Let $X = [0, 1]$. Then, $\mathcal{A} = \left\{\phi, X, \left[0, \frac{1}{2}\right], \left(\frac{1}{2}, 1\right]\right\}$ is a σ-algebra on X.

(4) Let $X = \{1, 2, 3\}$. Then, $\mathcal{A} = \{X, \phi, \{1\}, \{2,3\}\}$ is a σ-algebra.

Note 1.3.3

Let $X = \mathbb{R}$ and let $\mathcal{A}$ be a σ-algebra on X. If (A_n) is a sequence of sets in $\mathcal{A}$, then $\liminf_{n\to\infty} A_n \in \mathcal{A}$.

If S is any collection of subsets of X, then by taking the intersection of all σ-algebras containing S, we obtain the smallest σ-algebra containing S. Such a σ-algebra is said to be *generated by S* and denoted by $\sigma(S)$. It is clear that if S is a σ-algebra, then $\sigma(S) = S$.

Definition 1.3.4

The smallest σ-algebra containing all open subsets of $\mathbb{R}$ is called the Borel σ-algebra of $\mathbb{R}$ and is denoted by $\mathcal{B}(\mathbb{R})$. Elements of this σ-algebra are called Borel sets.

1.4 Measures

Definition 1.4.1

Let X be any set and $\mathcal{A}$ be a σ-algebra on X. A measure on $(X, \mathcal{A})$ is a function $\mu : \mathcal{A} \to [0, \infty]$ such that

1) $\mu(\varphi)=0$

2) if $A_i \in \mathcal{A}$, for each $i = 1, 2, 3,\ldots\ldots$, are pairwise disjoint, that is, $A_i \in \mathcal{A}$, for each $i = 1, 2, 3,\ldots\ldots$, and $A_i \cap A_j = \phi$ for every $i \neq j$, then

$$\mu\left(\bigcup_{i=1}^{\infty} A_i\right) = \sum_{i=1}^{\infty} A_i \ .$$

In the above definition, property (2) is known as the countable additivity property of the measure μ. Here, μ is finitely additive, if property (2) is replaced by $\mu\left(\bigcup_{i=1}^{n} A_i\right) = \sum_{i=1}^{n} A_i$ for every finite sequence A_1, A_2, ….., A_n of pairwise disjoint sets in $\mathcal{A}$.

Definition 1.4.2

A *measurable space* is a pair (X, $\mathcal{A}$), where X is a set and $\mathcal{A}$ is a σ-algebra on X. The elements of the σ-algebra $\mathcal{A}$ are called *measurable sets*.

Note 1.4.3

If a measure is countably additive, then it must also be *finitely additive*.

Definition 1.4.4

A measure space is a *triple* (X, $\mathcal{A}$, μ), where X is a set, $\mathcal{A}$ a σ-algebra in X and μ a measure on $\mathcal{A}$.

Note 1.4.5

Let (X, $\mathcal{A}$, μ) be a measure space. If $\mu(X) = 1$, then (X, $\mathcal{A}$, μ) is called a *probability space* and μ is called a *probability measure*.

Examples 1.4.6

1) Let X be a non-empty set and $\mathcal{A} = P(X)$. Define υ: $\mathcal{A} \to [0,\infty]$ by

$$\nu(A) = \begin{cases} n, & \text{if } A \text{ has } n \text{ elements} \\ \infty, & \text{otherwise} \end{cases}$$

Then, υ is a measure on X called the *counting measure*.

2) Let (X, $\mathcal{A}$) be a measurable space. Choose and fix $x \in X$. Define $\mu_x : \mathcal{A} \to [0,\infty]$ by

$$\mu_x(A) = \begin{cases} 1, & \text{if } x \in A \\ 0, & \text{otherwise} \end{cases}$$

Then, μ_x is a measure on X called the *unit point mass* at x.

Theorem 1.4.7

Let $(X, \mathcal{A}, \mu)$ be a measure space. Then the following statements hold:

1) If A, B $\in \mathcal{A}$ and $A \subseteq B$, then $\mu(A) \leq \mu(B)$.

2) If (A_n) is a sequence in $\mathcal{A}$, then

$$\mu\left(\bigcup_{n=1}^{\infty} A_n\right) \leq \sum_{n=1}^{\infty} \mu(A_n).$$

3) If (A_n) is a sequence in $\mathcal{A}$ such that $A_n \subseteq A_{n+1}$, for each $n \in \mathbb{N}$, then

$$\mu\left(\bigcup_{n=1}^{\infty} A_n\right) = \lim_{n\to\infty} \mu(A_n).$$

4) If (A_n) is a sequence in $\mathcal{A}$ such that $A_n \supseteq A_{n+1}$, for each $n \in \mathbb{N}$ and $\mu(A_1) < \infty$, then

$$\mu\left(\bigcap_{n=1}^{\infty} A_n\right) = \lim_{n\to\infty} \mu(A_n).$$

Proof

1) Take $B = A \cup (B - A)$, which is a disjoint union. Since μ is finitely additive, we have that

$$\mu(B) = \mu(A) + \mu(B - A) \geq \mu(A).$$

2) Let $B_1 = A_1$, $B_2 = A_2 - A_1$, $B_3 = A_3 - (A_1 \cup A_2), B_4 = A_4 - (A_1 \cup A_2 \cup A_3)$ and in general, we have

$$B_n = A_n - \left(\bigcup_{i=1}^{n-1} A_i\right),$$ for each natural number $n > 1$. Then,

$$B_n = \bigcap_{i=1}^{n-1} (A_n - A_i) = A_n \bigcap_{i=1}^{n-1} A_i^c.$$

Therefore, for each $n = 1, 2, 3, \ldots\ldots$, we have that $B_n \in \mathcal{A}$.

Clearly, $B_n \subseteq A_n$, for each $n = 1, 2, 3, \ldots\ldots$

Let m and k be integers such that $m < k$.

Then, $B_m \subset A_m$ and so

$$B_m \cap B_k \subset A_m \cap B_k = A_m \cap \left(A_k \bigcap_{i=1}^{k-1} A_i^c\right).$$

$$= A_m \cap A_k \cap ..... \cap A_m^c \cap .....$$

$$= A_m \cap A_m^c \cap A_k \cap ..... \cap ..... = \phi \cap A_k \cap ..... \cap ..... = \phi .$$

That is, $B_i \underset{i \neq j}{\cap} B_j = \varphi$.

Claim: $\overset{\infty}{\underset{n=1}{\cup}} A_n = \overset{\infty}{\underset{n=1}{\cup}} B_n$.

Since $B_n \subseteq A_n$, for each n = 1, 2, 3, ….., we have that $\overset{\infty}{\underset{n=1}{\cup}} B_n \subseteq \overset{\infty}{\underset{n=1}{\cup}} A_n$.

Let $x \in \overset{\infty}{\underset{n=1}{\cup}} A_n$.

Then, $x \in A_n$ for some n.

Let k be the smallest integer such that $x \in A_k$.

Then $x \in A_k$ and $x \notin A_j$, for each $j = 1, 2, 3, ..., k - 1$.

Therefore, $x \in A_j^c$, for each $j = 1, 2, 3, ..., k - 1$.

That is, $x \in B_k = A_k \overset{k-1}{\underset{j=1}{\cap}} A_j^c$, whenever $x \in \overset{\infty}{\underset{n=1}{\cup}} B_n$, which proves the claim.

Therefore, $\mu\left(\overset{\infty}{\underset{n=1}{\cup}} A_n\right) = \mu\left(\overset{\infty}{\underset{n=1}{\cup}} B_n\right) = \sum_{n=1}^{\infty} \mu(B_n) \leq \sum_{n=1}^{\infty} \mu(A_n)$, by part (1).

3) Let $B_1 = A_1$ and $B_n = A_n - A_{n-1}$ for all $n > 1$.

Then, $B_i \underset{i \neq j}{\cap} B_j = \varphi$, $A_k = \overset{k}{\underset{n=1}{\cup}} B_n$ and $\overset{\infty}{\underset{n=1}{\cup}} A_n = \overset{\infty}{\underset{n=1}{\cup}} B_n$.

Therefore, $\mu\left(\overset{\infty}{\underset{n=1}{\cup}} A_n\right) = \mu\left(\overset{\infty}{\underset{n=1}{\cup}} B_n\right) = \sum_{n=1}^{\infty} \mu(B_n) = \lim_{k\to\infty} \sum_{n=1}^{k} \mu(B_n) = \lim_{k\to\infty} \mu(A_k)$.

4) Let $A = \overset{\infty}{\underset{n=1}{\cap}} A_n$.

Then, $A_1 - A = A_1 - \overset{\infty}{\underset{n=1}{\cap}} A_n = \bigcup_{n=1}^{\infty} (A_1 - A_n)$, and

$A_1 - A_n \subset A_1 - A_{n+1}$, for each natural number n.

Therefore, by part (3), we have

$$\mu(A_1 - A) = \mu\left(\bigcup_{n=1}^{\infty} (A_1 - A_n)\right) = \lim_{n\to\infty} \mu(A_1 - A_n). \qquad .... (1.4.7.1)$$

Since $A \subset A_1$ and $\mu(A_1) < \infty$, we have that $\mu(A) < \infty$.

Also, since $A_n \subset A_1$, for every natural number *n*, it follows that $\mu(A_n) < \infty$, for each *n*.

Writing A_1 as a disjoint union $A_1 = (A_1 - A) \cup A$, we have that

$$\mu(A_1) = \mu(A_1 - A) + \mu(A).$$

$$\Rightarrow \mu(A_1 - A) = \mu(A_1) - \mu(A). \qquad \text{..........} (1.4.7.2)$$

Similarly, by expressing A_1 as $A_1 = (A_1 - A_n) \cup A_n$, we get that

$$\mu(A_1 - A_n) = \mu(A_1) - \mu(A_n). \qquad \text{..........} (1.4.7.3)$$

From equations (1.4.7.1), (1.4.7.2) and (1.4.7.3), we get that

$$\mu(A_1) - \mu(A) = \lim_{n\to\infty}[\mu(A_1) - \mu(A_n)] = \mu(A_1) - \lim_{n\to\infty}\mu(A_n).$$

Since $\mu(A_1) < \infty$, we have that

$$\mu(A) = \lim_{n\to\infty}\mu(A_n),$$

That is, $\mu(\bigcap_{n=1}^{\infty} A_n) = \lim_{n\to\infty}\mu(A_n)$.

Hence proved.

Definition 1.4.5

Let $(X, \mathcal{A}, \mu)$ be a measure space. The measure μ is said to be

1) *finite*, if $\mu(X) < \infty$, and
2) *σ-finite*, if there is a sequence (X_n) of sets in $\mathcal{A}$ with $\mu(X_n) < \infty$, for each *n* such that $X = \bigcup_{n=1}^{\infty} X_n$.

Definition 1.4.6

If μ is a finite measure, then $(X, \mathcal{A}, \mu)$ is called a *finite measure space*, and similarly, if μ is a σ-finite measure, then $(X, \mathcal{A}, \mu)$ is called a *σ-finite measure space*.

Definition 1.4.7

Let $(X, \mathcal{A}, \mu)$ be a measure space. A subset $A \subset X$ is a *null set* if there exists a set $B \in \mathcal{A}$ with $A \subset B$ and $\mu(B) = 0$. If $\mathcal{A}$ contains all the null sets, then

$(X, \mathcal{A}, \mu)$ is said to be a *complete measure space*. The completion of $\mathcal{A}$ is the smallest σ-algebra $\overline{\mathcal{A}}$ containing such that $(X, \overline{\mathcal{A}}, \mu)$ is complete.

1.5 Outer Measures

Definition 1.5.1

Let X be a set. An outer measure on X is a function $\mu^* : \mathcal{P}(X) \to [0, \infty]$ satisfying the following properties;

1) $\mu^*(\varphi) = 0$,
2) If $A \subseteq B$, then $\mu^*(A) \le \mu^*(B)$.
3) For any sequence (A_n) of subsets of X, $\mu^*\left(\bigcup_{n=1}^{\infty} A_n\right) \le \sum_{n=1}^{\infty} \mu^*(A_n)$.

In the above definition, property (2) is referred to as monotonicity, and property (3) is countable subadditivity.

Examples 1.5.2

1) Let X be a set. Define μ^* on $\mathcal{P}$(X) by

$$\mu^*(A) = \begin{cases} 1 & \text{if } A \ne \phi \\ 0 & \text{if } A = \phi \end{cases}$$

Then, μ^* is an outer measure on X.

2) Let X be an uncountable set. Define μ^* on $\mathcal{P}$(X) by

$$\mu^* = \begin{cases} 0 & \text{if } A \text{ is countable} \\ 1 & \text{if } A \text{ is uncountable} \end{cases}$$

Then, μ^* is an outer measure on X.

Definition 1.5.3

Let X be a set and μ^* an outer measure on X. A subset E of X is said to be μ^*-measurable if, for every subset A of X, we have

$$\mu^*(A) = \mu^*(A \cap E) + \mu^*(A \cap E^c).$$

Note 1.5.4

1) Since $A = (A \cap E) \cup (A \cap E^c)$ and μ^* is subadditive, we always have that $\mu^*(A) \le \mu^*(A \cap E) + \mu^*(A \cap E^c)$.

Therefore, a subset E of X is μ^*-measurable if, for every subset A of X,

$$\mu^*(A) \geq \mu^*(A \cap E) + \mu^*(A \cap E^c).$$

2) Replacing E by E^c in the definition of μ^*-measurability, we have that

$$\mu^*(A) = \mu^*(A \cap E^c) + \mu^*\left[A \cap (E^c)^c\right] = \mu^*(A \cap E^c) + \mu^*(A \cap E).$$

Thus, E is μ^*-measurable if and only if E^c is μ^*- measurable.

Lemma 1.5.5

Let X be a set, μ^* be an outer measure on X and E be a subset of X. If $\mu^*(E)=0$, then E is μ^*-measurable.

Proof

Let A be any subset of X.

Then, $A \cap E \subseteq E$.

Since μ^* is monotone, $\mu^*(A \cap E) \leq \mu^*(E) = 0$.

Also, since $A \cap E^c \subseteq A$, it follows that $\mu^*(A \cap E^c) \leq \mu^*(A)$.

Therefore, $\mu^*(A) \geq \mu^*(A \cap E) + \mu^*(A \cap E^c)$.

Hence, E is μ^*-measurable.

Note 1.5.6

The empty set ϕ is μ^*-measurable.

Theorem 1.5.7

Let X be a set, μ^* be an outer measure on X and E and F be μ^*- measurable subsets of X. Then, $E \cup F$ is μ^*- measurable.

Proof

Let A be any subset of X.

Since E is μ^*-measurable, $\mu^*(A) = \mu^*(A \cap E) + \mu^*(A \cap E^c)$.

Also, since F is μ^*-measurable,

$$\mu^*(A \cap E^c) = \mu^*\left[(A \cap E^c) \cap F\right] + \mu^*\left[(A \cap E^c) \cap F^c\right].$$

From the above two equations, we get

$$\mu^*(A) = \mu^*(A \cap E) + \mu^*\left[(A \cap E^c) \cap F\right] + \mu^*\left[(A \cap E^c) \cap F^c\right].$$

Therefore,

$$\mu^*(A) = \mu^*(A \cap E) + \mu^*\left[(A \cap E^c) \cap F\right] + \mu^*\left[(A \cap E^c) \cap F^c\right]$$

$$\geq \mu^*\left[(A \cap E) \cup \left((A \cap E^c) \cap F\right)\right] + \mu^*\left[(A \cap E^c) \cap F^c\right].$$

$$= \mu^*[A \cap (E \cup F)] + \mu^*\left[A \cap (E \cup F)^c\right],$$

where $E \cup F$ is μ^*-measurable.

Hence the theorem.

Theorem 1.5.8

Let X be a set, μ^* be an outer measure on X and let $\mathcal{A}$ be the collection of all μ^*- measurable subsets of X. Then, $\mathcal{A}$ is an algebra on X.

Proof

The proof of this theorem follows from note 1.5.4 (2), note 1.5.6 and theorem 1.5.7.

Theorem 1.5.9

Let X be a set, μ^* be an outer measure on X. If $E_1, E_2 \in \mathcal{A}$ and $E_1 \cap E_2 = \phi$, then

$$\mu^*[A \cap (E_1 \cup E_2)] = \mu^*(A \cap E_1) + \mu^*(A \cap E_2).$$

Proof

Since E_1 is μ^*-measurable,

$$\mu^*(A) = \mu^*(A \cap E_1) + \mu^*(A \cap E_1^c),$$

for each subset A of X.

Replacing A by $A \cap (E_1 \cup E_2)$, we have

$$\mu^*[A \cap (E_1 \cup E_2)] = \mu^*[(A \cap (E_1 \cup E_2)) \cap E_1] + \mu^*[(A \cap (E_1 \cup E_2)) \cap E_1^c]$$

$$= \mu^*[((A \cap E_1) \cup (A \cap E_2) \cap E_1)] + \mu^*[((A \cap E_1) \cup (A \cap E_2) \cap E_1^c)]$$

$$= \mu^*[(A \cap E_1 \cap E_1) \cup (A \cap E_2 \cap E_1)] + \mu^*[(A \cap E_1 \cap E_1^c) \cup (A \cap E_2 \cap E_1^c)]$$

$$= \mu^*(A \cap E_1) + \mu^*(A \cap E_2).$$

Hence the theorem.

Theorem 1.5.10

Let X be a set, μ^* be an outer measure on X. Suppose that (E_n) be a sequence of mutually disjoint sets in $\mathcal{A}$. Then for any $n \geq 1$ and any subset A of X,

$$\mu^*\left(A \cap \bigcup_{j=1}^{n} E_j\right) = \sum_{j=1}^{n} \mu^*(A \cap E_j). \qquad \text{.......... (1.5.10.1)}$$

Proof

We prove this theorem by induction.

When $n = 1$, the result is obviously true.

When $n = 2$, the result is true by the theorem 1.5.9.

Let us assume that

$$\mu^*\left(A \cap \bigcup_{j=1}^{n-1} E_j\right) = \sum_{j=1}^{n-1} \mu^*(A \cap E_j). \qquad \text{.......... (1.5.10.2)}$$

First, we note that

$$A \cap \left(\bigcup_{j=1}^{n} E_j\right) \cap E_n = A \cap E_n, \text{ and}$$

$$A \cap \left(\bigcup_{j=1}^{n} E_j\right) \cap E_n^c = A \cap \left(\bigcup_{j=1}^{n-1} E_j\right).$$

Since E_n is μ^*-measurable,

$$\mu^*\left[A \cap \left(\bigcup_{j=1}^{n} E_j\right)\right] = \mu^*\left[A \cap \left(\bigcup_{j=1}^{n} E_j\right) \cap E_n\right] + \mu^*\left[A \cap \left(\bigcup_{j=1}^{n} E_j\right) \cap E_n^c\right]$$

$$= \mu^*(A \cap E_n) + \mu^*\left[A \cap \left(\bigcup_{j=1}^{n-1} E_j\right)\right]$$

$$= \mu^*(A \cap E_n) + \sum_{j=1}^{n-1} \mu^*(A \cap E_j) \text{ [by equation (1.5.10.2)]}$$

$$= \sum_{j=1}^{n} \mu^*(A \cap E_j).$$

Hence the theorem.

Note 1.5.11

By assuming $A = X$ in equation (1.5.10.1) of theorem 1.5.10, we get

$$\mu^*\left(\bigcup_{j=1}^{n} E_j\right) = \sum_{j=1}^{n} \mu^*(E_j).$$

That is, μ^* is finitely additive on $\mathcal{A}$.

Theorem 1.5.12

Let X be a set, μ^* be an outer measure on X and let $\mathcal{A}$ be the collection of all μ^*- measurable subsets of X. Then,

i) $\mathcal{A}$ is a σ-algebra, and

ii) the restriction μ of μ^* to $\mathcal{A}$ is a measure on $(X, \mathcal{A})$.

Proof

i) In theorem 1.5.8, we have already proved that, $\mathcal{A}$ is an algebra.

We have only to prove that, $\mathcal{A}$ is closed under countable unions.

For that, we will prove that $\mathcal{A}$ is closed under pairwise disjoint countable unions.

Let (E_n) be a pairwise disjoint sequence of sets in $\mathcal{A}$, $B_n = \bigcup_{j=1}^{n} E_j$ and

$$B = \bigcap_{J=1}^{\infty} E_j .$$

Since $B_n \in \mathcal{A}$, for any $A \subseteq X$, we have,

$$\mu^*(A) = \mu^*(A \cap B_n) + \mu^*(A \cap B_n^c)$$

$$\geq \mu^*(A \cap B_n) + \mu^*(A \cap B^c) \qquad \text{[Since } B_n^c \supset B^c \text{ and } \mu^* \text{ is monotone]}$$

$$= \sum_{j=1}^{n} \mu^*(A \cap E_j) + \mu^*(A \cap B^c) \qquad \text{[By theorem 1.5.10]}$$

Since this is true for every natural number n, it follows that

$$\mu^*(A) \geq \sum_{j=1}^{\infty} \mu^*(A \cap E_j) + \mu^*(A \cap B^c)$$

$$\geq \mu^*(A \cap B) + \mu^*(A \cap B^c) \qquad \text{[Since } \mu^* \text{ is countably additive]}$$

Therefore, $\bigcup_{j=1}^{\infty} E_j \in \mathcal{A}$.

ii) By the definition of outer measure, $\mu(\phi) = 0$.

We have to prove that, μ^* is countably additive.

Let (E_n) be a pairwise disjoint sequence of sets in $\mathcal{A}$.

By i), for any $A \subseteq X$, we have

$$\mu^*(A) = \sum_{j=1}^{\infty} \mu^*(A \cap E_j) + \mu^*\left[A \cap \left(\bigcup_{j=1}^{\infty} E_j\right)^c\right].$$

If A is replaced by $\bigcup_{j=1}^{\infty} E_j$, we have

$$\mu^*\left(\bigcup_{j=1}^{\infty} E_j\right) \geq \sum_{j=1}^{\infty} \mu^*(E_j) \qquad \text{........... (1.5.12.1)}$$

By definition, since μ^* is countably subadditive, we have

$$\mu^*\left(\bigcup_{j=1}^{\infty} E_j\right) \leq \sum_{j=1}^{\infty} \mu^*(E_j) \qquad \text{........... (1.5.12.2)}$$

From equations (1.5.12.1) & (1.5.12.2), we get that

$$\mu^*\left(\bigcup_{j=1}^{\infty} E_j\right) = \sum_{j=1}^{\infty} \mu^*(E_j).$$

Thus, μ^* is a measure on $\mathcal{A}$.

Hence the theorem.

1.6 Lebesgue outer measure

Let $\mathcal{I}$ be the collection of open intervals in $\mathbb{R}$. Let $l(I)$ denote the length of I, for $I \in \mathcal{I}$.

Theorem 1.6.1

For any subset A of $\mathbb{R}$, define $m^* : \mathcal{P}(\mathbb{R}) \to [0, \infty]$ by

$$m^*(A) = \inf\left\{\sum_n l(I_n) : I_n \in \mathcal{I}, \text{ for each } n \text{ and } A \subseteq \bigcup_n I_n\right\}.$$

Then, m^* is an outer measure on $\mathbb{R}$.

Proof

a) Since $\phi \subseteq (a,a)$, for any real number a, it follows that $0 \leq m^*(\phi) \leq a - a = 0$.

Therefore, $m^*(\phi) = 0$.

b) Let A and B be subsets of $\mathbb{R}$ such that $A \subseteq B$.

If $B \subseteq \bigcup_n I_n$, where (I_n) is a sequence of open intervals in $\mathbb{R}$, then $A \subseteq \bigcup_n I_n$.

Therefore, $m^*(A) \le \sum_{n=1}^{\infty} l(I_n)$.

It implies that $m^*(A) \le m^*(B)$.

c) Let (A_n) be a sequence of subsets of $\mathbb{R}$.

If $m^*(A_n) = \infty$, for some n, then

$$m^*\left(\bigcup_{n=1}^{\infty} A_n\right) \le \sum_{n=1}^{\infty} m^*(A_n).$$

Suppose that $m^*(A_n) < \infty$,for each n.

Then, for given $\varepsilon > 0$, there is a sequence $(I_{nk})_k$ of open intervals in $\mathbb{R}$ such that $A_n \subseteq \bigcup_{k=1}^{\infty} I_{nk}$, and

$$\sum_{k=1}^{\infty} l(I_{nk}) < m^*(A_n) + \frac{\varepsilon}{2^n}.$$

Since $\bigcup_{n=1}^{\infty} A_n \subseteq \bigcup_{n=1}^{\infty} \bigcup_{k=1}^{\infty} I_{nk}$, it follows that

$$m^*\left(\bigcup_{n=1}^{\infty} A_n\right) \le \sum_{n=1}^{\infty} \sum_{k=1}^{\infty} l(I_{nk}) < \sum_{n=1}^{\infty}\left(m^*(A_n) + \frac{\varepsilon}{2^n}\right) = \sum_{n=1}^{\infty} m^*(A_n) + \varepsilon.$$

Since ε is arbitrary, we have

$$m^*\left(\bigcup_{n=1}^{\infty} A_n\right) \le \sum_{n=1}^{\infty} m^*(A_n).$$

Hence the theorem.

Note 1.6.2

The outer measure defined in the above theorem 1.6.1 is called the *Lebesgue outer measure.*

Definition 1.6.3

A set $E \subseteq \mathbb{R}$ is said to be *Lebesgue-measurable* (or *measurable*) if

$$m^*(A) = m^*(A \cap E) + m^*(A \cap E^c)$$

for every set $A \subseteq \mathbb{R}$.

Note 1.6.4

If $\mathcal{A}$ is the set of all Lebesgue-measurable subsets of $\mathbb{R}$, then, we have already proved that $\mathcal{A}$ is a σ-algebra and also the restriction μ of μ^* to $\mathcal{A}$ is a measure on $\mathcal{A}$. This measure is called the Lebesgue measure on $\mathbb{R}$.

Theorem 1.6.5

The outer measure of an interval I is its length. That is, $m^*(I) = l(I)$.

Proof

Case i)

Let I be a closed and bounded interval, say $I = [a, b]$.

Then, $[a,b] \subset (a-\varepsilon, b+\varepsilon)$, for each $\varepsilon > 0$.

Therefore, $m^*([a,b]) \leq l(a-\varepsilon, b+\varepsilon) = b-a+2\varepsilon$.

Since ε is arbitrary, $m^*(I) = m^*([a,b]) \leq b-a$.

Now, we have to prove that, $m^*(I) \geq b-a$.

Suppose that, $I \subset \bigcup_{k=1}^{\infty} I_k$, where I_k is open for each $k \in \mathbb{N}$.

Since I is compact, there is a finite subcollection $\{I_k\}_{k=1}^{m}$ of intervals such that $I \subset \bigcup_{k=1}^{m} I_k$.

Since $a \in I$, there is an interval (a_1, b_1) in the collection $\{I_k\}_{k=1}^{m}$ such that $a_1 < a < b_1$.

The result is obvious, if $b \leq b_1$.

Suppose not, that is, if $a < b_1 < b$.

Hence, $b_1 \in I$.

Therefore, there is an interval (a_2, b_2) in the collection $\{I_k\}_{k=1}^{m}$ such that $a_2 < b_1 < b_2$.

The result is obvious, if $b < b_2$.

Suppose not, that is, if $a < b_2 < b$.

Hence, $b_2 \in I$.

Therefore, there is an interval (a_3, b_3) in the collection $\{I_k\}_{k=1}^{m}$ such that $a_3 < b_2 < b_3$.

Continuing like this, we obtain a sequence of intervals

$(a_1, b_1), (a_2, b_2), \ldots\ldots, (a_r, b_r)$ from the collection $\{I_k\}_{k=1}^{m}$ such that

$a_i < b_{i-1} < b_i$, for $i = 2, 3, \ldots\ldots, r$.

Since $\{I_k\}_{k=1}^{m}$ is a finite collection, this process must terminate after $s \le m$ steps, with $b < b_s$.

Now, $\sum_{j=1}^{\infty} l(I_j) \ge \sum_{j=1}^{m} l(I_j) \ge \sum_{j=1}^{s} l(a_j, b_j)$

$$= (b_s - a_s) + (b_{s-1} - a_{s-1}) + (b_{s-2} - a_{s-2}) + \ldots\ldots + (b_1 - a_1)$$

$$= b_s - (a_s - b_{s-1}) - (a_{s-1} - b_{s-2}) - \ldots\ldots - (a_2 - b_1) - a_1$$

$$> b_s - a_1 > b - a.$$

Hence, we have that $m^*(I) \ge b - a = l(I)$.

Case ii)

Let I be an interval of the form (a, b), $(a, b]$ or $[a, b)$.

Then for each $0 < \varepsilon < (b - a)$ with $\left[a + \frac{\varepsilon}{2}, b - \frac{\varepsilon}{2}\right] \subset I \subset \left[a - \frac{\varepsilon}{2}, b + \frac{\varepsilon}{2}\right]$.

Therefore, $m^*\left[a + \frac{\varepsilon}{2}, b - \frac{\varepsilon}{2}\right] \le m^*(I) \le m^*\left[a - \frac{\varepsilon}{2}, b + \frac{\varepsilon}{2}\right]$

$$\Leftrightarrow l\left(\left[a + \frac{\varepsilon}{2}, b - \frac{\varepsilon}{2}\right]\right) \le m^*(I) \le l\left(\left[a - \frac{\varepsilon}{2}, b + \frac{\varepsilon}{2}\right]\right)$$

$$\Leftrightarrow b - a - \varepsilon \le m^*(I) \le b - a + \varepsilon \text{ [by case i)]}$$

Since ε is arbitrary, we have $m^*(I) = b - a = l(I)$.

Case iii)

Suppose that I is an unbounded interval.

Then, for any real number k, there is a closed interval $J \subset I$ such that $l(J) = k$.

Therefore, $m^*(I) \geq m^*(J) = l(J) = k$.

Hence, $m^*(I) = \infty$.

Hence the theorem.

Theorem 1.6.6

For each $x \in \mathbb{R}$, $m^*(\{x\}) = 0$.

Proof

For any $\varepsilon > 0$, we have $\{x\} \subset \left(x - \frac{\varepsilon}{2}, x + \frac{\varepsilon}{2}\right)$.

Thus, $0 \leq m^*(\{x\}) \leq m^*\left(x - \frac{\varepsilon}{2}, x + \frac{\varepsilon}{2}\right) = l\left(x - \frac{\varepsilon}{2}, x + \frac{\varepsilon}{2}\right) = \varepsilon$.

Since ε is arbitrary, $m^*(\{x\}) = 0$.

Hence the theorem.

Theorem 1.6.7

Every countable subset of $\mathbb{R}$ has outer measure zero.

Proof

Let A be a countable subset of $\mathbb{R}$.

Then, $A = \bigcup_n \{a_n\}$.

Therefore, $0 \leq m^*(A) = m^*\left(\bigcup_n \{a_n\}\right) \leq \sum_n m^*(\{a_n\}) = 0$.

Thus, $m^*(A) = 0$.

Hence the theorem.

Note 1.6.8

The interval [0, 1] is uncountable.

Theorem 1.6.9

The Lebesgue outer measure is translation-invariant. That is, $m^*(A + x) = m^*(A)$ for all $A \subset \mathbb{R}$ and $x \in \mathbb{R}$.

Proof

Let (I_n) be a sequence of open intervals such that $A \subset \bigcup_n I_n$.

Then, $A + x \subset \bigcup_n (I_n + x)$.

Therefore, $m^*(A + x) \le \sum_n l(I_n + x) = \sum_n l(I_n)$.

That is, $m^*(A + x)$ is a lower bound for the sums $\sum_n l(I_n)$, with $A \subset \bigcup_n I_n$.

Therefore, $m^*(A + x) \le m^*(A)$. .... (1.6.9.1)

To prove; $m^*(A) \le m^*(A + x)$.

Now, $m^*(A) = m^*(A + x + (-x)) \le m^*(A + x)$, [by a known result]

.... (1.6.9.2)

Hence from equations (1.6.9.1) and (1.6.9.2), we have $m^*(A + x) = m^*(A)$.

Hence the theorem.

Theorem 1.6.10

For any set $A \subset \mathbb{R}$ and any $\varepsilon > 0$, there is an open set $A \subset V$ and $m^*(V) < m^*(A) + \varepsilon$.

Proof

By the definition of $m^*(A)$, there is a sequence (I_n) of open intervals such that $A \subset \bigcup_n I_n$ and

$$\sum_n l(I_n) < m^*(A) + \frac{\varepsilon}{2}.$$

If $I_n = (a_n, b_n)$, let $J_n = \left(a_n - \frac{\varepsilon}{2^{n+1}}, b_n\right)$.

Then, $A \subset \bigcup_n J_n$.

Let $V = \bigcup_n J_n$.

Then V is an open set in $\mathbb{R}$ and

$$m^*(V) \le \sum_n l(J_n) = \sum_n l(I_n) + \frac{\varepsilon}{2} < m^*(A) + \varepsilon.$$

Hence the theorem.

Theorem 1.6.11

For any $a \in \mathbb{R}$, the set (a, ∞) is measurable.

Proof

Let A be any subset of $\mathbb{R}$.

We have to show that

$$m^*(A) \geq m^*(A \cap (a,\infty)) + m^*(A \cap (a,\infty)^c) = m^*(A \cap (a,\infty)) + m^*(A \cap (-\infty, a]).$$

Let $A_1 = A \cap (a,\infty)$ and $A_2 = A \cap (-\infty, a]$.

Then, we have to prove that

$$m^*(A) \geq m^*(A_1) + m^*(A_2).$$

If $m^*(A) = \infty$, then there is nothing to prove.

Let us assume that $m^*(A) < \infty$.

From the definition of m^*, for given $\varepsilon > 0$, there is a sequence (I_n) of open intervals such that

$$A \subset \bigcup_n I_n \text{ and } m^*(A) + \varepsilon > \sum_n l(I_n).$$

Let $J_n = I_n \cap (a,\infty)$ and $J_n' = I_n \cap (-\infty, a]$.

Then, J_n and J_n' are disjoint intervals and $I_n = J_n \cup J_n'$.

Therefore,

$$l(I_n) = l(J_n) + l(J_n') = m^*(J_n) + m^*(J_n').$$

Since $A_1 \subset \bigcup_n J_n$ and $A_2 \subset \bigcup_n J_n'$, it follows that

$$m^*(A_1) \leq m^*\left(\bigcup_n J_n\right) \leq \sum_n m^*(J_n) = \sum_n l(J_n), \text{ and}$$

$$m^*(A_2) \leq m^*\left(\bigcup_n J_n'\right) \leq \sum_n m^*(J_n') = \sum_n l(J_n').$$

Therefore,

$$m^*(A_1) + m^*(A_2) \leq \sum_n \left[l(J_n) + l(J_n')\right] = \sum_n l(I_n) < m^*(A) + \varepsilon.$$

Since ε is arbitrary,

$$m^*(A_1) + m^*(A_2) \leq m^*(A).$$

Hence the theorem.

Corollary 1.6.11

1) Every interval in $\mathbb{R}$ is measurable.
2) Every open set in $\mathbb{R}$ is measurable.
3) Every closed set in $\mathbb{R}$ is measurable.
4) Every set that is a countable intersection of open sets in $\mathbb{R}$ is measurable.
5) Every set that is a countable union of closed sets in $\mathbb{R}$ is measurable.

Definition 1.6.12

1) A set that is a union of a countable collection of closed sets is called a **F_σ - set.**
2) A set that is an intersection of a countable collection of open sets is called a **G_δ – set.**

Theorem 1.6.13

Let $E \subset \mathbb{R}$ and m^* be the Lebesgue outer measure on $\mathbb{R}$. The following statements are equivalent:

i) E is measurable.

ii) For each $\varepsilon > 0$, there is an open set V such that $E \subset V$ and $m^*(V \setminus E) < \varepsilon$.

iii) There is a G_δ-set G such that $E \subset G$ and $m^*(G \setminus E) = 0$.

iv) For each $\varepsilon > 0$, there is a closed set F such that $F \subset E$ and $m^*(E \setminus F) < \varepsilon$.

v) There is an F_σ-set H such that $H \subset E$ and $m^*(E \setminus H) = 0$.

Unit	
2	**MEASURABLE FUNCTIONS AND CONVERGENCE THEOREMS**

2.1 Introduction

In this chapter, we will study the definition of measurable functions and their properties, convergence of measurable functions, integration of nonnegative simple functions, integration of nonnegative measurable functions.

2.2 Measurability

Basic notions 2.2.1

The *extended real number system* $\overline{\mathbb{R}}$, is the set of real numbers together with two symbols -∞ and +∞. That is, $\overline{\mathbb{R}} = \mathbb{R} \cup \{-\infty, +\infty\} = [-\infty, \infty]$.

The algebraic operations for these two infinities are;

1) For $r \in \mathbb{R}$, $\pm\infty + r = \pm\infty$.
2) For $r \in \mathbb{R}, r(\pm\infty) = \pm\infty$, if $r > 0$ and $r(\pm\infty) = \mp\infty$, if $r < 0$.
3) $+\infty + (+\infty) = +\infty$ and $-\infty + (-\infty) = -\infty$.
4) $\infty + (-\infty)$ is undefined.
5) $0 \cdot (\pm\infty) = 0$.

Definition 2.2.2

A set X is said to be a *measure space*, if there exists a σ- ring M of subsets of X, which are called measurable sets and a non-negative countably additive set function μ defined on M. If $X = M$, then X is said to be a *measurable space*.

Definition 2.2.3

Let $(X, \mathcal{A})$ be a measurable space and $E \in \mathcal{A}$. A function $f : E \to \overline{\mathbb{R}}$ is said to be *measurable*, if for each $a \in \mathbb{R}$, the set $\{x \in E; f(x) > a\}$ is measurable.

A complex – valued function is measurable, if its real and imaginary parts are measurable.

Theorem 2.2.4

Let $(X, \mathcal{A})$ be a measurable space and $E \in \mathcal{A}$ and $f : E \to \overline{\mathbb{R}}$. Then the following are equivalent:

1) $\{x / f(x) > a\}$ is measurable for every real a.
2) $\{x / f(x) \geq a\}$ is measurable for every real a.
3) $\{x / f(x) < a\}$ is measurable for every real a.
4) $\{x / f(x) \leq a\}$ is measurable for every real a.

Proof

1) $\Rightarrow$ 2)

Let $\{x / f(x) > a\}$ be measurable for every real a.

To prove: $\{x / f(x) \geq a\}$ is measurable for every real a.

$$\begin{aligned}\{x / f(x) \geq a\} &= \{x / f(x) \in [a, \infty)\} \\ &= \{x / x \in f^{-1}([a, \infty))\} = f^{-1}([a, \infty)) \\ &= f^{-1}\left(\bigcap_{n=1}^{\infty}\left(a - \frac{1}{n}, \infty\right)\right) \\ &= \bigcap_{n=1}^{\infty}\left(f^{-1}\left(a - \frac{1}{n}, \infty\right)\right) \\ &= \bigcap_{n=1}^{\infty}\left\{x / f(x) > a - \frac{1}{n}\right\}\end{aligned}$$

By 1), $\left\{x / f(x) > a - \frac{1}{n}\right\}$ is measurable for all n.

Since countable intersection of measurable sets is measurable, $\bigcap_{n=1}^{\infty}\left\{x / f(x) > a - \frac{1}{n}\right\}$ is measurable.

Therefore, $\{x / f(x) \geq a\}$ is measurable for every real a.

2) $\Rightarrow$ 3)

Let $\{x / f(x) > a\}$ be measurable for every real a.

Now, $\{x / f(x) < a\} = X - \{x / f(x) \geq a\}$

Since X and $\{x / f(x) \geq a\}$ are measurable for every real a, $\{x / f(x) < a\}$ is measurable for every real a.

3) ⇒ 4)

Let $\{x / f(x) < a\}$ be measurable for every real a.

To prove: $\{x / f(x) \leq a\}$ is measurable for every real a.

Now, $\{x / f(x) \leq a\} = \{x / f(x) \in (-\infty, a]\}$.

$$= \{x / x \in f^{-1}((-\infty, a])\} = f^{-1}((-\infty, a])$$

$$= f^{-1}\left(\bigcap_{n=1}^{\infty}\left(-\infty, a+\frac{1}{n}\right)\right)$$

$$= \bigcap_{n=1}^{\infty}\left(f^{-1}\left(-\infty, a+\frac{1}{n}\right)\right)$$

$$= \bigcap_{n=1}^{\infty}\left\{x / f(x) < a+\frac{1}{n}\right\}$$

By the given data, $\left\{x / f(x) < a+\frac{1}{n}\right\}$ is measurable for all n.

Since countable intersection of measurable sets is measurable, $\bigcap_{n=1}^{\infty}\left\{x / f(x) < a+\frac{1}{n}\right\}$ is measurable.

Therefore, $\{x / f(x) \leq a\}$ is measurable for every real a.

4) ⇒ 1)

Let $\{x / f(x) \leq a\}$ is measurable for every real a.

To prove:

$\{x / f(x) > a\}$ is measurable for every real a.

Now, $\{x / f(x) > a\} = X - \{x / f(x) \leq a\}$.

Since X is measurable and $\{x / f(x) \leq a\}$ is measurable for every real a, $X - \{x / f(x) \leq a\}$ is measurable for every real a.

Therefore, $\{x / f(x) > a\}$ is measurable for every real a.

Hence the theorem.

Theorem 2.2.5

If f is a measurable real valued function, then $|f|$ is a measurable function.

Proof

Let a be any real number.

Now, $\{x / |f(x)| < a\} = \{x / -a < f(x) < a\}$

$$= \{x / f(x) < a\} \cap \{x / f(x) > -a\}$$

Since f is measurable, $\{x / f(x) < a\}$ and $\{x / f(x) > -a\}$ are measurable for every real a.

Since the intersection of measurable sets is measurable, $\{x / f(x) < a\} \cap \{x / f(x) > -a\}$ is measurable.

Therefore, $\{x / |f(x)| < a\}$ is measurable for every real a.

Hence $|f|$ is measurable.

Hence the theorem.

Example 2.2.6

1) The constant function is measurable. That is, if $(X, \mathcal{A})$ is a measurable space, $c \in \mathbb{R}$ and $E \in \mathcal{A}$, then the function $f : E \rightarrow \mathbb{R}$ given by $f(x) = c$, for each $x \in E$, is measurable.

Let $\alpha \in \mathbb{R}$.

If $\alpha \geq c$, then the set $\{x \in E : f(x) > \alpha\} = E$ and hence it is measurable. Therefore, f is measurable.

2) Let $(X, \mathcal{A})$ be a measurable space and let $A \in \mathcal{A}$. The characteristic function χ_A, is defined by

$$\chi_A(x) = \begin{cases} 1 & \text{if } x \in A \\ 0 & \text{if } x \notin A \end{cases}$$

The characteristic function χ_A is measurable. This follows immediately from the observation that, for each $\alpha \in \mathbb{R}$ and $E \in \mathcal{A}$, the set $\{x \in E : \chi_A > \alpha\}$ is either E, A or ϕ.

3) Let $\mathbb{B}$ be the Borel σ-algebra in $\mathbb{R}$ and $E \in \mathbb{B}$. Then, any continuous function $f : E \to \overline{\mathbb{R}}$ is measurable, since, if $f : E \to \overline{\mathbb{R}}$ is continuous and $\alpha \in \mathbb{R}$, then the set $\{x \in E : f(x) > \alpha\}$ is open and hence belongs to $\mathbb{B}$.

Theorem 2.2.7

Let $|f_n|$ be a sequence of measurable function on *X*. Put $g(x) = \sup. f_n(x)$, $h(x) = \limsup_{n\to\infty} f_n(x)$, $u(x) = \inf. f_n(x)$ and $v(x) = \liminf_{n\to\infty} f_n(x)$, then *g*, *h*, *u* and *v* are measurable.

Proof

Let $\{f_n\}$ be a sequence of measurable function on *X* and $g(x) = \sup. f_n(x)$.

i) To prove: *g* is measurable.

We will prove that, $\{x / g(x) > a\} = \bigcup_{n-1}^{\infty} \{x / f_n(x) > a\}$.

Let $y \in \{x / g(x) > a\}$.

$\Rightarrow g(y) > a$.

Hence, $g(y) - a > 0$.

Therefore, there exists $m \in J$, such that $f_m(y) > g(y) - (g(y) - a)$.

$\Rightarrow f_m(y) > a$.

Hence, $y \in \{x / f_m(x) > a\} \subseteq \bigcup_{n=1}^{\infty} \{x / f_n(x) > a\}$.

Therefore, $\{x / g(x) > a\} \subseteq \bigcup_{n=1}^{\infty} \{x / f_n(x) > a\}$ .... (2.2.7.1)

Let $y \in \bigcup_{n=1}^{\infty} \{x / f_n(x) > a\}$.

Hence, $y \in \{x / f_k(x) > a\}$ for some *k*.

$\Rightarrow f_k(y) > a$.

Now, $g(y) = \sup. f_n(y) \geq f_k(y) > a$.

Therefore, $g(y) > a$.

Hence, $y \in \{x / f(x) > a\}$.

Therefore, $\bigcup_{n=1}^{\infty}\{x / f_n(x) > a\} \subseteq \{x / g(x) > a\}$. ....(2.2.7.2)

From (2.2.7.1) & (2.2.7.2), we get that

$$\{x / g(x) > a\} = \bigcup_{n=1}^{\infty}\{x / f_n(x) > a\}.$$

Since $\{f_n\}$ is measurable for each n, $\{x / f_n(x) > a\}$ is measurable for every n.

Since countable union of measurable sets is measurable, $\bigcup_{n=1}^{\infty}\{x / f_n(x) > a\}$ is measurable.

Therefore, from our claim we get that, $\{x / g(x) > a\}$ is measurable.

iii) To prove: u is measurable.

We will prove that, $\{x / u(x) < a\} = \bigcup_{n=1}^{\infty}\{x / f_n(x) < a\}$.

Let $y \in \{x / u(x) < a\}$.

$\Rightarrow u(y) < a$.

Hence, $a - u(y) > 0$.

Therefore, there exists $m \in J$ such that $f_m(y) < u(y) + (a - u(y)) = a$.

$\Rightarrow f_m(y) < a$.

Hence, $y \in \{x / f_m(x) < a\}$.

Therefore, $\{x / u(x) < a\} \subseteq \bigcup_{n=1}^{\infty}\{x / f_n(x) < a\}$. .... (2.2.7.3)

Let $y \in \bigcup_{n=1}^{\infty}\{x / f_n(x) < a\}$.

Hence, $y \in \{x / f_k(x) < a\}$ for some k.

$\Rightarrow f_k(y) < a$.

Now, $u(y) = \text{Inf}.f_n(y) \leq f_k(y) < a$.

Therefore, $u(y) < a$.

Hence, $y \in \{x / u(x) < a\}$.

Therefore, $\bigcup_{n=1}^{\infty}\{x / f_n(x) < a\} \subseteq \{x / u(x) < a\}$. .... (2.2.7.4)

From (2.2.7.1) & (2.2.7.2), we get that

$$\{x / u(x) < a\} = \bigcup_{n=1}^{\infty} \{x / f_n(x) < a\}.$$

Since $\{f_n\}$ is measurable for each n, $\{x / f_n(x) < a\}$ is measurable for every n.

Since countable union of measurable sets is measurable, $\bigcup_{n=1}^{\infty}\{x / f_n(x) < a\}$ is measurable.

Therefore, from our claim we get that, $\{x / u(x) < a\}$ is measurable.

ii) To prove: $h(x) = \limsup_{n\to\infty} f_n(x)$ is measurable.

Put $g_1(x) = \sup\{f_1(x), f_2(x), ...\}$

$g_2(x) = \sup\{f_2(x), f_3(x), ...\}$

....

$g_m(x) = \sup\{f_m(x), f_{m+1}(x), ...\}$

....

Hence, $\{g_m\}$ is decreasing.

Therefore, $\limsup_{n\to\infty} f_n(x) = \lim_{m\to\infty} g_m(x) = \inf . g_m(x)$.

By (i), for each m, g_m is measurable.

Also, by (iii), inf. $g_m(x)$ is measurable.

Therefore, $\limsup_{n\to\infty} f_n(x)$ is measurable.

Hence, h is measurable.

iv) To prove: $v(x) = \liminf_{n\to\infty} f_n(x)$ is measurable.

Put $u_1(x) = \inf\{f_1(x), f_2(x), ...\}$

$u_2(x) = \inf\{f_2(x), f_3(x), ...\}$

....

$u_m(x) = \inf\{f_m(x), f_{m+1}(x), ...\}$

....

Hence $\{u_m\}$ is increasing.

Therefore, $\liminf_{n\to\infty} f_n(x) = \lim_{n\to\infty} u_m(x) = \sup . u_m(x)$.

By (iii), for each m, u_m is measurable.

Also, by (i), sup. $g_m(x)$ is measurable.

Therefore, $\liminf_{n\to\infty} f_n(x)$ is measurable.

Hence, v is measurable.

Hence the theorem.

Theorem 2.2.8

The limit of a convergent sequence of measurable sequence is measurable.

Proof

Let $\{f_n\}$ be a sequence of measurable functions, such that $f_n(x) \to f(x)$.

To prove: f is measurable.

Since $f_n(x) \to f(x)$,

$$f(x) = \lim_{n\to\infty} f_n(x) = \lim_{n\to\infty} \sup.f_n(x).$$

Since each f_n is measurable, $\limsup_{n\to\infty}.f_n(x)$ is also measurable.

Therefore, f is measurable.

Hence the theorem.

Theorem 2.2.9

Let f, g be measurable real valued function on X. Let F be a real continuous function on R^2. Put $h(x) = F(f(x), g(x)), x \in X$. Then, h is measurable.

Proof

Given f, g are measurable real valued functions on X, such that $f, g : X \to \mathbb{R}$.

Also, $F : \mathbb{R}^2 \to \mathbb{R}$ is continuous.

We know that, $h : X \to \mathbb{R}$.

To prove: h is measurable.

Let a be any real number.

Define $G_a = \{(u,v) / F(u,v) > a\}$.

$$= \{(u,v) / F(u,v) \in (a,\infty)\}.$$

$$= \left\{(u,v) / (u,v) \in F^{-1}((a,\infty))\right\}.$$

$$= F^{-1}((a,\infty)).$$

Since (a,∞) is an open set in $\mathbb{R}$, and F is continuous, $F^{-1}((a,\infty))$ is open in $\mathbb{R}^2$.

Therefore, G_a is an open set in $\mathbb{R}^2$.

Since any open set in $\mathbb{R}^2$ can be written as a countable union of open intervals in $\mathbb{R}^2$,

$$G_a = \bigcup_{n=1}^{\infty} I_n \text{, where } I_n \text{ is an open interval in } \mathbb{R}^2.$$

Take $I_n = (a_n, b_n) \times (c_n, d_n)$.

Now, $\{x / h(x) > a\} = \{x / F(f(x), g(x)) > a\}$.

$$= \{x / F(f(x), g(x)) \in (a,\infty)\}.$$

$$= \left\{ x / (f(x), g(x)) \in F^{-1}((a,\infty)) = G_a = \bigcup_{n=1}^{\infty} I_n \right\}.$$

$$= \bigcup_{n=1}^{\infty} \{x / (f(x), g(x)) \in I_n\}.$$

$$= \bigcup_{n=1}^{\infty} \{x / (f(x), g(x)) \in (a_n, b_n) \times (c_n, d_n)\}.$$

$$= \bigcup_{n=1}^{\infty} \{x / a_n < f(x) < b_n, c_n < g(x) < d_n\}.$$

$$= \bigcup_{n=1}^{\infty} [\{x / f(x) > a_n\} \cap \{x / f(x) < b_n\} \cap \{x / g(x) > c_n\} \cap \{x / g(x) < d_n\}].$$

Since f and g are measurable functions, $\{x / f(x) > a_n\}$, $\{x / f(x) < b_n\}$, $\{x / g(x) > c_n\}$ and $\{x / g(x) < d_n\}$ are measurable sets.

Hence, their intersection is also measurable.

Since countable union of measurable sets is measurable, $\{x / h(x) > a\}$ is a measurable set.

Therefore, h is measurable.

Hence the theorem.

Theorem 2.2.10

If f, g are measurable real function on X, then $f + g, f - g, fg$ are measurable. If $g(x) \neq 0$, for all $x \in X$, then f / g is measurable.

Proof

Given f and g are measurable functions such that $f, g: X \to \mathbb{R}$.

1. Define $F: \mathbb{R}^2 \to \mathbb{R}$ as $F((x, y)) = x + y$.

We claim that, F is continuous in $\mathbb{R}^2$.

That is, to prove that, $(x_n, y_n) \to (x, y) \Rightarrow F((x_n, y_n)) \to F((x, y))$.

Now, $(x_n, y_n) \to (x, y) \Rightarrow x_n \to x$ and $y_n \to y$.

$$\Rightarrow x_n + y_n \to x + y.$$

$$\Rightarrow F((x_n, y_n)) \to F((x, y))$$

Therefore, F is continuous on $\mathbb{R}^2$.

Define $h: X \to \mathbb{R}$ as $h(x) = F(f(x), g(x))$.

Therefore, $h(x) = f(x) + g(x)$.

$= (f + g)(x)$.

Hence, by the previous theorem 2.2.9, h is measurable.

Therefore, $f + g$ is measurable.

2. Define $F: \mathbb{R}^2 \to \mathbb{R}$ as $F((x, y)) = x - y$.

We claim that, F is continuous on $\mathbb{R}^2$.

That is, to prove that, $(x_n, y_n) \to (x, y) \Rightarrow F((x_n, y_n)) \to F((x, y))$.

Now, $(x_n, y_n) \to (x, y) \Rightarrow x_n \to x$ and $y_n \to y$.

$$\Rightarrow x_n - y_n \to x - y.$$

$$\Rightarrow F((x_n, y_n)) \to F((x, y)).$$

Therefore, F is continuous on $\mathbb{R}^2$.

Define $h: X \to R$ by $h(x) = F(f(x), g(x))$.

Therefore, $h(x) = f(x) - g(x)$.

$= (f - g)(x)$.

Hence, by the previous theorem 2.2.9, h is measurable.

Therefore, $f - g$ is measurable.

3. Define $F: \mathbb{R}^2 \to \mathbb{R}$ as $F(x, y) = xy$.

We claim that, F is continuous on $\mathbb{R}^2$.

That is, to prove that, $(x_n, y_n) \to (x, y) \Rightarrow F\big((x_n, y_n)\big) \to F((x, y))$.

Now, $(x_n, y_n) \to (x, y) \Rightarrow x_n \to x$ and $y_n \to y$.

$$\Rightarrow x_n y_n \to xy.$$

$$\Rightarrow F\big((x_n, y_n)\big) \to F((x, y)).$$

Therefore, F is continuous on $\mathbb{R}^2$.

Define $h : X \to \mathbb{R}$ as $h(x) = F(f(x), g(x))$.

Therefore, $h(x) = f(x)\, g(x) = (fg)(x)$.

Hence, by the previous theorem 2.2.9, h is measurable.

Therefore, $f\,g$ is measurable.

4. Define $F : \mathbb{R}^2 \to \mathbb{R}$ as $F((x, y)) = \dfrac{x}{y}$, where $y \neq 0$.

We claim that, F is continuous on $\mathbb{R}^2$.

That is, prove that, $(x_n, y_n) \to (x, y) \Rightarrow F\big((x_n, y_n)\big) \to F((x, y))$.

Now, $(x_n, y_n) \to (x, y) \Rightarrow x_n \to x$ and $y_n \to y$.

$$\Rightarrow \left(\frac{x_n}{y_n}\right) \to \left(\frac{x}{y}\right).$$

$$\Rightarrow F\big((x_n, y_n)\big) \to F((x, y)).$$

Therefore, F is continuous on $\mathbb{R}^2$.

Define $h : X \to \mathbb{R}$ as $h(x) = F((f(x), g(x))$.

Therefore, $h(x) = \dfrac{f(x)}{g(x)}$, where $g(x) \neq 0$.

$$= \left(\frac{f}{g}\right)(x).$$

Hence, by the previous theorem 2.2.9, h is measurable.

Therefore, $\dfrac{f}{g}$ is measurable.

Hence the theorem.

Theorem 2.2.11

If f, g are measurable real functions on X, then max. (f, g) and min. (f, g) are measurable.

Proof

Let $\max.(f,g)=\frac{f+g}{2}+\frac{|f-g|}{2}$ and $\min.(f,g)=\frac{f+g}{2}-\frac{|f-g|}{2}$.

Since f and g are measurable, $f+g$ and $f-g$ are measurable.

Since $f+g$ and $f-g$ are measurable, $\frac{f+g}{2}+\frac{|f-g|}{2}$, $\frac{f+g}{2}-\frac{|f-g|}{2}$ are measurable.

Therefore, $\max.\left\{\frac{f+g}{2}+\frac{|f-g|}{2}\right\}$ and $\min.\left\{\frac{f+g}{2}-\frac{|f-g|}{2}\right\}$ are measurable.

That is, max.(f, g) and min.(f, g) are measurable.

Hence the theorem.

Definition 2.2.12

Let f be a real - valued function defined on a set X. The *positive part of* f, denoted by f^+, is the function $f^+=\max.(f,0)$ and the *negative part of* f, denoted by f^-, is the function $f^-=\min.(-f,0)$.

If f is a real valued function defined on X, then $f=f^+-f^-$ and $|f|=f^++f^-$. We also have, $f^+=\frac{1}{2}\left[|f|+f\right]$ and $f^-=\frac{1}{2}\left[|f|-f\right]$.

Note 2.2.13

Let $f:X\to\mathbb{R}$ and define $f^+=\max.(f,0)$ and $f^-=\min.(-f,0)$. Then, f^+ and f^- are measurable if and only if f is measurable.

Proof

First, we will prove that, if f is measurable, then f^+ and f^- are measurable.

Suppose $f(x)>0$, then $f^+(x)=f(x)>0$.

Suppose $f(x)\leq 0$, then $f^+(x)=0$.

Therefore, $f^+(x)\geq 0$.

Suppose $f(x) \geq 0$, then $f^{-}(x) = 0$.

Suppose $f(x) < 0$, then $f^{-}(x) = -f(x) > 0$.

Therefore, $f^{-}(x) \geq 0$.

Hence, f^{+} and f^{-} are non – negative on *X*.

Therefore, since f is measurable, by theorem 2.2.11, f^{+} and f^{-} are measurable.

Second part:

Let f^{+} and f^{-} be measurable.

To prove: *f* is measurable.

Now, $f^{+} = \max.(f, 0) = \frac{f+0}{2} + \frac{|f-0|}{2} = \frac{f}{2} + \frac{|f|}{2}$. .... (2.2.13.1)

$$f^{-} = -\min.(f, 0) = -\left[\frac{f+0}{2} - \frac{|f-0|}{2}\right] = -\frac{f}{2} + \frac{|f|}{2}. \quad \text{.......... (2.2.13.2)}$$

From (2.2.13.1) and (2.2.13.2), we get that, $f^{+} - f^{-} = f$.

Therefore, f is measurable.

Hence proved.

Problem 2.2.14

If $\{f_n\}$ is a sequence of measurable functions, then prove that the set of points x at which $\{f_n(x)\}$ converges is measurable.

Proof

Given $\{f_n\}$ is a sequence of measurable functions.

Let $A = \{x \in E \,/\, f_n(x) \text{ is convergent}\}$, where $E \subset X$.

To prove that, *A* is measurable.

Now, $A = \{x \in E \,/\, f_n(x) \text{ is convergent}\}$

$$= \left\{x \in E \,/\, \lim_{n\to\infty} \sup . f_n(x) = \lim_{n\to\infty} \inf . f_n(x)\right\}.$$

Let $P(x) = \lim_{n\to\infty} \sup . f_n(x)$ and $Q(x) = \lim_{n\to\infty} \inf . f_n(x)$.

Since each f_n is measurable, $\lim_{n\to\infty} \sup . f_n(x)$ and $\lim_{n\to\infty} \inf . f_n(x)$ are measurable.

Hence, *P* and *Q* are measurable functions.

Therefore, $P - Q$ is measurable.

Now, $A = \{x \in E / P(x) = Q(x)\} = \{x \in E / (P-Q)(x) = 0\}$

Therefore, A is measurable.

Definition 2.2.15

Let $(X, \mathcal{A})$ be a measurable space. A *simple function* on X is a function of the form

$$S = \sum_{j=1}^{n} c_j \chi_{E_j}$$, where, for each $j = 1, 2, \ldots, n$, c_j is an extended real number

and $E_j \in \mathcal{A}$. Since χ_{E_j} is measurable for each $j = 1, 2, \ldots, n$, from theorem 2.2.10, it follows that S is also measurable. That is, a simple function is said to have a finite range. Every characteristic function is a simple function.

Result 2.2.16

Every simple function is a linear combination of its characteristic function.

Proof

Let s be a simple function on S.

Let the range of s be $\{c_1, c_2, \ldots, c_n\}$.

Let $A_i = \{x \in X / s(x) = c_i\}$.

$$X = \bigcup_{i=1}^{n} A_i, \quad A_i \cap A_j = 0, \quad \text{if } i \neq j.$$

Then, $S = \sum_{i=1}^{n} c_i \chi_{A_i}$, where χ_{A_i} is the characteristic function of A_i.

Therefore, every simple function is a linear combination of its characteristic function.

2.3 Types of Convergence

Definition 2.3.1

Let $(X, \mathcal{A}, \mu)$ be a measure space. A sequence (f_n) of a.e. real – valued functions on X is said to

1) *converge almost everywhere* to an a.e. real – valued measurable function *f*, if for each $\varepsilon > 0$ and each $x \in X$, there is a set $E \in \mathcal{A}$ and a natural number *N* such that $\mu(E) < \varepsilon$ and $|f_n(x) - f(x)| < \varepsilon$, for each $x \in X \setminus E$ and $n \geq N$. It is denoted by $f_n \xrightarrow{a.e.} f$.

2) *converge almost uniformly* to an a.e. real – valued measurable function *f*, if for each $\varepsilon > 0$, there is a set $E \in \mathcal{A}$ and a natural number N such that $\mu(E) < \varepsilon$ and $\|f_n - f\|_\infty = \sup_{x \in X \setminus E} |f_n(x) - f(x)| < \varepsilon$, for each $n \geq N$. It is denoted by $f_n \xrightarrow{a.u.} f$.

3) *converge in measure* to an a.e. real – valued measurable function *f*, if for every $\varepsilon > 0$, $\lim_{n \to \infty} \mu(\{x \in X : |f_n(x) - f(x)| \geq \varepsilon\}) = 0$. If μ is a probability measure, then this mode of convergence is called *convergence in probability*.

Theorem 2.3.2

Let *f* be a real valued function on *X*. Then, there exists a sequence $\{s_n\}$ of simple functions such that $s_n(x) \to f(x)$ as $n \to \infty$ for all $x \in X$. If f is measurable, then $\{s_n\}$ may be chosen to be a sequence of measurable function. If $f \geq 0$, then $\{s_n\}$ may be chosen to be an increasing function.

Proof

Step 1:

Let $f \geq 0$.

Take $E_{n_i} = \left\{ x \in X / \frac{i-1}{2^n} \leq f(x) < \frac{i}{2^n} \right\}$.

and $F_n = \{x \in X / f(x) \geq n\}$, where $i = 1, 2, \ldots, n2^n$, and $n = 1, 2, \ldots$

Let us take, $s_n = \sum_{i=1}^{n2^n} \frac{i-1}{2^n} \chi_{E_{n_i}} + n\chi_{F_n}$.

Therefore, s_n is a simple function, for each *n*.

Claim 1:

$s_n(x) \le f(x)$, for all $x \in X$ and for all n.

Suppose $f(x) \ge n$, then $x \in F_n$.

Therefore, $s_n(x) = n \le f(x)$.

Suppose $f(x) < n$, then $\frac{i-1}{2^n} \le f(x) < \frac{i}{2^n}$, for some $1 \le i \le n2^n$.

Therefore, $x \in E_{n_i}$.

$$\Rightarrow s_n(x) = \frac{i-1}{n} \le f(x).$$

Hence, $s_n(x) \le f(x)$, for all $x \in X$ and for all n.

Claim 2:

$s_n(x) \le s_{n+1}(x)$, for all $x \in X$ and for all n.

Suppose $f(x) \ge n+1$, then $x \in F_{n+1}$.

Therefore, $s_{n+1}(x) = n + 1$.

Also, we have, $f(x) \ge n$.

Therefore, $x \in F_n$.

Hence, $s_n(x) = n$.

Since $n + 1 > n$, we have that, $s_{n+1}(x) \ge s_n(x)$.

Suppose $n \le f(x) < n+1$, then $f(x) > n$.

Therefore, $x \in F_n$.

Hence, $s_n(x) = n$.

Since $f(x) < n + 1$, we have $\frac{i-1}{2^{n+1}} \le f(x) < \frac{i}{2^{n+1}}$, for some $1 \le i \le (n+1)2^{n+1}$.

Therefore, $x \in E_{(n+1)i}$.

Hence, $s_{n+1}(x) = \frac{i-1}{2^{n+1}}$.

Since, $n \le f(x)$, we have, $n.2^{n+1} \le 2^{n+1} f(x) < i$.

Therefore, $n.2^{n+1} \le i-1$.

That implies, $n \le \dfrac{i-1}{2^{n+1}}$.

Hence, $s_n(x) \le s_{n+1}(x)$.

Suppose, $f(x) < n$, then $\dfrac{i-1}{2^n} \le f(x) < \dfrac{i}{2^n}$, for some $1 \le i \le n.2^n$.

Therefore, $x \in E_{n_i}$.

Hence, $s_n(x) = \dfrac{i-1}{2^n}$.

Now, $\dfrac{2i-2}{2^{n+1}} \le f(x) < \dfrac{2i}{2^{n+1}}$.

That is, $\dfrac{2i-2}{2^{n+1}} \le f(x) < \dfrac{2i-1}{2^{n+1}}$ or $\dfrac{2i-1}{2^{n+1}} \le f(x) < \dfrac{2i}{2^{n+1}}$.

Hence, $s_{n+1}(x) = \dfrac{2i-2}{2^{n+1}}$ or $\dfrac{2i-1}{2^{n+1}}$

$$\Rightarrow s_{n+1}(x) = \frac{i-1}{2^n} \text{ or } \frac{i-(1/2)}{2^n}.$$

Therefore, $s_n(x) \le s_{n+1}(x)$, for all $x \in X$ and for all n.

Claim 3:

$s_n(x) \to f(x)$ pointwise on X.

Let $x \in X$ and $\varepsilon > 0$.

Choose a positive integer m, such that $f(x) < m$, and $\dfrac{1}{2^m} < \varepsilon$.

Therefore, $\dfrac{i-1}{2^m} \le f(x) < \dfrac{i}{2^m}$, for some $1 \le i < m.2^m$.

Hence, $s_m(x) = \dfrac{i-1}{2^m}$.

That implies, $|s_m(x) - f(x)| < \dfrac{1}{2^m} < \varepsilon$.

Let $n \ge m$.

Hence, by claim (2), we have, $s_n(x) \ge s_m(x)$.

Therefore, $|s_n(x) - f(x)| = f(x) - s_n(x) \le f(x) - s_m(x) = |s_m(x) - f(x)| < \varepsilon$.

$\Rightarrow |s_n(x) - f(x)| < \varepsilon$, for all $n \geq m$.

Hence, $s_n(x) \to f(x)$ pointwise on *X*.

Step 2:

Let *f* be a real – valued function on *X*.

Therefore, $f = f^+ - f^-$, where $f^+, f^- \geq 0$.

Since $f^+ \geq 0$, then by step (1), there exists a sequence $\{s'_n\}$ of simple functions such that $s'_n \to f^+$ pointwise on *X*.

Also, since $f^- \geq 0$, then by step (1), there exists a sequence $\{s''_n\}$ of simple functions such that $s''_n \to f^-$ pointwise on *X*.

Let us take, $s_n = s'_n - s''_n$.

Therefore, $\{s_n\}$ is a sequence of simple functions such that $s_n \to f^+ - f^- = f$ pointwise on *X*.

Step 3:

If $f \geq 0$ and is measurable.

Therefore, $E_{n_i} = \left\{ x \in X / \frac{i-1}{2^n} \leq f(x) < \frac{i}{2^n} \right\}$.

$$\Rightarrow E_{n_i} = \left\{ x \in X / f(x) \geq \frac{i-1}{2^n} \right\} \cap \left\{ x \in X / f(x) < \frac{i}{2^n} \right\}.$$

Since f is measurable, $\left\{ x \in X / f(x) \geq \frac{i-1}{2^n} \right\}$ and $\left\{ x \in X / f(x) < \frac{i}{2^n} \right\}$ are measurable.

Hence, their intersection is also measurable.

Therefore, E_{n_i} is measurable.

Also, F_n is measurable.

Hence, $s_n = \sum_{i=1}^{n2^n} \frac{i-1}{2^n} \chi_{E_{n_i}} + n\chi_{F_n}$ is also measurable.

Therefore, $\{s_n\}$ is a sequence of simple measurable functions converging to f pointwise on *X*.

Step 4:

Let f be a measurable real – valued function on X.

Therefore, $f = f^{+} - f^{-}$, where $f^{+}, f^{-} \geq 0$.

Since $f^{+} \geq 0$, by step (3), there exists a sequence $\{s'_n\}$ of simple measurable functions such that $s'_n \to f^{+}$ pointwise on X.

Also, since $f^{-} \geq 0$, by step (3), there exists a sequence $\{s''_n\}$ of simple measurable functions such that $s''_n \to f^{-}$ pointwise on X.

Let us take, $s_n = s'_n - s''_n$.

Therefore, $\{s_n\}$ is a sequence of simple measurable functions such that $s_n \to f^{+} - f^{-} = f$ pointwise on X.

Hence the theorem.

Theorem 2.3.3

Let f be a bounded function on X. Then, there is a sequence $\{s_n\}$ of simple functions such that $\{s_n\} \to f$ uniformly on X.

Proof

Case 1)

Let f be a bounded real – valued function on X and $f \geq 0$.

Let us take, $E_{n_i} = \left\{ x \in X / \dfrac{i-1}{2^n} \leq f(x) < \dfrac{i}{2^n} \right\}$ and

$F_n = \{ x \in X / f(x) \geq n \}$, for n = 1, 2, ….. and i = 1, 2, ….., $n.2^n$.

Also, we assume that, $s_n = \sum_{i=1}^{n2^n} \dfrac{i-1}{2^n} \chi_{E_{n_i}} + n \chi_{F_{n_i}}$.

Then, $\{s_n\}$ is a sequence of simple functions.

Claim:

$\{s_n\} \to f$ uniformly on X.

Since f is bounded, we can find a positive integer m, such that $f(x) < m$, for all $x \in X$ and $(1/2^m) < \varepsilon$.

Therefore, $|s_m(x) - f(x)| < \dfrac{1}{2^m} < \varepsilon$, for all $x \in X$.

If $n \geq m$, then $s_m(x) \leq s_n(x) \leq f(x)$, for all $x \in X$.

Therefore, $|s_n(x) - f(x)| \leq |s_m(x) - f(x)| < \varepsilon$, for all $x \in X$.

$\Rightarrow |s_n(x) - f(x)| < \varepsilon$, for all $x \in X$ and for all $n \geq m$.

Therefore, $\{s_n\} \to f$ uniformly on X.

Case 2)

Let f be a bounded real – valued function on X, such that $f = f^+ - f^-$, where $f^+, f^- \geq 0$.

Since f is bounded, f^+ and f^- are bounded.

By case (1), there exists sequences $\{s_n'\}$ and $\{s_n''\}$ of simple functions such that $\{s_n'\} \to f^+$ and $\{s_n''\} \to f^-$.

Let us assume that, $s_n = s_n' - s_n''$.

Then, $\{s_n\}$ is a sequence of simple functions such that $s_n \to f^+ - f^- = f$ uniformly on X.

Hence the theorem.

2.4 Lebesgue integral of Non - negative simple functions

Definition 2.4.1

Let ϕ be a nonnegative simple function with the canonical representation $\phi = \sum_{i=1}^{n} a_i \chi_{E_i}$. The Lebesgue integral of ϕ with respect to μ, is the extended real number

$$\int_X \phi d\mu = \sum_{i=1}^{n} a_i \mu(E_i).$$

If $A \in \mathcal{A}$, we define $\int_A \phi d\mu = \int_X \chi_A \phi d\mu$.

The function ϕ is integrable, if $\int_X \phi d\mu$ is finite.

If A is measurable and ϕ is defined as above, then

$$\int_A \phi d\mu = \sum_{i=1}^{n} a_i \mu(A \cap E_i).$$

Furthermore,

$$\int_A d\mu = \int_A \chi_A d\mu = \int_X \chi_A d\mu = \mu(A).$$

Theorem 2.4.2

Let $(X, \mathcal{A}, \mu)$ be a measure space, ϕ and ψ be nonnegative simple functions and c be a nonnegative real number. Then,

1) $\int_X (\varphi+\psi)d\mu = \int_X \varphi d\mu + \int_X \psi d\mu$.

2) $\int_X c\varphi d\mu = c\int_X \varphi d\mu$.

3) If $\phi \leq \psi$, then $\int_X \varphi d\mu \leq \int_X \psi d\mu$.

4) If A and B are disjoint measurable sets, then $\int_{A\cup B} \varphi d\mu = \int_A \varphi d\mu + \int_B \varphi d\mu$.

5) The set function $\nu : \mathcal{A} \to [0,\infty]$ defined by $\nu(A) = \int_A \varphi d\mu$, for $A \in \mathcal{A}$, is a measure on X.

6) If $A \in \mathcal{A}$ and $\mu(A) = 0$, then $\int_A \varphi d\mu = 0$.

Theorem 2.4.3

Let $(X, \mathcal{A}, \mu)$ be a measure space and ϕ be a nonnegative simple function. If A and B are measurable sets such that $A \subseteq B$ and $\mu(B \setminus A) = 0$, then

$$\int_A \phi d\mu = \int_B \phi d\mu.$$

Proof

We know that, $B = A \cup (B \setminus A)$, is a disjoint union.

By theorem 5.3.2, (4) and (6), we have

$$\int_B \phi d\mu = \int_{A\cup(B\setminus A)} \phi d\mu = \int_A \phi d\mu + \int_{B\setminus A} \phi d\mu = \int_A \phi d\mu + 0 = \int_A \phi d\mu.$$

Hence the theorem.

2.5 Lebesgue integral of non - negative measurable functions

Definition 2.5.1

Let f be a nonnegative measurable function. The Lebesgue integral of f with respect to μ, is defined as

$$\int_X f d\mu = \sup.\left\{\int_X \varphi d\mu : 0 \le \varphi \le f,\ \varphi \text{ is a simple function}\right\}.$$

It is denoted by $\int_X f d\mu$.

If $E \in \mathcal{A}$, then we define the *Lebesgue integral of f over E with respect to* μ as

$$\int_E f d\mu = \int f \chi_E d\mu.$$

Theorem 2.5.2

1) If $f \le g$, then $\int_X f d\mu \le \int_X g d\mu$.

Let f and g be a nonnegative functions and c be a nonnegative real number. Then,

$$\int_X cf d\mu = c\int_X f d\mu \;.$$

2) If A and B are measurable sets such that $A \subseteq B$, then

$$\int_A f d\mu \le \int_B f d\mu.$$

Proof

1) If c = 0, then the result is obvious.

Assume that, c > 0. Then,

$$\int_X cf d\mu = \sup.\left\{\int_X \phi d\mu : 0 \le \phi \le cf,\ \phi \text{ a simple function}\right\}.$$

$$= \sup.\left\{c\int_X \frac{\phi}{c} d\mu : 0 \le \frac{\phi}{c} \le f,\ \phi \text{ a simple function}\right\}.$$

$$= c.\sup.\left\{\int_X \frac{\phi}{c} d\mu : 0 \le \frac{\phi}{c} \le f,\ \phi \text{ a simple function}\right\}.$$

$$= c\int_X f\delta\mu .$$

2) Since $f \le g$, it follows that

$\{\varphi : 0 \le \varphi \le f,\ \varphi \text{ a simple function}\} \subset \{\varphi : 0 \le \varphi \le g,\ \varphi \text{ a simple function}\}$.

Hence, $\int_X f d\mu = \sup_{0\le\phi\le f} \int_X \phi d\mu \le \sup_{0\le\phi\le g} \int_X \phi d\mu = \int_X g d\mu$.

3) If $A \subseteq B$, then $\chi_A \le \chi_B$.

Therefore, for any nonnegative measurable function f, we have that $f\chi_A \le f\chi_B$.

Then, by (2), it follows that

$$\int_A f d\mu = \int_X f\chi_A d\mu \le \int_X f\chi_B d\mu = \int_B f d\mu .$$

Hence the theorem.

Theorem 2.5.3

The following inequality is known as the ***Chebyshev's inequality***.

Let $(X, \mathcal{A}, \mu)$ be a measure space, f be a nonnegative measurable function and c be a positive real number. Then,

$$\mu(\{x \in X : f(x) \ge c\}) \le \frac{1}{c}\int_X f d\mu .$$

Proof

Let $A = \{x \in X : f(x) \ge c\}$.

Then, since $c \le f$ on A and $A \subset X$, we have,

$$\chi_A \le \chi_A f \le \chi_X f = f .$$

By theorem 2.5.2, we have that, $\int_X \chi_A c d\mu \le \int_X f d\mu$.

$$\Rightarrow c\int_X \chi_A d\mu \le \int_X f d\mu .$$

$$\Rightarrow c\int_A d\mu \le \int_X f d\mu .$$

$$\Rightarrow c\mu(A) \le \int_X f d\mu .$$

$$\Rightarrow \mu(A) \le \frac{1}{c}\int_X f d\mu .$$

That is, $\mu(\{x \in X : f(x) \ge c\}) \le \frac{1}{c}\int_X f d\mu$.

Hence proved.

Theorem 2.5.4

Let (X, $\mathcal{A}$, μ) be a measure space and f be a nonnegative measurable function on X. Then, $\int_X f d\mu = 0$ if and only if $f = 0$ a.e. on X.

Proof

Assume that $\int_X f d\mu = 0$.

For each $n \in \mathrm{N}$, let $E_n = \left\{x \in X : f(x) \ge \frac{1}{n}\right\}$.

Then, by theorem 2.5.3 (Chebyshev's inequality), we have

$$0 \le \mu(E_n) \le n\int_X f d\mu = 0 .$$

Hence, $\mu(E_n) = 0$, for each $n \in \mathrm{N}$.

Since $E_n \subset E_{n+1}$, for each $n \in \mathrm{N}$ and $E = \{x \in X : f(x) > 0\} = \bigcup_{n=1}^{\infty} E_n$, by a known theorem, it follows that

$$\mu(E) = \mu\left(\bigcup_{n=1}^{\infty} E_n\right) = \lim_{n\to\infty} \mu(E_n) = 0 .$$

That is, f = 0 a.e. on X.

Conversely,

Assume that f = 0 a.e. on X.

Let $\phi = \sum_{i=1}^{n} a_i \chi_{E_i}$ be a canonical form of a nonnegative simple function, such that $\phi \le f$.

Then, $\phi = 0$ a.e. on X.

Since $E_i = \{x \in X : \phi(x) = a_i, i = 1,2,\ldots\ldots,n\}$, we have that $\mu\left(\bigcup_{i=1}^{n} E_i\right) = 0$.

But since, $\mu\left(\bigcup_{i=1}^{n} E_i\right) = \sum_{i=1}^{n} \mu(E_i)$, we have that $\mu(E_i) = 0$,

for each i = 1, 2, ….., n.

Therefore, $\int_X \phi d\mu = \sum_{i=1}^{n} a_i \mu(E_i) = 0$.

Then, it follows that $\int_X f d\mu = \sup_{0 \le \phi \le f} \int_X \phi d\mu = 0$.

Hence the theorem.

Theorem 2.5.5

Let (X, $\mathcal{A}$, μ) be a measure space and f be a nonnegative measurable function. If $A \in \mathcal{A}$ and $\mu(A) = 0$, then $\int_A f d\mu = 0$.

Proof

Let ϕ be a nonnegative simple function such that $\phi \le f$.

Then, by theorem 5.3.2 (6), we have that $\int_A \phi d\mu = 0$.

Therefore, $\int_A f d\mu = \sup_{0 \le \phi \le f} \int_A \phi d\mu = \sup_{0 \le \phi \le f} \{0\} = 0$.

Hence the theorem.

Theorem 2.5.6

a) Suppose f is a nonnegative measurable function on X. For $A \in M$, define $\phi(A) = \int_A f d\mu$, then ϕ is countably additive on M.

b) the same conclusion holds if $f \in L(\mu)$ on E.

Proof

a) Given that $f \geq 0$ and measurable on X.

For $A \in M$, $\phi(A) = \int_A f d\mu$.

Then, ϕ is a set function on M.

Now, $A_n \in M$, $n = 1,2,3,........$

If $n \neq m$, then $A_n \cap A_m = 0$.

If $A = \bigcup_{n=1}^{\infty} A_n$, then, we have to prove that, ϕ is countably additive.

That is, we have to prove that, $\phi(A) = \sum_{n=1}^{\infty} \phi(A_n)$.

Case i)

Let $f = K_E$, where $E \in M$.

Now, $\varphi(A) = \int_A f d\mu = \int_K K_E d\mu = \mu(E \cap A) = \mu\left(\left(\bigcup_{n=1}^{\infty} A_n\right) \cap E\right) = \mu\left(\bigcup_{n=1}^{\infty} (A_n \cap E)\right)$.

Since μ is countably additive,

$$\varphi(A) = \sum_{n=1}^{\infty} \mu(A_n \cap E) = \sum_{n=1}^{\infty} \int_{A_n} K_E d\mu = \sum_{n=1}^{\infty} \int_{A_n} f d\mu = \sum_{n=1}^{\infty} \varphi(A_n).$$

Case ii)

Let f be a simple nonnegative measurable function.

Therefore, $f = \sum_{i=1}^{n} c_i K_{E_i}$, $c_i \geq 0$, $E_i \in M$.

Now, $\phi(A) = \int_A f d\mu = \sum_{i=1}^{m} \int_A c_i K_{E_i} d\mu = \sum_{i=1}^{m} \mu(A \cap E_i) = \sum_{i=1}^{m} \mu\left(\bigcup_{n=1}^{\infty} A_n \cap E_i\right)$.

That is,

$$\varphi(A)=\sum_{i=1}^{m}\sum_{n=1}^{\infty}\mu(A_n\cap E_i)=\sum_{n=1}^{\infty}\sum_{i=1}^{m}\mu(A_n\cap E_i)=\sum_{n=1}^{\infty}\sum_{i=1}^{m}\int_{A_n}c_iK_{E_i}d\mu=\sum_{n=1}^{\infty}\int_{A_n}fd\mu=\sum_{n=1}^{\infty}\varphi(A_n).$$

Case iii)

Let $0\le s\le f$ be a simple nonnegative measurable function on X.

Now, by case (ii), we have

$$\int_A sd\mu=\sum_{n=1}^{\infty}\int_{A_n}sd\mu\le\sum_{n=1}^{\infty}\int_{A_n}fd\mu.$$

That is, $\sup_{0\le s\le f}\int_A sd\mu\le\sum_{n=1}^{\infty}\int_{A_n}fd\mu$.

That implies, $\int_A fd\mu\le\sum_{n=1}^{\infty}\int_{A_n}fd\mu$.

Therefore, $\varphi(A)\le\sum_{n=1}^{\infty}\int_{A_n}fd\mu$. .... (2.5.6.1)

To prove: $\sum_{n=1}^{\infty}\phi(A_n)\le\phi(A)$.

Suppose $\phi(A_m)=+\infty$, for some m.

Then, $\sum_{n=1}^{\infty}\phi(A_n)=+\infty$.

Since $A\supset A_m$, $\phi(A)\ge\phi(A_m)$.

Hence, $\phi(A)=+\infty$.

That implies, $\phi(A)=\sum_{n=1}^{\infty}\phi(A_n)$.

Suppose $\phi(A_n)<\infty$, for all n.

Let $\varepsilon>0$ be given.

Now, $\phi(A_1)=\int_{A_1}fd\mu=\sup_{0\le s\le f}\int_{A_1}sd\mu$.

Therefore, there exists a simple measurable function s_1 such that $0 \le s_1 \le f$ and $\int_{A_1} s d\mu > \phi(A_1) - \in$.

Similarly, there exists a simple measurable function s_2 such that $0 \le s_2 \le f$ and $\int_{A_2} s d\mu > \phi(A_2) - \varepsilon$.

Let $s = \max.\{s_1, s_2\}$.

Therefore, s is a simple measurable function such that $0 \le s \le f$.

Hence, $\int_{A_1} s d\mu + \int_{A_2} s d\mu > \phi(A_1) + \phi(A_2) - 2\varepsilon$.

That implies, $\int_{A_1 \cup A_2} s d\mu > \phi(A_1) + \phi(A_2) - 2\varepsilon$.

Now, $\phi(A_1 \cup A_2) = \int_{A_1 \cup A_2} f d\mu \ge \int_{A_1 \cup A_2} s d\mu > \phi(A_1) + \phi(A_2) - 2\varepsilon$.

Since ε is arbitrary, $\phi(A_1 \cup A_2) \ge \phi(A_1) + \phi(A_2)$.

Proceeding like this, we get

$$\phi\left(\bigcup_{i=1}^{n} A_i\right) \ge \sum_{i=1}^{n} \phi(A_i), \text{ for each } n \in J.$$

Since $A \supset \bigcup_{i=1}^{n} A_i$, $\phi(A) \ge \phi\left(\bigcup_{i=1}^{n} A_i\right) \ge \sum_{i=1}^{n} \phi(A_i)$, for all n.

As it is true for every integer, we have

$$\phi(A) \ge \sum_{n=1}^{\infty} \phi(A_n). \qquad \text{.......... (2.5.6.2)}$$

Thus, from (1) and (2), we get

$$\phi(A) = \sum_{n=1}^{\infty} \phi(A_n).$$

Hence, ϕ is countably additive on m.

Hence part (a) is proved.

b) Given that $f \in L(\mu)$ on X.

Put $f = f^+ - f^-$.

Since $f \in L(\mu)$ on X, f is measurable and $\int_X f^+ d\mu < \infty$ and $\int_X f^- d\mu < \infty$.

Since f^+, f^- are measurable and $f^+, f^- \geq 0$, let $A_n \in M$ for $n = 1,2,3,........$

and $A_n \cap A_m = 0$, if $n \neq m$ and put $A = \bigcup_{n=1}^{\infty} A_n$.

Since $A \subset X$, $\int_A f^+ d\mu < \infty$ and $\int_A f^- d\mu < \infty$.

Therefore, by (a), we have $\int_A f^+ d\mu = \sum_{n=1}^{\infty} \int_{A_n} f^+ d\mu$ and $\int_A f^- d\mu = \sum_{n=1}^{\infty} \int_{A_n} f^- d\mu$.

and hence $\int_A (f^+ - f^-) d\mu = \sum_{n=1}^{\infty} \int_{A_n} (f^+ - f^-) d\mu$.

That implies, $\int_A f d\mu = \sum_{n=1}^{\infty} \int_{A_n} f d\mu$.

That is, $\phi(A) = \sum_{n=1}^{\infty} \phi(A_n)$.

Therefore, ϕ is countably additive on X.

Thus, part (b) is proved.

Hence the theorem.

Theorem 2.5.7

If $A \in M$, $B \subset A$ and $\mu(A - B) = 0$, then $\int_A f d\mu = \int_B f d\mu$.

Proof

We know that, $A = B \cup (A - B)$ and $B \cap (A - B) = 0$.

Therefore, by the previous theorem 2.5.6,

$$\int_A f d\mu = \int_B f d\mu + \int_{A-B} f d\mu.$$

Since $\mu(A - B) = 0$, we have $\int_A f d\mu = \int_B f d\mu$.

Hence the theorem.

Theorem 2.5.8

If $f \in L(\mu)$ on E, then $|f| \in L(\mu)$ on E and $\left|\int_E f d\mu\right| \leq \int_E |f| d\mu$.

Proof

First part

Given that $f \in L(\mu)$ on E.

Hence, $\int_E f d\mu < +\infty$.

Let us take, $f = f^+ - f^-$.

Therefore, $\int_E f^+ d\mu < \infty$ and $\int_E f^- d\mu < \infty$.

Let $A = \{x \in E / f(x) \geq 0\}$ and $B = \{x \in E / f(x) < 0\}$.

Now, $A \cup B = E$, $A \cap B = 0$ and $A, B \in \mathfrak{m}$.

Hence, $\int_E |f| d\mu = \int_A |f| d\mu + \int_B |f| d\mu$. .... (2.5.8.1)

When $x \in A$, $f(x) \geq 0$.

Therefore, $|f|(x) = |f(x)| = f(x)$.

Also, $f^+(x) = f(x)$.

Hence, $|f| = f^+$ on A.

When $x \in B$, $f(x) < 0$.

Therefore, $|f|(x) = |f(x)| = -f(x)$.

Also, $f^-(x) = -f(x)$.

Hence, $|f| = f^-$ on B.

Since $\int_E f^+ d\mu < +\infty$ and $A \subset E$, $\int_A f^+ d\mu < +\infty$.

Since $\int_E f^- d\mu < +\infty$ and $B \subset E$, $\int_B f^- d\mu < +\infty$.

Substituting the above results in equation (2.5.8.1), we get

$$\int_E |f| d\mu = \int_A f^+ d\mu + \int_B f^- d\mu < +\infty.$$

Therefore, $|f| \in L(\mu)$ on E.

Second part

To prove that, $\left|\int_E f d\mu\right| \leq \int_E |f| d\mu$.

Since $f \leq |f|$ on E, we have $\int_E f d\mu \leq \int_E |f| d\mu$. .... (2.5.8.2)

Also, $-f \leq |f|$ on E.

Hence, $-\int_E f d\mu \leq \int_E |f| d\mu$.

That implies, $\int_E f d\mu \geq -\int_E |f| d\mu$.

That is, $-\int_E |f| d\mu \leq \int_E f d\mu$. .... (2.5.8.3)

From equations (2.5.8.2) and (2.5.8.3), we get

$$-\int_E |f| d\mu \leq \int_E f d\mu \leq \int_E |f| d\mu.$$

Therefore, $\left|\int_E f d\mu\right| \leq \int_E |f| d\mu$.

Hence the theorem.

Theorem 2.5.9

Suppose *f* is a measurable function on *E* and $|f| \leq g$ on *E*. If $g \in L(\mu)$ on *E*, then $f \in L(\mu)$ on *E*.

Proof

Given that *f* is a measurable on *E*, $|f| \leq g$ on *E* and $g \in L(\mu)$ on *E*.

To prove that, $f \in L(\mu)$ on *E*.

We know that, $f^+ = \max.(f,0) = \frac{f}{2} + \frac{|f|}{2}$ and

$$f^- = -\min.(f,0) = -\frac{f}{2} + \frac{|f|}{2}.$$

Therefore, $f^+ + f^- = |f| \leq g$ on *E*,

Since $f^+ \geq 0$ and $f^- \geq 0$, we have $f^+ \leq g$ on *E* and $f^- \leq g$ on *E*.

That implies, $\int_E f^+ d\mu \le \int_E g d\mu$ and $\int_E f^- d\mu \le \int_E g d\mu$.

Since $g \in L(\mu)$ on *E*, $\int_E g d\mu$ is finite.

That is, $\int_E f^+ d\mu$ and $\int_E f^- d\mu$ are finite.

Therefore, $f \in L(\mu)$ on *E*. Hence the theorem.

Corollary 2.5.10

f is measurable on *E* and $|f| \in L(\mu)$ on *E*.

Proof

We know that $f = f^+ - f^-$, $\quad f^+, f^- \ge 0$.

Also, $f^+ \le |f|$ on E and

$$f^- \le |f| \text{ on } E.$$

Since $|f| \in L(\mu)$, by the previous theorem 2.5.9, $f^+, f^- \in L(\mu)$.

Therefore, $f \in L(\mu)$.

Hence the theorem.

Theorem 2.5.11

This theorem is known as **Lebesgue Monotone Convergence theorem**.

Suppose $E \in \mathcal{M}$ and $\{f_n\}$ is a sequence of measurable functions on E, such that $0 \le f_1(x) \le f_2(x) \le \ldots\ldots.,$ $x \in E$. If f is defined by $f_n(x) \to f(x),$ $x \in E$ as $n \to \infty$, then

$$\int_E f_n d\mu \to \int_E f d\mu \text{ as } n \to \infty.$$

Proof

Given that $E \in \mathcal{M}$ and $0 \le f_1(x) \le f_2(x) \le \ldots\ldots.,$ $x \in E$, where each f_n is measurable on E.

Also, $\lim_{n\to\infty} f_n(x) = f(x)$.

To prove that, $\lim_{n\to\infty} \int_E f_n d\mu = \int_E f d\mu$.

Since $\{f_n(x)\}$ is an increasing sequence, $f(x) = \sup_{n \in J} f_n(x)$.

Now, for all n, $f_n \le f_{n+1}$ on E.

Therefore, $\left\{ \int_E f_n d\mu \right\}$ is an increasing sequence.

That implies, $\lim_{n\to\infty} \int_E f_n d\mu$ exist.

Let $\alpha = \lim_{n\to\infty} \int_E f_n d\mu$.

We have to prove that, $\alpha = \int_E f d\mu$.

We know that, for all n, $f_n \le f$ on E.

That implies, $\int_E f_n d\mu \le \int_E f d\mu$.

Therefore, $\lim_{n\to\infty} \int_E f_n d\mu \le \int_E f d\mu$.

That is, $\alpha \le \int_E f d\mu$. .... (2.5.11.1)

Let us choose c such that $0 < c < 1$ and s be a simple measurable function such that $0 \le s \le f$.

Therefore, $\int_E f d\mu = \sup_{0 \le s \le f} \int_E s d\mu$.

Let $E_n = \{x \in E / f_n(x) \ge c(s(x))\}$.

That is, $E_n = \{x \in E / f_n(x) - c(s(x)) \ge 0\}$.

Since f_n is measurable for each n and s is measurable, $f_n - cs$ is a measurable function.

Hence, $E_n \in \mathcal{M}$.

Claim: $E_n \subset E_{n+1}$, for all n.

Let $x \in E_n$.

Therefore, $f_n(x) \ge cs(x)$.

Now, for all n, $f_{n+1}(x) \ge f_n(x) \ge c.s(x)$.

That implies, $x \in E_{n+1}$.

Hence, $E_n \subset E_{n+1}$.

Claim: $E = \bigcup_{n=1}^{\infty} E_n$.

Now, for all n, $E_n \subset E$. That implies, $\bigcup_{n=1}^{\infty} E_n \subset E$.

We have to prove that, $E \subset \bigcup_{n=1}^{\infty} E_n$.

Let $x \in E$.

Suppose $f(x) = 0$.

Now, $f(x) = \sup_{n \in J} f_n(x)$.

Therefore, for all n, $f_n(x) = 0$.

Since, $0 \le s \le f$, $\quad s(x) = 0$.

Hence, $f_n(x) = 0 = s(x) = c.s(x)$.

That is, $f_n(x) \ge c.s(x)$.

Therefore, $x \in E_n$. That implies, $x \in \bigcup_{n=1}^{\infty} E_n$.

Hence, $E \subset \bigcup_{n=1}^{\infty} E_n$.

Suppose $f(x) > 0$.

If $s(x) = 0$, then $cs(x) = 0 < f(x)$.

That is, $f(x) - cs(x) > 0$.

If $s(x) > 0$, then since $0 < c < 1$, we have $cs(x) < s(x) \le f$.

That implies, $f(x) - cs(x) > 0$.

Now, since $f(x) = \sup_{n \in J} f_n(x)$, there exists $m \in J$ such that

$$f_m(x) > f(x) - \left(f(x) - cs(x)\right).$$

That is, $f_m(x) > cs(x)$.

Hence, $x \in E_m \subseteq \bigcup_{n=1}^{\infty} E_n$.

Therefore, $E = \bigcup_{n=1}^{\infty} E_n$.

Hence, for any $A \in \mathcal{M}$, define $\phi(A) = \int_A s d\mu$.

Therefore, by theorem 2.5.6, ϕ is countably additive on $\mathcal{M}$.

That implies, $\lim_{n\to\infty} \phi(E_n) = \phi(E)$.

That is, $\lim_{n\to\infty} \int_{E_n} s d\mu = \int_E s d\mu$. .... (2.5.11.2)

Since $E \supset E_n$, for all n, we have

$$\int_E f_n d\mu \geq \int_{E_n} f_n d\mu \geq \int_{E_n} cs d\mu .$$

That implies, $\lim_{n\to\infty} \int_E f_n d\mu \geq c \lim_{n\to\infty} \int_{E_n} s d\mu$.

Then, by equation (2.5.11.2), we have $\alpha \geq c \int_E s d\mu$.

This is true for every c with $0 < c < 1$.

Thus, taking limit as $c \to 1$, we get $\alpha \geq \int_E s d\mu$.

Hence, $\alpha \geq \sup_{0 \leq s \leq f} \int_E s d\mu$.

That implies, $\alpha \geq \int_E f d\mu$. .... (2.5.11.3)

From equations (2.5.11.1) and (2.5.11.3), we get

$$\alpha = \int_E f d\mu .$$

Therefore, $\lim_{n\to\infty} \int_E f_n d\mu = \int_E f d\mu$.

Hence the theorem.

Theorem 2.5.12

Suppose $E \in \mathcal{M}$ and $\{f_n\}$ is a sequence of non – negative measurable functions and

$$f(x) = \sum_{n=1}^{\infty} f_n(x), \ x \in E \text{, then } \int_E f d\mu = \sum_{n=1}^{\infty} \int_E f_n d\mu .$$

Proof

Let $g_n = \sum_{i=1}^{n} f_i$.

Since each f_i is measurable, g_n is measurable for each $n \in J$.

Also, $\lim_{n\to\infty} g_n(x) = \lim_{n\to\infty} \sum_{i=1}^{\infty} f_i(x) = \sum_{i=1}^{\infty} f_i(x) = f(x), \quad x \in E$.

Therefore, by Lebesgue Monotone convergence theorem, we have

$$\int_E f d\mu = \lim_{n\to\infty} \int_E g_n d\mu = \lim_{n\to\infty} \int_E \sum_{i=1}^{n} f_i d\mu = \sum_{i=1}^{\infty} \int_E f_i d\mu = \sum_{n=1}^{\infty} \int_E f_n d\mu .$$

Hence the theorem.

Theorem 2.5.13

This theorem is known as ***Fatou's Lemma***.

Suppose $E \in \mathcal{M}$. If $\{f_n\}$ is a sequence of non – negative measurable function and $f(x) = \liminf_{n\to\infty} .f_n(x), \ x \in E$, then $\int_E f d\mu \le \liminf_{n\to\infty} . \int_E f_n d\mu$.

Proof

Let us assume that $g_1(x) = \inf .\{f_1(x), f_2(x), ...\}$,

$g_2(x) = \inf .\{f_2(x), f_3(x), ...\}$,

....

$g_n(x) = \inf .\{f_n(x), f_{n+1}(x), ...\}$.

....

Now, $\{g_n(x)\}$ is increasing and $\liminf_{n\to\infty} .f_n(x) = \liminf_{n\to\infty} .g_n(x)$.

Hence we have, $\lim_{n\to\infty} g_n(x) = f(x)$.

Also, for all n and $x \in E$ and g_n is measurable, by Lebesgue Monotone Convergence theorem, we have $\lim_{n\to\infty}\int_E g_n d\mu = \int_E f d\mu$. .... (2.5.13.1)

Again, for all $x \in E$, $g_n \leq f_n$ on E implies that $\int_E g_n d\mu \leq \int_E f_n d\mu$.

That implies, $\liminf_{n\to\infty} . \int_E g_n d\mu \leq \liminf_{n\to\infty} . \int_E f_n d\mu$. .... (2.5.13.2)

Now, since $\lim_{n\to\infty}\int_E g_n d\mu$ exists, by equation (2.5.13.1), we have

$$\liminf_{n\to\infty} . \int_E g_n d\mu = \lim_{n\to\infty}\int_E g_n d\mu = \int_E f d\mu.$$

Therefore, substituting in equation (2.5.13.2), we get

$$\int_E f d\mu \leq \liminf_{n\to\infty} . \int_E f_n d\mu.$$

Hence the theorem.

Theorem 2.5.14

This theorem is known as **Lebesgue Dominated Convergence theorem.** Suppose $E \in \mathcal{M}$. If suppose $\{f_n\}$ is a sequence of measurable functions and $f_n(x) \to f(x)$ as $n \to \infty$ and for all $x \in E$, if there exists $g \in L(\mu)$ on E such that $|f_n(x)| \leq g(x)$ for all n and $x \in E$, then $\int_E f d\mu = \lim_{n\to\infty}\int_E f_n d\mu$.

Proof

Since f_n is measurable, $|f_n| \leq g$ and $g \in L(\mu)$ on E, by theorem 2.5.9, we have

$f_n \in L(\mu)$ on E.

Also, given that $|f_n(x)| \leq g(x)$, for all n and $x \in E$.

That implies, $\lim_{n\to\infty}|f_n(x)| \leq g(x)$, for all $x \in E$.

That is, $|f(x)| \leq g(x)$, for all $x \in E$.

Therefore, we have $|f| \leq g$ on E, $g \in L(\mu)$ and f is measurable.

Since, "limit of convergent sequence of measurable functions is measurable",

$f \in L(\mu)$ on E.

Now, given that, $|f_n| \le g$ on E.

That is, $-g \le f_n \le g$. .... (2.5.14.1)

Therefore, $f_n + g \ge 0$.

Also, $f_n + g \to f + g$ as $n \to \infty$.

Hence by Fatou's lemma, we have $\int_E (f+g)d\mu \le \liminf_{n\to\infty} . \int_E (f_n + g)d\mu$.

That is, $\int_E fd\mu + \int_E gd\mu \le \liminf_{n\to\infty} . \int_E f_n d\mu + \int_E gd\mu$.

Therefore, $\int_E fd\mu \le \liminf_{n\to\infty} . \int_E f_n d\mu$. .... (2.5.14.2)

Now, from equation (2.5.14.1), we have

$g - f_n \ge 0$.

Also, $g - f_n \to g - f$ as $n \to \infty$.

Hence by Fatou's lemma, we have

$$\int_E (g-f)d\mu \le \liminf_{n\to\infty} . \int_E (g - f_n)d\mu .$$

That is, $\int_E gd\mu - \int_E fd\mu \le \int_E gd\mu - \liminf_{n\to\infty} . \int_E f_n d\mu$.

That implies, $\limsup_{n\to\infty} . \int_E f_n d\mu \le \int_E fd\mu$. .... (2.5.14.3)

Therefore, from equations (2.5.14.2) and (2.5.14.3), we have

$$\int_E fd\mu \le \liminf_{n\to\infty} . \int_E f_n d\mu \le \limsup_{n\to\infty} . \int_E f_n d\mu \le \int_E fd\mu .$$

Hence $\int_E fd\mu = \liminf_{n\to\infty} . \int_E f_n d\mu = \limsup_{n\to\infty} . \int_E f_n d\mu$.

That implies, $\left(\int_E f_n d\mu \right)$ is convergent.

Therefore, $\lim_{n\to\infty} \int_E f_n d\mu = \int_E fd\mu$.

Hence the theorem.

Corollary 2.5.15

If $\mu(E) < \infty$ and $\{f_n\}$ is a uniformly bounded sequence of measurable functions such that $f_n(x) \to f(x)$ as $n \to \infty$ for every $x \in E$, then $\int_E f d\mu = \lim_{n\to\infty} \int_E f_n d\mu$.

Proof

Since $\{f_n\}$ is uniformly bounded, there exists $k > 0$ such that $|f_n(x)| < k,$ for all $x \in E$.

Let us take $g(x) = k$.

Hence $|f_n(x)| \leq g(x),$ for all $x \in E$.

That is, $|f_n| \leq g$ on *E*.

Now, $\int_E g d\mu = \int_E k d\mu = k\mu(E) < \infty$.

Hence, $g \in L(\mu)$ on *E*.

Therefore, by Lebesgue Dominated Convergence theorem, we have

$$\int_E f d\mu = \lim_{n\to\infty} \int_E f_n d\mu .$$

Hence the corollary.

Note 2.5.16

1. We say that *f* is equivalent to *g* on *E*, denoted by $f \sim g$, if the set $\{x \in E / f(x) \neq g(x)\}$ has measure zero.
2. The relation "~" is an equivalence relation.

Proof

i) *Reflexive:*

$\{x \in E / f(x) \neq f(x)\} = 0$ has measure zero.

Therefore, $f \sim f$.

Hence, '~' is reflexive.

ii) *Symmetric:*

We have to prove that, $f \sim g \Rightarrow g \sim f$.

Now, $f \sim g \Rightarrow \{x \in E / f(x) \neq g(x)\}$ has measure zero.

$\Rightarrow \{x \in E ? g(x) \neq f(x)\}$ has measure zero.

$\Rightarrow g \sim f$.

Hence, '~' is symmetric.

iii) *Transitive:*

We have to prove that, $f \sim g, \quad g \sim h \Rightarrow f \sim h$.

$f \sim g, \quad g \sim h \Rightarrow \{x \in E / f(x) \neq g(x)\}$ has measure zero, and

$\{x \in E / g(x) \neq h(x)\}$ has measure zero.

Let $E_1 = \{x \in E / f(x) \neq g(x)\}$ and $E_2 = \{x \in E / g(x) \neq h(x)\}$.

Therefore, E_1 and E_2 has measure zero.

Let $E_3 = \{x \in E / f(x) \neq h(x)\}$.

We have to prove that, $\mu(E_3) = 0$.

We claim that, $E_3 \subseteq E_1 \cup E_2$.

Let $x \in E_3$. Then, $f(x) \neq h(x)$.

Suppose $f(x) = g(x)$ and $g(x) = h(x)$.

That implies, $f(x) = h(x)$, which is a contradiction.

Therefore, either $f(x) \neq g(x)$ or $g(x) \neq h(x)$.

That is, $x \in E_1$ or $x \in E_2$, which implies $x \in E_1 \cup E_2$.

Hence, $E_3 \subseteq E_1 \cup E_2$.

Therefore, $\mu(E_3) \leq \mu(E_1) + \mu(E_2) \leq 0 + 0 = 0$.

That implies, $f \sim h$.

Hence, '~' is transtive.

Therefore, '~' is an equivalence relation.

Hence proved.

3. $f \sim g$ on E, implies $\int_E f d\mu = \int_E g d\mu$.

Proof

Given that $f \sim g$ on E.

Let us assume that, $E_1 = \{x \in E / f(x) \neq g(x)\}$ and $E_2 = \{x \in E / f(x) = g(x)\}$.

Therefore, $E = E_1 \bigcup E_2$, $E_1 \bigcap E_2 = 0$ and since $f \sim g$, we have $\mu(E_1) = 0$.

Hence, $\int_E f d\mu = \int_{E_1} f d\mu + \int_{E_2} f d\mu = 0 + \int_{E_2} g d\mu = \int_{E_1} g d\mu + \int_{E_2} g d\mu = \int_E g d\mu$.

Hence proved.

Definition 2.5.17

If a property *p* holds on $E - A$ and if $\mu(A) = 0$, then we say *p* holds almost everywhere on *E*.

That is, $f \sim g$ on *E* implies $f = g$ almost everywhere.

Problems 2.5.18

1. If $f \geq 0$ and $\int_E f d\mu = 0$, then prove that $f(x) = 0$ almost everywhere on *E*.

Solution

Given that $f \geq 0$ and $\int_E f d\mu = 0$.

For each $n \in J$, let us take $A_n = \{x \in E / f(x) > 1/n\}$.

Since f is measurable, A_n is measurable for all *n*.

We claim that $A_n \subseteq A_{n+1}$, for all *n*.

Let $x \in A_n$. Then, $f(x) > 1/n$.

We know that, $n + 1 > n \Rightarrow \frac{1}{n+1} < \frac{1}{n}$.

Hence, $f(x) > \frac{1}{n} > \frac{1}{n+1}$.

Therefore, $x \in A_{n+1}$.

That implies, $A_n \subseteq A_{n+1}$, for all *n* .

Let $A = \{x \in E / f(x) > 0\}$.

We claim that, $A = \bigcup_{n=1}^{\infty} A_n$.

For each *n*, $A_n \subseteq A$.

Hence, $\bigcup_{n=1}^{\infty} A_n \subseteq A$.

Let $x \in A$. Then, $f(x) > 0$.

That implies, $f(x) > \frac{1}{m}$, for some $m \in J$.

That is, $x \in A_m$, for some m, which implies $x \in \bigcup_{m=1}^{\infty} A_m$.

Hence, $A \subseteq \bigcup_{n=1}^{\infty} A_n$.

Therefore, $A = \bigcup_{n=1}^{\infty} A_n$.

Since f is measurable, $A \in \mathcal{M}$.

We claim that, $\mu(A_n) = 0$, for all n.

Since $A_n \subset E$, by the given data, we have, $\int_{A_n} f d\mu \leq \int_E f d\mu = 0$.

Now, on A_n, $\int_{A_n} f d\mu > \int_{A_n} \frac{1}{n} d\mu$.

That is, $0 \geq \frac{1}{n}\mu(A_n)$.

Hnece, $\mu(A_n) = 0$, for all n.

Again, we claim that, $\mu(A) = 0$.

Now, μ is countably additive on $\mathcal{M}$.

For $n = 1, 2, 3, \ldots\ldots$, $A_n \in \mathcal{M}$, and also, $A_1 \subseteq A_2 \subseteq A_3 \subseteq \ldots\ldots\ldots$ and $A = \bigcup_{n=1}^{\infty} A_n$.

Hence, by a known theorem, we have $\mu(A) = \lim_{n\to\infty} \mu(A_n)$.

Since $\mu(A_n) = 0$, for all n, $\mu(A) = 0$.

Therefore, $f(x) = 0$, for all $x \in E - A$ and $\mu(A) = 0$.

That is, $f(x) = 0$, almost everywhere on E.

Hence proved.

2. If f is measurable, and $\int_A f d\mu = 0$, for every measurable subset A of a measurable set E. Prove that $f(x) = 0$ almost everywhere on E.

Solution

Given that, $\int_A f d\mu = 0,\ A \in \mathcal{M}$ and $A \subseteq E$.

For each $n \in J$, put $A_n = \{x \in E / f(x) > 1/n\}$.

Since f is measurable, A_n is measurable for all n.

We claim that, $A_n \subseteq A_{n+1}$, for all n.

Let $x \in A_n$.

Hence, $f(x) > \frac{1}{n}$.

We know that, $n+1 > n \Rightarrow \frac{1}{n+1} < \frac{1}{n}$.

That is, $f(x) > \frac{1}{n} > \frac{1}{n+1}$.

That implies, $x \in A_{n+1}$.

Therefore, $A_n \subseteq A_{n+1}$, for all n.

Let $A = \{x \in E / f(x) > 0\}$.

We claim that, $A = \bigcup_{n=1}^{\infty} A_n$.

We know that, for each n, $A_n \subseteq A$, which implies, $\bigcup_{n=1}^{\infty} A_n \subseteq A$.

Let $x \in A$. Then, $f(x) > 0$.

That is, $f(x) > \frac{1}{m}$, for some $m \in J$.

Hence, $x \in A_m$, for some m.

That is, $x \in \bigcup_{m=1}^{\infty} A_m$, which implies $A \subseteq \bigcup_{n=1}^{\infty} A_n$.

Therefore, $A = \bigcup_{n=1}^{\infty} A_n$.

Since f is measurable, $A \in \mathcal{M}$.

We claim that, $\mu(A_n) = 0$, for all n.

Since $A_n \subset A$, we have $\int_{A_n} f d\mu \leq \int_{A} f d\mu = 0$.

Now on A_n, $\int_{A_n} f d\mu > \int_{A_n} \frac{1}{n} d\mu$.

That is, $\frac{1}{n}.\mu(A_n) \leq 0$.

Hence, $\mu(A_n) = 0$ for all n.

We claim that, $\mu(A) = 0$.

Now, μ is countably additive on $\mathcal{M}$.

For $n = 1,2,3,......$, $A_n \in \mathcal{M}$, and also $A_1 \subseteq A_2 \subseteq ....$ and $A = \bigcup_{n=1}^{\infty} A_n$.

Hence, by a known theorem, we have $\mu(A) = \lim_{n\to\infty} \mu(A_n)$.

Since $\mu(A_n) = 0$, for all n, we have $\mu(A) = 0$.

Given that, $\int_{A} f d\mu = 0$, for all $A \in \mathcal{M}$ and $A \subset E$.

Hence, $\int_{A} - f d\mu = 0$, for all $A \in \mathcal{M}$ and $A \subset E$.

Let $B = \{x \in E / f(x) < 0\} = \{x \in E / - f(x) > 0\}$.

By the previous case, we get that $\mu(B) = 0$.

Therefore, $f(x) = 0$ on $E - (A \cup B)$.

Also, $\mu(A \cup B) = \mu(A) + \mu(B) = 0$.

Therefore, $f(x) = 0$ almost everywhere on E.

Hence proved.

2.6 Lebesgue Integral of complex functions

Definition 2.6.1

Let $f = u + iv$ be a complex function defined on a measurable space X. We say that f is measurable if and only if both u and v are measurable.

Note 2.6.2

1. If f and g are complex measurable functions, then $f+g, fg$ are measurable functions.
2. If $f = u+iv$ is measurable, then $|f| = \sqrt{u^2+v^2}$ is measurable.

Definition 2.6.3

Let μ be a measure and X be a measurable space. Let E be a measurable subset of X. Let $f = u+iv$ be a complex function on X. We say $f \in L(\mu)$ on E, if f is measurable and $\int_E |f| d\mu < \infty$. In this case, we define $\int_E f d\mu = \int_E u d\mu + i\int_E v d\mu$.

Results 2.6.4

1. $f \in L(\mu)$ on E if and only if $u, v \in L(\mu)$ on E.

Proof

Direct part,

Given that $f \in L(\mu)$ on E.

Therefore, $\int_E |f| d\mu < \infty$.

That implies, $|f| \in L(\mu)$ on E.

Also, $|u| \leq f$ and $|v| \leq f$.

Hence, by theorem 2.5.9, $u, v \in L(\mu)$ on E.

Converse part,

Given that $u, v \in L(\mu)$ on E.

Therefore, $\int_E |u| d\mu < \infty$ and $\int_E |v| d\mu < \infty$.

Now, $|f| = |u+iv| \leq |u| + |v|$.

That implies, $\int_E |f| d\mu \leq \int_E |u| d\mu + \int_E |v| d\mu$.

That is, $\int_E |f| d\mu < \infty$.

Therefore, $f \in L(\mu)$ on E.

Hence proved.

2. If $f \in L(\mu)$ on E, then $cf \in L(\mu)$ on E, for all constant c, and $\int_E cf d\mu = c\int_E f d\mu$.

3. If $f_1, f_2 \in L(\mu)$ on E, then $f_1 + f_2 \in L(\mu)$ on E, and $\int_E (f_1 + f_2) d\mu = \int_E f_1 d\mu + \int_E f_2 d\mu$.

4. If $\mu(E) = 0$ and f is a complex measurable function on E, then $\int_E f d\mu = 0$.

5. If $f \in L(\mu)$ on E and $A \subseteq E$ and $A \in \mathcal{M}$, then $f \in L(\mu)$ on E.

6. If $\{f_n\}$ is a sequence of complex measurable functions, such that $\lim_{n\to\infty} f_n(x) = f(x)$, for all $x \in E$. If there exists $g \in L(\mu)$ on E such that $|f_n(x)| \le g(x)$, for all $x \in E$ and for all n. Then, $\lim_{n\to\infty}\int_E f_n d\mu = \int_E f d\mu$.

7. If $f \in L(\mu)$ on E, then $|f| \in L(\mu)$ on E and $\left|\int_E f d\mu\right| \le \int_E |f| d\mu$.

Unit 3

SIGNED MEASURES AND RADON NIKODYM THEOREM

3.1 Introduction

In this chapter, we will discuss the most important results in Measure theory like Hahn decomposition theorem, Jordon decomposition theorem, Radon-Nikodym theorem, and Lebesgue decomposition theorem.

3.2 Positive and Negative sets

Definition 3.2.1

Let $(X, \mathcal{A})$ be a measurable space. A *signed measure* on $\mathcal{A}$ is an extended real-valued set function ν such that

1) ν assumes atmost one of the values $-\infty$ and ∞,
2) $\nu(\phi) = 0$,
3) For any sequence (A_n) of disjoint measurable sets,

$$\nu\left(\bigcup_{n\in N} A_n\right) = \sum_{n\in N} \nu(A_n).$$

Note 3.2.2

Every measure space is a signed measure.

Example 3.2.3

Let $(X, \mathcal{A}, \mu)$ be a measure space and f be a measurable function on X such that f^+ and f^- is integrable. For any $A \in \mathcal{A}$, define ν on $\mathcal{A}$ by

$$\nu(A) = \int_A f d\mu.$$

Then, ν is a signed measure on $\mathcal{A}$.

Definition 3.2.4

Let ν be a signed measure on a measurable space $(X, \mathcal{A})$. A set $A \in \mathcal{A}$ is said to be a

1) *Positive set* with respect to ν, if $\nu(A \cap B) \geq 0$, for any $B \in \mathcal{A}$.
2) *Negative set* with respect to ν, if $\nu(A \cap B) \leq 0$, for any $B \in \mathcal{A}$.

Note 3.2.5

1) A set $A \in \mathcal{A}$ is positive with respect to ν if and only if $\nu(B) \geq 0$, for every measurable subset B of A. Similarly, a set $A \in \mathcal{A}$ is negative with respect to ν if and only if $\nu(B) \leq 0$, for every measurable subset B of A.
2) A set $A \in \mathcal{A}$ is a null set if and only if $\nu(B) = 0$, for all $B \in \mathcal{A}$ such that $B \subset A$.
3) Any measurable subset of a positive set is positive and a countable union of positive sets is positive. Similarly, any measurable subset of a negative set is negative and a countable union of negative sets is negative.
4) If A is positive for each set with respect to ν, then $\nu(A) = 0$. Generally, the converse is not true.

Theorem 3.2.6

Let $(X, \mathcal{A})$ be a measurable space and ν a signed measure on $\mathcal{A}$. If $E \in \mathcal{A}$ and $0 < \nu(E) < \infty$, then E contains set F with $\nu(F) > 0$.

Proof

If E is positive with respect to ν, then take $F = E$.

Assume that E is not positive.

Then there is a set $A \in \mathcal{A}$ with $A \subset E$ and $\nu(A) < 0$.

Let k_1 be the smallest positive integer such that there is an $E_1 \in \mathcal{A}$ with $E_1 \subset E$ and $\nu(E_1) < -\dfrac{1}{k_1}$.

Since $0 < \nu(E) + \dfrac{1}{k_1} < \nu(E) - \nu(E_1) = \nu(E - E_1) < \infty$, we can repeat the above argument used for E in the case of $E - E_1$.

Let k_1 be the smallest positive integer such that there is an $E_2 \in \mathcal{A}$ with $E_2 \subset E - E_1$ and $\nu(E_2) < -\frac{1}{k_2}$. Then

$$0 < \nu(E - E_1) + \frac{1}{k_2} < \nu(E - E_1) - \nu(E_2) = \nu(E - (E_1 \cup E_2)) < \infty .$$

Continuing in this way, we obtain a sequence (k_n) of positive integers such that for each $n \in \mathbb{N}$, k_n is the smallest positive integer for which there is a measurable set E_n such that

$$E_n \subset E - \bigcup_{j=1}^{n-1} E_j$$

and $\nu(E_n) \subset E - \bigcup_{j=1}^{n-1} E_j$ and $\nu(E_n) < -\frac{1}{k_n}$.

If the process stops at n_s, then let $F = E - \bigcup_{j=1}^{s} E_j$.

Then, F is a positive set and $\nu(F) > 0$, [since, if $\nu(F) = 0$, then $\nu(E) = \sum_{j=1}^{s} \nu(E_j) < 0$, which contradicts the fact that $\nu(E) > 0$].

Otherwise, let $F = E - \bigcup_{j=1}^{\infty} E_j$.

Then, $E = F \cup \bigcup_{j=1}^{\infty} \nu(E_j)$, a disjoint union.

Hence, $\nu(E) = \nu(F) + \sum_{j=1}^{\infty} \nu(E_j)$.

If $\nu(F) = 0$, then $\nu(E) = \sum_{j=1}^{\infty} \nu(E_j) < 0$, which contradicts the hypothesis that $\nu(E) > 0$.

Similarly, if $\nu(F) > 0$, then $\nu(E) < 0$.

Thus, $\nu(F) > 0$.

Since $0 < \nu(E) < \infty$, the series $\sum_{j=1}^{\infty} \nu(E_j)$ converges.

Therefore, $\sum_{j=1}^{\infty} \nu(E_j) > -\infty$, whenever $\sum_{j=1}^{\infty} \frac{1}{k_j} < \infty$.

In particular, we have that $k_j \to \infty$ as $j \to \infty$.

We show that, F is a positive set.

Since $\lim_{n\to\infty} k_j = \infty$, there is a $j_0 \in \mathbb{N}$ such that $k_j > 1$, for $j \geq j_0$.

Let A be a measurable subset of F and $j > j_0$.

Then, $A \subset E - \bigcup_{i=1}^{j} E_i$ and so

$$\nu(A) \geq -\frac{1}{k_j - 1}.$$

This is true for all $j \geq j_0$.

Letting $j \to \infty$, we get that $\nu(A) \geq 0$.

Therefore, F is a positive set.

Hence proved.

3.3 Hahn Decomposition theorem

The following theorem is known as ***Hahn decomposition theorem***.

Theorem 3.3.1

Let ν be a signed measure on a measurable space (X, $\mathcal{A}$). Then there is a pair (P, N) of measurable subsets of X such that

1) P is a positive set and N is a negative set.
2) $P \cap N = \varphi$..
3) $X = P \cup N$.

Proof

Since ν assumes atmost one of the values of $-\infty$ or ∞, we may assume that ∞ is the value that is never attained.

That is, $\nu(E) < \infty$, for all $E \in \mathcal{A}$.

Let $\mathcal{P}$ be the collection of all sets in $\mathcal{A}$ that are positive with respect to ν.

Then, $\mathcal{P}$ is nonempty, since $\phi \in \mathcal{P}$.

Let $\alpha = \sup\{\nu(A) : A \in \mathcal{P}\}$.

Then, $\alpha \geq 0$, since $\phi \in \mathcal{P}$.

Let (A_n) be a sequence in $\mathcal{P}$ such that $\alpha = \lim_{n\to\infty} \nu(A_n)$ and let $P = \bigcup_{n\in N} A_n$.

Since, a countable union of positive sets is positive, we have that P is positive with respect to ν.

By the definition of α, we have that $\alpha \geq \nu(P)$.

Since $P - A_n \subset P$, for each $n \in \mathbb{N}$ and P is positive with respect to ν, it follows that

$$\nu(P - A_n) \geq 0, \text{ for each } n \in \mathbb{N}.$$

Therefore, $\nu(P) = \nu(A_n) + \nu(P - A_n) \geq \nu(A_n)$, for each $n \in \mathbb{N}$.

Thus, $\alpha \leq \nu(P)$.

Hence, $\nu(P) = \alpha$.

Let $N = X - P$.

We show that N is negative with respect to ν.

Let E be a measurable subset of N.

If $\nu(E) > 0$, then, by theorem 3.2.6, E contains a subset B such that $\nu(B) > 0$.

But then, the disjoint union $P \cup B$ would be a positive set with $\nu(P \cup B) = \nu(P) + \nu(B) > \alpha$, which contradicts the definition of α.

From the above, it is clear that $P \cap N = \phi$ and $X = P \cup N$.

Hence proved.

Definition 3.3.2

The decomposition $X = P \cup N$, if X is the disjoint union of a positive set and a negative set is called a *Hahn decomposition* for ν. The Hahn decomposition (P, N) is not unique. If M is a null set with respect to ν, then the pairs $(P \cup M, N - M)$ and $(P - M, N \cup M)$ are also Hahn decomposition of X with respect to ν.

Result 3.3.3

Let $(X, \mathcal{A})$ be a measure space and ν a signed measure on X. If (P_1, N_1) and (P_2, N_2) are Hahn decompositions of X with respect to ν, then, for all $E \in \mathcal{A}$,

$$\nu(E \cap P_1) = \nu(E \cap P_2) \text{ and } \nu(E \cap N_1) = \nu(E \cap N_2).$$

Definition 3.3.4

Let ν be a signed measure on a measurable space $(X, \mathcal{A})$ and let $\{P, N\}$ be a Hahn decomposition of X with respect to ν. The *positive variation* ν^+, *negative variation* ν^- and *total variation* $|\nu|$ of ν are finite measures defined on $\mathcal{A}$ by

$$\nu^+(E) = \nu(E \cap P),$$

$$\nu^-(E) = -\nu(E \cap N)$$

$$|\nu|(E) = \nu(E \cap P) - \nu(E \cap N) = \nu^+(E) + \nu^-(E).$$

From the above result 3.3.3, it is clear that the definitions of ν^+, ν^- and $|\nu|$ are independent of any Hahn Decomposition of X with respect to the signed measure ν.

Definition 3.3.5

Let (P, N) be a Hahn decomposition of X with respect to a signed measure ν. Then $X = P \cup N$ and $P \cap N = \phi$. Let $X \in \mathcal{A}$, then

$E = E \cap X = E \cap (P \cup N) = (E \cap P) \cup (E \cap N)$, which is a disjoint union.

Therefore, $\nu(E) = \nu(E \cap P) + \nu(E \cap N) = \nu^+(E) - \nu^-(E)$.

Hence, $\nu = \nu^+ - \nu^-$.

This is called the *Jordon decomposition of* ν. Since ν assumes one of the values of $-\infty$ and ∞, either ν^+ or ν^- must be finite. If both ν^+ and ν^- are finite, then v is called a *finite signed measure.*

Example 3.3.6

Let $(X, \mathcal{A}, \mu)$ be a measure space and $f \in L^1(\mu)$. Let ν be a set function defined on $\mathcal{A}$ by

$$\nu(E) = \int_E f d\mu, \qquad E \in \mathcal{A}.$$

Then, ν is a signed measure on X and

$$\nu^+(E) = \int_E f^+ d\mu, \qquad \nu^-(E) = \int_E f^- d\mu \text{ and } \qquad |\nu|(E) = \int_E |f| d\mu.$$

Definition 3.3.7

Two measures λ and μ on a measurable space $(X, \mathcal{A})$ are said to be *mutually singular*, denoted by $\lambda \perp \mu$, if there is an $A \in \mathcal{A}$ such that $\lambda(A) = 0 = \mu(A^c)$.

If λ and μ are signed measures, then $\lambda \perp \mu$ if $|\lambda| \perp |\mu|$.

Example 3.3.8

Let v be a signed measure on a measurable space $(X, \mathcal{A})$. Then, the measures v^+ and v^- are mutually singular. Let (P, N) be a Hahn decomposition of X with respect to v. Then $X = P \cup N$ and $P \cap N = \phi$. Therefore,

$$\nu^+(N) = \nu(N \cap P) = \nu(\varphi) = 0 \text{ and}$$

$$\nu^-(P) = -\nu(N \cap P) = -\nu(\varphi) = 0.$$

Thus, $\nu^+ \perp \nu^-$.

3.4 Jordon Decomposition theorem

The following theorem is known as ***Jordon Decomposition theorem***.

Theorem 3.4.1

If ν is a signed measure on a measurable space $(X, \mathcal{A})$, then there exists positive measures ν^+ and ν^- such that $\nu = \nu^+ - \nu^-$ and ν^+ and ν^- are mutually singular. This decomposition is unique.

Proof

Let E and F be the negative and positive sets respectively for ν, such that $X = E \cup F$ and $E \cap F = \phi$.

Let $\nu^+(A) = \nu(A \cap F)$ and $\nu^-(A) = -\nu(A \cap E)$.

Therefore, by the definition of Hahn decomposition, we have $\nu = \nu^+ - \nu^-$.

Suppose there exists another decomposition such that

$$\nu = \mu^+ - \mu^- \text{ and } \mu^+ \perp \mu^- . \qquad \text{..........} (3.4.1.1)$$

Let E' be the set such that $\mu^+(E') = 0$ and $\mu^-\left((E')^c\right) = 0$.

Set $(E')^c = F'$.

Hence, $X = E' \cup F'$ and $E' \cap F' = \varphi$.

If $A \subset F'$, then $\mu^-(A) \leq \mu^-(F') = 0$.

Therefore, $\nu(A) = \mu^+(A) - \mu^-(A) = \mu^+(A) \geq 0$.

This implies that, F' is a positive set for ν.

Similarly, E' is a negative set for ν.

Therefore, E' and F' are another Hahn decomposition of X.

To prove: The Uniqueness part.

That is, to prove that, $\nu^+ = \mu^+$ and $\nu^- = \mu^-$.

By the uniqueness part of Hahn decomposition theorem, we have,

$F \Delta F'$ is a null set with respect to ν.

Since $\mu^+(E') = 0$ and $\mu^-(F') = 0$, if $A \in \mathcal{A}$, then

$$\mu^+(A) = \mu^+(A \cap F') = \mu^+(A \cap F') - \mu^-(A \cap F')$$

[Since $A \cap F' \subset F' \Rightarrow \mu^+(A \cap F') = 0$ and $\mu^-(A \cap F') = 0$]

Hence, by equation (3.4.1.1), we have $\mu^+(A) = \nu(A \cap F')$.

Since $F \Delta F'$ is a null set, we have $\mu^+(A) = \nu(A \cap F)$.

Now, by our assumption, we get $\mu^+(A) = \nu^+(A)$.

Similarly, we can prove that, $\mu^-(A) = \nu^-(A)$.

Hence the theorem.

Note 3.4.2

A signed measure ν is called *finite*, if $|\nu|$ is finite.

Also, it is said to be σ - *finite*, if $|\nu|$ is σ-finite.

3.5 The Radon - Nikodym theorem

Definition 3.5.1

Let λ and μ be measures on a measurable space $(X,\mathcal{A})$. We say that λ is *absolutely continuous* with respect to μ, if $\lambda(E)=0$, for every $E\in\mathcal{A}$, for which $\mu(E)=0$. It is denoted by $\lambda<<\mu$.

If λ and μ are signed measures, then $\lambda<<\mu$, if $|\lambda|<<|\mu|$.

Example 3.5.2

Let $(X,\mathcal{A},\mu)$ be a measure space and *f* be a nonnegative measurable function on *X*. We know that the set function

$$\lambda(E)=\int_E f d\mu, \quad E\in\mathcal{A}$$

defines a measure on *X*. The measure λ will be finite if and only if *f* is integrable. Since the integral over a set $E\in\mathcal{A}$ with $\mu(E)=0$ is zero, it follows that λ is absolutely continuous with respect to μ.

Theorem 3.5.3

Let λ,μ and ν be measures on a measurable space $(X,\mathcal{A})$ and c_1 and c_2 be numbers. Then

1) If $\lambda\ll\mu$ and $\nu\ll\mu$, then $(c_1\lambda+c_2\nu)\ll\mu$.
2) If $\lambda\perp\mu$ and $\nu\perp\mu$, then $(c_1\lambda+c_2\nu)\perp\mu$.
3) If $\lambda\perp\mu$ and $\nu\perp\mu$, then $\lambda=0$.

Theorem 3.5.4

Let λ,μ and ν be finite positive measures on a measurable space $(X,\mathcal{A})$. Either $\mu\perp\nu$ or else, there exists $\varepsilon>0$ and $G\in\mathcal{A}$ such that $\mu(G)>0$ and *G* is a positive set for $\nu-\varepsilon\mu$.

Theorem 3.5.5

This theorem is known as ***Radon - Nikodym theorem***.

Suppose μ is a σ-finite positive measure on a measurable space $(X,\mathcal{A})$ and ν is a finite positive measure on $(X,\mathcal{A})$ such that ν is absolutely continuous with respect to μ. Then, there exists μ-integrable nonnegative function f which is measurable with respect to $\mathcal{A}$ such that

$$\nu(A) = \int_A f d\mu, \text{ for all } A \in \mathcal{A}.$$

Moreover, if g is another such function, then $f = g$ almost everywhere (a.e) with respect to μ.

Proof

Let us prove the theorem in four steps.

Step 1:

Let us first prove the uniqueness part.

Suppose f and g are two functions, then for all $A \in \mathcal{A}$, we have

$$\int_A f d\mu = \nu(A) = \int_A g d\mu.$$

Now, for every set A, we have

$$\int_A (f - g) d\mu = \nu(A) - \nu(A) = 0.$$

By the theorem that, "Suppose f is real valued and measurable function and for every measurable set A, we have $\int_A f d\mu = 0$. Then, f = 0 almost everywhere", we have

$$\text{f} - \text{g} = 0 \text{ almost everywhere with respect to } \mu.$$

Step 2:

Let us assume that μ is a finite measure.

Define $\mathcal{F} = \left\{ g \text{ is measurable; } g \geq 0, \int_A g d\mu \leq \nu(A), \text{ for all } A \in \mathcal{A} \right\}$.

Here, $\mathcal{F}$ is not empty, because $0 \in \mathcal{F}$.

Let $L = \sup.\left\{\int g d\mu ; g \in \mathcal{F}\right\}$ and g_n be a sequence in $\mathcal{F}$ such that $\int g_n d\mu \to L$.

Let $h_n = \max.(g_1, g_2, \ldots\ldots, g_n)$.

We claim that, if g_1 and g_2 are in $\mathcal{F}$, then $h_2 = \max.(g_1, g_2)$ is also in $\mathcal{F}$.

Let $B = \{x; g_1(x) \geq g_2(x)\}$.

Therefore, $\int_A h_2 d\mu = \int_{A\cap B} h_2 d\mu + \int_{A\cap B^c} h_2 d\mu$.

$$= \int_{A\cap B} g_1 d\mu + \int_{A\cap B^c} g_2 d\mu$$

$$= \nu(A\cap B) + \nu(A\cap B^c) = \nu(A).$$

Hence, $h_2 \in \mathcal{F}$.

By induction hypothesis, we prove that $h_n \in \mathcal{F}$.

Let us assume that h_n increases to f.

Therefore, by Monotone Convergence theorem, we have

$\int_A f d\mu \le \nu(A)$, for all $A \in \mathcal{A}$ and

$\int f d\mu \ge \int h_n d\mu \ge \int g_n d\mu$, for each n.

Hence, $\int f d\mu = L$.

Step 3:

Next, we prove that, f is the desired function.

Let us define λ by $\lambda(A) = \nu(A) - \int_A f d\mu$.

Now, λ is a positive measure, since $f \in \mathcal{F}$.

Suppose λ is not mutually singular to μ.

Then, by the previous theorem 3.5.4, there exists $\varepsilon > 0$ and G such that G is measurable,

$\mu(G) > 0$ and G is a positive set for $\lambda - \varepsilon\mu$.

For any $A \in \mathcal{A}$,

$$\nu(A) - \int_A f d\mu = \mu(A) \ge \lambda(A\cap G) \ge \varepsilon\, \mu(A\cap G) = \int_A \varepsilon\, \chi_G d\mu.$$

That implies, $\nu(A) \ge \int_A (f + \varepsilon\, \chi_G) d\mu$.

Hence, $f + \varepsilon\, \chi_G \in \mathcal{F}$.

But, $\int_X (f + \varepsilon\, \chi_G) d\mu = L + \varepsilon\, \mu(G) > L$.

This is a contradiction to the definition of L.

Therefore, $\lambda \perp \mu$.

Then, there exists $H \in \mathcal{A}$ such that $\mu(H)=0$ and $\mu(\mathrm{H}^c)=0$.

Since $\nu << \mu$, then $\nu(H)=0$.

Hence, $\lambda(H)=\nu(H)-\int_H fd\mu=0$.

This implies that, $\lambda=0$ or $\nu(A)=\int_A fd\mu$, for all A.

Step 4:

Suppose μ is σ-finite.

Then, there exists $F_i \to X$ such that $\mu(F_i)<\infty$, for each i.

Let μ_i be the restriction of μ to F_i, that is, $\mu_i(A)=\mu(A\cap F_i)$.

Similarly, define ν_i, the restriction of ν to F_i.

If $\mu_i(A)=0$, then $\mu(A\cap F_i)=0$ and hence $\nu_i(A)=0$.

Therefore, $\nu_i << \mu_i$.

If f_i is the function such that $d\nu_i = f_i d\mu_i$, then the argument of step 1 shows that $f_i = f_j$ on F_i, if $i \le j$.

Define f by $f(x)=f_i(x)$, if $x \in F_i$.

Then, for each $A \in \mathcal{A}$,

$$\nu(A\cap F_i)=\nu_i(A)=\int_A f_i d\mu_i = \int_{A\cap F_i} fd\mu .$$

Letting $i \to \infty$, we get that

$$\nu(A)=\int_A fd\mu .$$

Hence the theorem.

Note 3.5.6

The function *f* described in the Radon-Nikodym theorem is also called the Radon-Nikodym derivative of ν with respect to μ. We write, $f=\frac{d\nu}{d\mu}$ or $d\nu = fd\mu$.

Theorem 3.5.7

This theorem is known as ***Lebesgue-Radon-Nikodym Theorem.***

Let $(X, \mathcal{A}, \mu)$ be a σ-finite measure space and ν be a σ-finite measure on $\mathcal{A}$. Then, there is a unique pair of measures λ and ρ, with $\nu = \lambda + \rho$ such that $\lambda << \mu$ and $\rho << \mu$.

Proof

Let $\delta = \mu + \nu$.

Then, δ is a σ-finite measure with $\mu << \delta$ and $\nu << \delta$.

By the Radon-Nikodym theorem, there are nonnegative measurable functions f and g on X such that

$$\mu(E) = \int_E f d\delta \text{ and } \nu(E) = \int_E g d\delta,\ E \in \mathcal{A}.$$

Let $A = \{x \in X : f(x) > 0\}$ and $B = \{x \in X : f(x) = 0\}$.

Then, $X = A \cup B, A \cap B = \phi$ and $\mu(B) = \int_B f d\delta = 0$.

Define λ and ρ by,

$$\lambda(E) = \nu(E \cap A) \text{ and } \rho(E) = \nu(E \cap B).$$

Let $E \in \mathcal{A}$.

Then,

$$E = E \cap X = E \cap (A \cup B) = (E \cap A) \cup (E \cap B) \text{ is a disjoint union.}$$

Therefore,

$$\nu(E) = \nu(E \cap A) + \nu(E \cap B) = \lambda(E) + \rho(E) = (\lambda + \rho)(E).$$

Hence, $\nu = \lambda + \rho$.

Since, $\rho(A) = \nu(A \cap B) = \nu(\varphi) = 0$, we have that $\rho(A) = 0 = \mu(B)$.

That is, $\rho \perp \mu$.

Now, we will show that $\lambda << \mu$.

Let $E \in \mathcal{A}$, such that $\mu(E) = 0$.

Then,

$$0 = \mu(E) = \int_E f d\rho.$$

Therefore, $f = 0$ a.e. $[\rho]$.

Now, $0 \le \int_{A\cap E} fd\rho \le \int_E fd\rho = 0$.

Hence, by a known theorem, we have

$$\int_{A\cap E} fd\rho = 0$$

Since $f > 0$ on $A \cap E$, we must have that $\rho(A \cap E) = 0$.

Since $\nu << \delta$, it follows that $\nu(A \cap E) = 0$.

Therefore, $\lambda(E) = 0$.

That is, $\lambda << \mu$.

Uniqueness: Let λ_1 and ρ_1 be another pair of measures with $\nu = \lambda_1 + \rho_1$ such that $\lambda_1 << \mu$ and $\rho_1 \perp \mu$.

Then, $\lambda + \rho = \lambda_1 + \rho_1 \Leftrightarrow \lambda - \lambda_1 = \rho_1 - \rho$.

Hence, $(\lambda - \lambda_1) << \mu$ and $(\rho_1 - \rho) \perp \mu$.

Since $\lambda - \lambda_1 = \rho_1 - \rho$, it follows that $(\lambda - \lambda_1) \perp \mu$.

That is,

$$(\lambda - \lambda_1) << \mu, (\lambda - \lambda_1) \perp \mu \text{ and}$$

$$(\rho_1 - \rho) << \mu, (\rho_1 - \rho) \perp \mu.$$

Therefore, by theorem 3.5.3, we have that

$$\lambda - \lambda_1 = 0 \text{ and } \rho_1 - \rho = 0.$$

Hence, $\lambda = \lambda_1$ and $\rho_1 = \rho$.

Hence the theorem.

3.6 Complex Measures

Definition 3.6.1

A *complex measure* on a measurable space $(X, \mathcal{A})$ is a map $\nu : \mathcal{A} \to \mathbb{C}$ such that

1) $\nu(\varphi) = 0$

2) If $\{E_i\}$ is a sequence of disjoint sets in $\mathcal{A}$, then $\nu\left(\bigcup_{i=1}^{\infty} E_i\right) = \sum_{i=1}^{\infty} \nu(E_i)$, where the series converges absolutcly.

A positive measure is a complex measure only if it is finite.

Example 3.6.2

If μ is a positive measure and $f \in L^1(\mu)$, then $fd\mu$ is a complex measure.

Note 3.6.3

If ν is a complex measure such that $\nu = \nu_r + \nu_i$, where ν_r and ν_i are the real and imaginary parts of ν. Therefore, ν_r and ν_i are signed measures and they do not assume the values $+\infty$ and $-\infty$. Hence they are finite, and so the range of ν is a bounded subset of $\mathbb{C}$.

Theorem 3.6.4

This theorem is known as ***Lebesgue – Radon - Nikodym Theorem*** for complex measures.

Let $(X, \mathcal{A}, \mu)$ be a σ-finite measure space and ν be a complex measure on $\mathcal{A}$. Then, there exist a complex measure λ and $f \in L^1(\mu)$ such that $\lambda \perp \mu$ and $d\nu = d\lambda + fd\mu$. Also, if $\lambda' \perp \mu$ and $d\nu = d\lambda' + f'd\mu$, then $\lambda = \lambda'$ and $f = f'$ μ-almost everywhere.

Theorem 3.6.5

Let ν be a complex measure on $(X, \mathcal{A})$.

1) $|\nu(E)| \leq |\nu|(E)$ for all $E \in \mathcal{A}$.

2) $\nu << |\nu|$ and $d\nu / d|\nu|$ has absolute value 1 $|\nu|$ - almost everywhere.

3) $L^1(\nu) = L^1(|\nu|)$, and if $f \in L^1(\nu)$, then $\left|\int fd\nu\right| \leq \int |f|\, d|\nu|$.

Theorem 3.6.6

If ν_1 and ν_2 are complex measures on $(X, \mathcal{A})$, then $|\nu_1 + \nu_2| \leq |\nu_1| + |\nu_2|$.

Proof

We know that, for i = 1, 2, we have $\nu_i = f_i d\mu$.

Therefore, $d|\nu_1 + \nu_2| = |f_1 + f_2| d\mu \leq |f_1| d\mu + |f_2| d\mu = d|\nu_1| + d|\nu_2|$.

Hence, $|\nu_1 + \nu_2| \leq |\nu_1| + |\nu_2|$.

Hence the theorem.

3.7 Functions of Bounded Variations

Let X be a measure space $[a,b]$, with $\mu = m$ on the family of all Lebesgue measurable subsets m of $[a,b]$. Let $\int_a^b f dx$ denote the Lebesgue integral of f on $[a, b]$. Let $R\int_a^b f dx$ denote the Riemann integral on $[a,b]$.

Theorem 3.7.1

1) If $f \in R$ on $[a,b]$, then $f \in L$ on $[a,b]$ and $\int_a^b f dx = R\int_a^b f dx$.

2) Let f be a bounded function on $[a,b]$. Then, $f \in R$ on $[a,b]$ if and only if f is continuous almost everywhere on $[a,b]$.

Proof

Suppose f is a bounded function on $[a,b]$.

We can find a sequence $\{P_k\}$ of partitions of $[a,b]$, such that

a) $\{P_{k+1}\}$ is a refinement of P_k,

b) $\|P_k\| < \frac{1}{k}$,

c) $R\int_{\underline{a}}^{b} f dx = \lim_{k\to\infty} L(P_k, f)$,

d) $R\int_a^{\overline{b}} f dx = \lim_{k\to\infty} U(P_k, f)$.

If $P_k = \{a = x_0, x_1, \ldots\ldots, x_n = b\}$, define $U_k(a) = L_k(a) = f(a)$.

Let m_i = g.l.b. of $f(x)$,

M_i = l.u.b. of $f(x)$, where $x_{i-1} \le x \le x_i$.

Put $U_k(x) = M_i$ and $L_k(x) = m_i$.

Clearly, $L_k(x) \le f(x) \le U_k(x)$.

Given that, P_{k+1} is the refinement of P_k.

Therefore, $L_k(x) \le L_{k+1}(x)$ and $U_{k+1}(x) \le U_k(x)$.

Hence, $L_1(x) \le L_2(x) \le ..... \le f(x) \le ..... \le U_2(x) \le U_1(x)$.

Since $\{L_k(x)\}$ is increasing and bounded above by $f(x)$, $\{L_k(x)\}$ converges to $\sup\limits_{k \in J} L_k(x)$.

Similarly, $\{U_k(x)\}$ converges to $\inf\limits_{k \in J} U_k(x)$.

Define, $L(x) = \lim\limits_{k \to \infty} L_k(x)$ and $U(x) = \lim\limits_{k \to \infty} U_k(x)$.

Since L_k and U_k are measurable, L and U are measurable.

Now, since $L_k(x) \le f(x) \le U_k(x)$, for all $x \in [a,b]$ and for all $k \in J$, we have

$$\lim_{k \to \infty} L_k(x) \le f(x) \le \lim_{k \to \infty} U_k(x).$$

That is, $L(x) \le f(x) \le U(x)$, for all $x \in [a,b]$.

Now, $L(P_k, f) = \sum\limits_{i=1}^{n} m_i \Delta x_i = \sum\limits_{i=1}^{n} m_i (x_i - x_{i-1})$.

Also, we have, $\int\limits_a^b L_k(x)dx = \sum\limits_{i=1}^{n} m_i m([x_{i-1}, x_i]) = \sum\limits_{i=1}^{n} m_i (x_i - x_{i-1})$.

Therefore, $L(P_k, f) = \int\limits_a^b L_k dx$.

That implies, $\lim\limits_{k \to \infty} L(P_k, f) = \lim\limits_{k \to \infty} \int\limits_a^b L_k dx$.

Since L_k is a sequence of measurable functions such that $0 \le L_1(x) \le L_2(x) \le .....$ and $\lim\limits_{k \to \infty} L_k(x) = L(x)$, by Lebesgue Monotone Convergence theorem, we have

$$\lim_{k \to \infty} \int_a^b L_k(x)dx = \int_a^b L(x)dx.$$

That implies, $R\int\limits_{\underline{a}}^{b} fdx = \int\limits_a^b Ldx$. .... (3.7.1.1)

Similarly, we have, $R\int\limits_a^{\bar{b}} fdx = \int\limits_a^b Udx$. .... (3.7.1.2)

1) Given that, $f \in R$ on $[a, b]$.

Therefore, we have, $R\underline{\int_a^b} fdx = R\overline{\int_a^b} fdx$.

Hence, from equations (3.7.1.1) and (3.7.1.2), we get, $\int_a^b Ldx = \int_a^b Udx$.

Therefore, $L(x) = U(x)$ almost everywhere on $[a,b]$.

But, since $L(x) \leq f(x) \leq U(x)$, for all $x \in [a,b]$, we have

$$L(x) = f(x) = U(x) \text{ almost everywhere on } [a,b].$$

That implies, $\int_a^b L\,dx = \int_a^b f\,dx = \int_a^b U\,dx$.

Therefore, $R\int_a^b f\,dx = \int_a^b f\,dx$.

Therefore, $f \in L$ on $[a, b]$ and $\int_a^b fdx = R\int_a^b fdx$.

Hence the first part.

2) Let $A = \bigcup_{k=1}^{\infty} P_k$.

Since each P_k is finite, A is countable.

Therefore, $m(A) = 0$.

Let $x \notin A$.

To prove: $L(x) = P(x)$ if and only if f is continuous at x.

First, we will assume that $L(x) = U(x)$, and prove that f is continuous at x.

Now, since $L(x) = U(x)$, we have

$$\lim_{k\to\infty} U_k(x) = \lim_{k\to\infty} L_k(x).$$

$$\Rightarrow \lim_{k\to\infty}(U_k - L_k)(x) = 0.$$

Therefore, there exists a positive integer $k \geq N$, such that $|(U_k - L_k)(x)| < \varepsilon$, for all $k \geq N$.

$$\Rightarrow U_k(x) - L_k(x) < \varepsilon, \text{ for all } k \geq N. \quad \text{.......... (3.7.1.3)}$$

Let $P_k = \{a = x_0, x_1, \ldots\ldots, x_n = b\}$.

Since $x \notin A$, we have, $x \notin P_k$.

Therefore, $x_{i-1} < x < x_i$, for some i.

Let $\delta = \min.\{x - x_{i-1}, x_i - x\}$ and $|x - t| < \delta$.

That implies, $t \in (x_{i-1}, x_i)$.

Therefore, $m_i \le f(x)$ and $f(t) \le M_i$.

We have, $U_k(x) = M_i$ and $L_k(x) = m_i$.

Hence, $|f(x) - f(t)| \le M_i - m_i = |U_k(x) - L_k(x)| < \varepsilon$. [By (3.7.1.3)]

Therefore, there exists $\delta > 0$ such that $|x - t| < \delta \Rightarrow |f(x) - f(t)| < \varepsilon$.

Hence, f is continuous at x.

Converse part,

Suppose f is continuous at x.

We have to prove that, $U(x) = L(x)$.

That is, to prove that, $\lim\limits_{k \to \infty}(U_k - L_k)(x) = 0$.

Let $\varepsilon > 0$ be given.

Since f is continuous at x, there exists $\delta > 0$ such that $|x - t| < \delta \Rightarrow |f(x) - f(t)| < \varepsilon/3$. .... (3.7.1.4)

Choose $N \in J$, such that $\dfrac{1}{N} < \delta$.

Let $k \in J$, such that $k \ge N$.

Hence, we have $\dfrac{1}{k} \le \dfrac{1}{N} < \delta$.

Now, $\|P_k\| < \dfrac{1}{k} < \delta$.

Since $x \notin A$, we have $x \notin P_k$.

Therefore, $x_{i-1} < x < x_i$, for some i.

Now, for all $s, t \in [x_{i-1}, x_i]$, we have $|s - x| < \delta$ and $|t - x| < \delta$.

Then, by (3.1.7.4), we have,

$$|f(s)-f(x)|<\varepsilon/3 \text{ and } |f(t)-f(x)|<\varepsilon/3.$$

Therefore, $|f(s)-f(t)|\leq|f(s)-f(x)|+|f(x)-f(t)|<\dfrac{2\varepsilon}{3}$.

Hence, $M_i-m_i<2\varepsilon/3<\varepsilon$.

That is, $U_k(x)-L_k(x)<\varepsilon$.

Therefore, $|U_k(x)-L_k(x)|<\varepsilon$, for all $k\geq N$.

$$\Rightarrow \lim_{k\to\infty}(U_k-L_k)(x)=0.$$

$$\Rightarrow U(x)=L(x).$$

Hence, if $x\notin A$, then $U(x)=L(x)$ if and only if *f* is continuous at *x*.

Now, $f\in R$ on $[a, b]$ $\Leftrightarrow R\underline{\int_a^b} fdx=R\overline{\int_a^b} fdx$.

$$\Leftrightarrow \int_a^b Udx=\int_a^b Ldx.$$

$\Leftrightarrow U=L$ a.e. on $[a, b]$.

$\Leftrightarrow f$ is continuous a. e. on $[a, b]$.

Thus, the second part is proved.

Hence the theorem.

Theorem 3.7.2

The continuous functions form a dense subset of L^2 on $[a, b]$. That is, for any $f\in L^2$ on $[a, b]$ and for any $\varepsilon>0$, there is a function *g* continuous on $[a, b]$, such that $\|f-g\|=\left(\int_a^b (f-g)^2\,dx\right)^{1/2}<\varepsilon$.

Proof

We shall say that, *f* is approximated in L^2 by a sequence $\{g_n\}$ if $\|f-g_n\|\to 0$ as $n\to\infty$.

Let *A* be a closed subset of $[a,b]$ and χ_A is the characteristic function.

Let us take, $t(x) = \inf .|x - y|$, $y \in A$ and $g_n(x) = \dfrac{1}{1 + nt(x)}$, $n = 1, 2, \ldots\ldots$

Then, g_n is continuous on $[a,b]$ and $g_n(x) = 0$ on A and $g_n(x) \to 0$ on B, where $B = [a,b] - A$.

Hence, $\|g_n - \chi_A\| = \left\{ \int_B g_n^2 dx \right\}^{1/2} \to 0$.

Therefore, the characteristic function of closed sets can be approximated in L^2 by continuous functions.

The same is true for the characteristic function of any measurable set and hence also, for simple measurable functions.

If $f \geq 0$ and $f \in L^2$, then there exists a monotonically increasing sequence $\{s_n\}$ of simple nonnegative measurable functions such that $s_n(x) \to f(x)$.

Therefore, $\|f - s_n\| \to 0$.

Let *f* be any real function.

Then, $f = f^+ - f^-$, where $f^+, f^- \geq 0$.

Since $f^+ \geq 0$, there exists a monotonically increasing sequence $\{s_n'\}$ of simple nonnegative measurable functions such that $s_n'(x) \to f^+(x)$.

Since $f^- \geq 0$, there exists a monotonically increasing sequence $\{s_n''\}$ of simple nonnegative measurable functions such that $s_n''(x) \to f^-(x)$.

That is, $s_n'(x) - s_n''(x) \to f^+(x) - f^-(x) = f(x)$.

Therefore, $\|f - s_n\| \to 0$ as $n \to \infty$, where $s_n = s_n' - s_n''$.

Problem 3.7.3

If $f \in L(\mu)$ on *E* and *g* is bounded and measurable on *E*,

then $fg \in L(\mu)$ on *E*.

Solution

Since *g* is bounded on *E*, there exists $k > 0$ such that $|g(x)| \leq k$, for all $x \in E$.

Therefore, $|f(x)g(x)| = |f(x)||g(x)|$, for all $x \in E$.

$$\leq k\ f(x), \text{ for all } x \in E.$$

Hence, $|fg| \leq k|f|$ on E.

Since $f \in L(\mu)$ on E, f is measurable.

Given, g is measurable.

Therefore, fg is measurable.

Since $f \in L(\mu)$ on E, $|f| \in L(\mu)$ on E.

$$\Rightarrow k|f| \in L(\mu) \text{ on } E.$$

Therefore, $fg \in L(\mu)$ on E.

Hence proved.

Unit	
4	**CONCEPTS OF FUNCTIONAL ANALYSIS**

4.1 Normed Linear Spaces

Definition 4.1.1

Let V be a vector space. The *norm*, denoted by $\| \ \|$, is a real valued function defined on V, such that, for all $x, y \in V$,

1) $\|x\| \geq 0$,
2) $\|x\| = 0 \Leftrightarrow x = 0$,
3) $\|x + y\| \leq \|x\| + \|y\|$, (the triangle inequality)
4) $\|\alpha x\| = |\alpha| \ \|x\|$, where α is a scalar.

The norm of x is a nonnegative number. A linear space together with the norm $\| \ \|$ on it is called a *normed linear space* or *normed vector space*.

Examples 4.1.2

1) $\mathbb{R}$ is a linear space over itself. Define $\|x\| = |x|$ for all $x \in \mathbb{R}$.

Proof

Clearly, i) $\|x\| = |x| > 0$.

ii) $\|x\| = |x| = 0 \Leftrightarrow x = 0$.

iii) $\|x + y\| = |x + y| \leq |x| + |y| = \|x\| + \|y\|$.

iv) $\|\alpha x\| = |\alpha x| = |\alpha| \ |x| = |\alpha| \ \|x\|$.

Therefore, $\| \ \|$ is a norm on $\mathbb{R}$.

Hence, $\mathbb{R}$ is a normed linear space.

2) $\mathbb{R}^2$ is a linear space over $\mathbb{R}$.

Define $\| \ \|: \mathbb{R}^2 \to \mathbb{R}$ by $\|(x, y)\| = \sqrt{x^2 + y^2}$.

Proof

i) $\|(x, y)\| = \sqrt{x^2 + y^2} \geq 0$.

ii) $\|(x, y)\| = 0 \Leftrightarrow \sqrt{x^2 + y^2} = 0 \Leftrightarrow x = y = 0 \Leftrightarrow (x, y) = 0$.

iii) Claim: $\|(x, y) + (p, q)\| \leq \|(x, y)\| + \|(p, q)\|$.

Now, $\|(x, y) + (p, q)\| = \|(x + p), (y + q)\| = \sqrt{(x + p)^2 + (y + q)^2}$.

Also, we have, $\|(x, y)\| = \sqrt{x^2 + y^2}$ and $\|(p, q)\| = \sqrt{p^2 + q^2}$.

To prove: $\sqrt{(x + p)^2 + (y + q)^2} \leq \sqrt{x^2 + y^2} + \sqrt{p^2 + q^2}$.

That is, to prove: $(x + p)^2 + (y + q)^2 \leq \left[\sqrt{x^2 + y^2} + \sqrt{p^2 + q^2}\right]^2$.

That implies to prove: $xp + yq \leq \sqrt{x^2 + y^2}\sqrt{p^2 + q^2}$.

That is, to prove: $(xp + yq)^2 \leq (x^2 + y^2)(p^2 + q^2)$.

Hence to prove: $(yp - xq)^2 \geq 0$.

It is trivial.

Therefore, $\|(x, y) + (p, q)\| \leq \|(x, y)\| + \|(p, q)\|$.

iv) $\|\alpha(x, y)\| = \|(\alpha x, \alpha y)\| = \sqrt{(\alpha x)^2 + (\alpha y)^2} = \alpha\sqrt{x^2 + y^2} = |\alpha|\|(x, y)\|$.

Thus, $\| \ \|$ is a norm on $\mathbb{R}^2$.

Therefore, $\mathbb{R}^2$ is a normed linear space.

3) $\| \ \|_1$ is a norm on $\mathbb{R}^2$.

Define $\| \ \|$ on $\mathbb{R}^2$ by $\|(x, y)\|_1 = \max.\{|x|, |y|\}$.

Proof

i) $\|(x, y)\|_1 = \max.\{|x|, |y|\} \geq 0$.

ii) $\|(x, y)\|_1 = 0 \Leftrightarrow \max.\{|x|, |y|\} = 0 \Leftrightarrow |x| = |y| = 0 \Leftrightarrow x = 0, y = 0 \Leftrightarrow (x, y) = 0.$

iii) $\|(x, y) + (p, q)\|_1 \leq \|(x, y)\|_1 + \|(p, q)\|_1$.

iv) $\|\alpha(x,y)\|_1 = \|(\alpha x, \alpha y)\|_1 = \max.\{|\alpha x|, |\alpha y|\} = |\alpha|\|(x,y)\|_1$.

Therefore, $\| \; \|_1$ is a norm on $\mathbb{R}^2$.

4) $\mathbb{R}^n$ is a normed linear space.

Note 4.1.3

1) The set of all bounded continuous real functions defined on $[0,1]$, denoted as $C([0,1])$, is a linear space.
2) Every normed linear space is a metric space. That is, every norm will induce a metric.

Proof

Let $\mathbb{N}$ be a normed linear space.

Define $d : \mathbb{N} \times \mathbb{N} \to \mathbb{R}$ by $d(x,y) = \|x - y\|$, for all $x, y \in \mathbb{N}$.

Claim: d is a metric on $\mathbb{N}$.

i) $d(x,y) = \|x - y\| \geq 0$.

ii) $d(x,y) = 0 \Leftrightarrow \|x - y\| = 0 \Leftrightarrow x = y$.

iii) $d(x,z) = \|x - z\| = \|x - y + y - z\| \leq \|x - y\| + \|y - z\| = d(x,y) + d(y,z)$.

Therefore, every norm induces a metric.

Hence proved.

Definition 4.1.4 (Banach spaces)

A normed linear space which is complete as a metric space with respect to the induced metric is called a *Banach space*. $\mathbb{R}$, $\mathbb{C}$, $\mathbb{R}^n$ are Banach spaces.

Note 4.1.5

1. Let us define another norm $f \in \mathbb{C}([0,1])$, such that $\|f\| = \sup.\{|f(x)|, x \in [0,1]\}$.

In general, if X is a topological space, then $\mathbb{C}(X)$ is the set of all bounded continuous scalar functions defined on X, and, for any $f \in \mathbb{C}(X)$, let us define $\|f\| = \sup.\{|f(x)|; x \in X\}$.

Then, $\| \; \|$ is called uniform norm on $\mathbb{C}(X)$ and hence $\mathbb{C}(X)$ is a normed linear space. Also, $\mathbb{C}(X)$ is a Banach space.

2. $\mathbb{R}^n$ is a Banach space.

Proof

Let $x = (x_1, x_2, \ldots\ldots, x_n) \in \mathbb{R}^n$ and $y = (y_1, y_2, \ldots\ldots, y_n) \in \mathbb{R}^n$.

With respect to pointwise addition and scalar multiplication, $\mathbb{R}^n$ is a linear space over $\mathbb{R}$.

Define $\|x\| = \sqrt{x_1^2 + x_2^2 + \cdots + x_n^2} = [\sum_{i=1}^{n} x_i^2]^{1/2}$.

i) Clearly, $\|x\| \geq 0$.

ii) Now, $\|x\| = 0 \Leftrightarrow \sum_{i=1}^{n} x_i^2 = 0 \Leftrightarrow x_i^2 = 0,$ for $i = 1,2, \ldots\ldots, n.$

$$\Leftrightarrow x = 0.$$

iii) $\|x + y\| = \|x_1 + y_1\| + \|x_2 + y_2\| + \cdots + \|x_n + y_n\|$

$$= [\sum_{i=1}^{n} |x_i + y_i|^2]^{1/2}.$$

By Minkowski's inequality, we have

$$\|x + y\| \leq [\sum_{i=1}^{n} |x_i|^2]^{1/2} + [\sum_{i=1}^{n} |y_i|^2]^{1/2} \leq \|x\| + \|y\|.$$

iv) $\|\alpha x\| = [\sum_{i=1}^{n} |\alpha x_i|^2]^{1/2} = [\sum_{i=1}^{n} |\alpha|^2 |x_i|^2]^{1/2} = |\alpha| [\sum_{i=1}^{n} |x_i|^2]^{1/2}$

$$= |\alpha| \|x\|.$$

Hence, $\mathbb{R}^n$ is a normed linear space.

Now, $d(x, y) = \|x - y\| = [\sum_{i=1}^{n} |x_i - y_i|^2]^{1/2}$.

We claim that, $\mathbb{R}^n$ is complete with respect to this metric.

Consider a Cauchy sequence $(X_p) = (X_1, X_2, \ldots X_n, \ldots)$ in $\mathbb{R}^n$, where $X_p = (x_{p_1}, x_{p_2}, \ldots, x_{p_n})$.

Let $\epsilon > 0$ be given.

Then, there exists a positive integer n_0, such that $d(x_p, x_q) < \epsilon$, for all $p, q \geq n_0$.

Therefore, $\left[\sum_{k=1}^{n} \left|x_{p_k} - y_{q_k}\right|^2\right]^{1/2} < \epsilon, for\ all\ p, q \geq n_0.$

That is, for each $k = 1, 2, 3, \ldots\ldots, n$, we have $\left|x_{p_k} - y_{q_k}\right| < \epsilon, for\ all$ $p, q \geq n_0$.

Therefore, (x_{p_k}) is a Cauchy sequence in $\mathbb{R}$, for each $k = 1, 2, 3, \ldots\ldots, n$.

Since $\mathbb{R}$ is complete, there exists $y_k \in \mathbb{R}$, such that $(x_{p_k}) \to y_k$.

Let $y = (y_1, y_2, \ldots\ldots, y_n)$.

We claim that, $(x_p) \to y$.

Since $(x_{p_k}) \to y_k$, there exists a positive integer m_k, such that

$|x_{p_k} - y_k| < \frac{\epsilon}{\sqrt{n}}, for\ all\ p > m_k$.

Let $m_0 = max.\{m_1, m_2, \ldots\ldots, m_n\}$.

Then, $d(x_p, y) = \left[\sum_{k=1}^{n}(x_{p_k} - y_k)^2\right]^{1/2} < \left[n\left(\epsilon/\sqrt{n}\right)\right]^{1/2} = \epsilon,$

$for\ all\ p \geq m_0$.

Therefore, $(x_p) \to y$.

That implies, $\mathbb{R}^n$ is complete.

Therefore, $\mathbb{R}^n$ is a Banach space.

Hence proved.

Properties 4.1.6

1) Let N be a normed linear space. Then, for all $x, y \in \mathbb{N}$, we have $\left\|\|x\| - \|y\|\right\| \leq \|x - y\|$.

Proof

Now, we have to prove that,

$$-\|x - y\| \leq \|x\| - \|y\| \leq \|x - y\|.$$

Consider, $\|x\| = \|x - y + y\| \leq \|x - y\| + \|y\|$.

Therefore, $\|x\| - \|y\| \leq \|x - y\|$. .... (4.1.6.1)

Now, $-(\|x\| - \|y\|) = \|y\| - \|x\| \leq \|y - x\|$. [by (4.1.6.1)]

$$= \|-1\|\|x - y\| = |(-1)|\|x - y\| = \|x - y\|.$$

That implies, $-\|x - y\| \leq \|x\| - \|y\|$ .... (4.1.6.2)

Hence, from (4.1.6.1) & (4.1.6.2), we get

$$-\|x - y\| \leq \|x\| - \|y\| < \|x - y\|.$$

Hence proved.

2) Norm is a continuous function.

Proof

Let $\varepsilon > 0$ be given.

We have to find a $\delta > 0$ such that $\|x-y\| < \delta \Rightarrow \left| \|x\| - \|y\| \right| < \varepsilon$.

Let us choose $\delta < \varepsilon$.

Then, by the above property (1), we have

$$\left| \|x\| - \|y\| \right| < \|x-y\| < \delta < \varepsilon .$$

This is true for any $x, y \in \mathrm{N}$.

That implies, $\| \ \|$ is uniformly continuous.

Hence, $\| \ \|$ is continuous.

3) Addition and scalar multiplication are jointly continuous in N.

Proof

First, we will prove that "+" is jointly continuous.

That is, to prove;

For $x_n \to x$ and $y_n \to y \Rightarrow x_n + y_n \to x + y$.

Since, $x_n \to x, y_n \to y$, we have $\|x_n - x\| \to 0, \|y_n - y\| \to 0$. .... (4.1.6.3)

Now, $\|(x_n + y_n) - (x + y)\| = \|(x_n - x) + (y_n - y)\| \le \|x_n - x\| + \|y_n - y\|$.

Hence, by equation (4.1.6.3), the left hand side of the above equation converges to zero.

Therefore, $(x_n + y_n) \to (x + y)$.

Second, we prove that, scalar multiplication is jointly continuous.

Since, $(\alpha_n) \to \alpha$, we have $\|\alpha_n - \alpha\| \to 0 \Rightarrow |\alpha_n - \alpha| \to 0$. .... (4.1.6.4)

Also, $(x_n) \to x \quad \Rightarrow \quad \|x_n - x\| \to 0$. .... (4.1.6.5)

Now, $\|\alpha_n x_n - \alpha x\| = \|\alpha_n (x_n - x) + (\alpha_n - \alpha) x\| \le |\alpha_n| \ \|x_n - x\| + |\alpha_n - \alpha| \ \|x\|$.

Hence, by equations (4.1.6.4) & (4.1.6.5), $\|\alpha_n x_n - \alpha x\| \to 0$.

Therefore, $(\alpha_n x_n) \to \alpha x$.

Hence proved.

4) $||*||_p$ is a norm, where the metric induced is

$$d(x,y) = [\Sigma_{i=1}^{n} |x_i - y_i|^p]^{1/p}.$$

Proof

To prove; $\mathbb{R}^n$ is complete, with respect to the given norm.

Consider a Cauchy sequence (x_k) in $\mathbb{R}^n$, where $(x_k) = \left(x_{k_1}, x_{k_2}, \ldots\ldots, x_{k_n}\right)$.

Now, (x_k) is a Cauchy sequence if and only if, for given $\epsilon > 0$, there exists a positive integer n_0, such that $d(x_s, x_t) < \epsilon, for\ all\ s, t \geq n_0$.

That is, $\left[\sum_{i=1}^{n} \left|x_{s_i} - x_{t_i}\right|^p\right]^{1/p} < \epsilon, for\ all\ s, t \geq n_0$.

That implies, $\left|x_{s_i} - x_{t_i}\right| < \epsilon, for\ i = 1, 2, 3, \ldots\ldots, n\ \ and\ for\ all\ s, t \geq n_0$.

That is, $d\left(x_{s_i}, x_{t_i}\right) < \epsilon, for\ i = 1, 2, 3, \ldots\ldots, n\ \ and\ for\ all\ s, t \geq n_0$.

This shows that, for each $i = 1, 2, 3, \ldots\ldots, n$, $\left(x_{s_i}\right)$ is a Cauchy sequence in $\mathbb{R}$.

But, $\mathbb{R}$ is complete.

Therefore, for i =1, 2, 3, ….., n, sequence $\left(x_{s_i}\right)$ converges.

Suppose $\left(x_{s_i}\right) \to y_i$.

Let $y = y_1, \ldots\ldots, y_n$.

We claim that, the sequence (x_k) in $\mathbb{R}^n$ converges to y.

Now, $\left(x_{s_i}\right) \to y_i$ means, for given $\epsilon > 0$, there exists a positive integer m_i, such that

$$d\left(x_{s_i}, y_i\right) < \frac{\epsilon}{n^{1/p}},\ for\ all\ s \geq m_i.$$

Therefore, $\left|x_{s_i} - y_i\right|^p < \frac{\epsilon^p}{n}, for\ all\ i = 1, 2, \ldots\ldots, n\ and\ s \geq m_i$.

Let $m = max.\{m_1, m_2, \ldots\ldots, m_n\}$.

Now, $d(x_k, y) = \left[\sum_{i=1}^{n} \left|x_{k_i} - y_i\right|^p\right]^{1/p} < \left[n\frac{\epsilon^p}{n}\right]^{1/p} = \epsilon,\ for\ all\ k \geq m.$

Thus, the sequence $(x_k) \to y$.

Therefore, $\mathbb{R}^n$ is complete, with respect to the given norm.

Hence proved.

Note 4.1.7

In $\mathbb{N}$, if sequence $(x_n) \to x$, then $\|x_n\| \to \|x\|$ in $\mathbb{R}$.

Proof

Now, $(x_n) \to x \Rightarrow \|x_n - x\| \to 0$ in $\mathbb{N}$.

Now, $\left| \|x_n\| - \|x\| \right| < \|x_n - x\| \to 0$.

Therefore, $\|x_n\| \to \|x\|$.

Hence proved.

Definition 4.1.8

Let $1 \le p < \infty$ and $\mathbb{R}^n$ be the set of all n-tuples of scalars. Define $\|x\|_p = \left[\sum_{i=1}^{n} |x_i|^p\right]^{1/p}$. Then, $\| \ \|_p$ is a norm in $\mathbb{R}^n$, called the pth *norm.* The induced metric is $d(x, y) = \|x - y\| = \left[\sum_{i=1}^{n} |x_i - y_i|^p\right]^{1/p}$.

$\mathbb{R}^n$ is a Banach space, with respect to this metric. This space is denoted by l_p^n.

Examples 4.1.9

1) Let p be a real number, such that $1 \le p < \infty$. Let l_p denote the linear space of all infinite sequences, $x = \{x_1, x_2, \ldots\ldots, x_n, \ldots\ldots\}$ of scalars, such that $\sum_{n=1}^{\infty} |x_n|^p < \infty$, with the norm

$$\|x\|_p = \left(\sum_{n=1}^{\infty} |x_n|^p\right)^{1/p}$$. Here, l_p is a Banach space.

2) Consider the linear space of all n-tuples $x = (x_1, x_2, \ldots\ldots, x_n)$ of scalars with the norm $\|x\|_\infty = \max.\{|x_1|, |x_2|, \ldots\ldots, |x_n|\}$. Now, $d(x, y) = \max.\{|x_1 - y_1|, \ldots\ldots, |x_n - y_n|\}$. This metric is called square metric. Here, l_∞^n is a Banach space.

3) Consider the linear space of all bounded sequences $x = \{x_1, x_2, \ldots\ldots, x_n, \ldots\ldots\}$ of scalars with the norm $\|x\| = \sup.\{|x_n|\}$. Now, $d(x, y) = \sup.\{|x_n - y_n|\}$. Here, l_∞ is a Banach space.

4) Let C denote the set of all convergent sequences of real numbers. Clearly, $C \subseteq l_\infty$. Also, C is a linear space and it is a Banach space in itself.

5) Let C_0 be the space of all convergent sequence each of which converges to zero. Then, C_0 is a Banach space.

Note 4.1.10

Let $X = \{1, 2, \ldots..,n\}$. Consider the discrete topology on X. Then, $\mathbb{C}(X)$ coincides with l_∞^n.

Let $X = \mathbb{N}$. If we consider the discrete topology on X, then $\mathbb{C}(X)$ coincides with l_∞.

Unit sphere 4.1.11

Let $\mathbb{N}$ be a normed linear space with $\| \ \|$. A unit sphere in $\mathbb{N}$, denoted by S is defined as $S = \{x; x \in \mathbb{N} \ \& \ \|x\| \leq 1\}$.

Property 4.1.12

S is a convex set.

Proof

Let x and y be two arbitrary vectors in S.

To prove: $\lambda x + (1-\lambda)y \in S, \quad \forall \lambda \in (0,1)$.

$\|\lambda x + (1-\lambda)y\| \leq \|\lambda x\| + \|(1-\lambda)y\| = |\lambda| \ \|x\| + |1-\lambda| \ \|y\| = \lambda\|x\| + (1-\lambda)\|y\|$, since $\lambda \in (0,1)$.

Since $x, y \in S$, we have $\|\lambda x + (1-\lambda)y\| \leq \lambda.1 + (1-\lambda).1 = 1$.

Therefore, $\lambda x + (1-\lambda)y \in S, \quad \forall \lambda \in (0,1)$ and $\forall x, y \in S$.

That implies, S is compact.

Hence proved.

Problem 4.1.13

Examine the shape of the unit sphere S in $\mathbb{R}^2$, with respect to the following norms:

1) $\|x\|_1 = \|x_1\| + \|x\|_2$.
2) $\|x\|_2 = \sqrt{|x_1|^2 + |x_2|^2}$.
3) $\|x\|_\infty = Max.\{\ |x_1|,\ |x_2|\}$ where $(x_1, x_2) \in \mathbb{R}^2$.

Solution

1) With respect to $\| \|_1$:

$S = \{x; \|x\|_1 \le 1\} = \{(x_1, x_2); \|x_1\| + \|x_2\| \le 1\}$

= Square with vertices (0, 1), (-1, 0), (0, -1), (1, 0).

2) With respect to $\| \|_2$:

$S = \{x; \|x\|_2 \le 1\} = \{(x_1, x_2); \sqrt{x_1^2 + x_2^2} \le 1\}$

= Unit circle.

3) With respect to $\| \|_\infty$:

$S = \{x; \|x\|_\infty \le 1\} = \{(x_1, x_2); \text{Max.}\{|x_1|, |x_2|\} \le 1\}$.

= Unit square whose vertices are (1, 1), (-1, 1), (-1, -1), (1, -1).

Theorem 4.1.14

Let M be a closed linear subspace of a normed linear space N. If the norm of a coset $x + M$ in the quotient space $\frac{N}{M}$ is defined by $\|x + M\| = \inf.\{\|x + m\|; m \in M\}$. Then, $\frac{N}{M}$ is a normed linear space. Further, if N is a Banach space, then so is $\frac{N}{M}$.

Proof

Clearly, $\frac{N}{M}$ is a linear space.

For any, $x + m \in \frac{N}{M}$, define $\|x + M\| = \inf.\{\|x + m\|; m \in M\}$.

Each $\|x + m\| \ge 0$, for $m \in M$, implies $\inf.\{\|x + m\|; m \in M\} \ge 0$.

That implies, $\|x + M\| \ge 0$.

Since M is closed, $\|x + M\| = 0$,

if and only if, there exists a sequence $\{m_k\}$ in M, such that $\|x + m_k\| \to 0$.

if and only if, $x \in M$, [since M is a subspace, it contains zero vector].

if and only if $x + M = M$, which is the zero element of $\frac{N}{M}$.

Now, $\|(x+M)+(y+M)\| = \|x+y+M\|$.

$$= \inf.\{\|x+y+m\|; m \in M\}.$$

$$= \inf.\{\|x+y+m+m'\|; m, m' \in M\}.$$

$$= \inf.\{\|(x+m)+(y+m')\|; m, m' \in M\}.$$

$$\leq \inf.\{\|x+m\|; m \in M + \|y+m'\|; m' \in M\}.$$

$$= \|x+M\| + \|y+M\|.$$

Again, $\|\alpha(x+M)\| = \|\alpha x + \alpha M\| = \|\alpha x + M\|$.

$$= \inf.\{\|\alpha x + m\|; m \in M\}.$$

$$= \inf.\{\|\alpha x + \alpha M\|; m \in M\}.$$

$$= \inf.\{|\alpha| \|x+m\|; m \in M\}.$$

$$= |\alpha| \inf.\{\|x+m\|; m \in M\}.$$

$$= |\alpha| \|x+M\|.$$

Thus, $\frac{N}{M}$ is a normed linear space.

Consider a Cauchy sequence $\{v_n + M\}$ in $\frac{N}{M}$.

We know that, a Cauchy sequence is convergent if and only if it has a convergent subsequence.

Hence, it is enough to prove that, $\{v_n + M\}$ has a convergent subsequence.

Since, $\{v_n + M\}$ is a Cauchy sequence, we have

$$\|(v_m + M) - (v_n + M)\| < \frac{1}{2}, \quad \forall m, n \geq n_1.$$

$$\|(v_m + M) - (v_n + M)\| < \frac{1}{2^2}, \quad \forall m, n \geq n_2.$$

$$\|(v_m + M) - (v_n + M)\| < \frac{1}{2^3}, \quad \forall m, n \geq n_3.$$

....

$\|(v_m + M) - (v_n + M)\| < \frac{1}{2^k}, \quad \forall m, n \geq n_k$ and so on.

Put $x_k = v_{n_k}$.

Then, we get a subsequence $\{x_n + M\}_1^\infty$ of $\{v_n + M\}$ such that

$$\|(x_1 + M) - (x_2 + M)\| < \frac{1}{2}.$$

$$\|(x_2 + M) - (x_3 + M)\| < \frac{1}{2^2}.$$

....

$$\|(x_n + M) - (x_{n+1} + M)\| < \frac{1}{2^n} \text{ and so on.}$$

Claim: This subsequence is convergent.

Choose $y_1 \in x_1 + M$ and $y_2 \in x_2 + M$ such that $\|y_1 - y_2\| < \frac{1}{2}$.

Similarly, choose $y_3 \in x_3 + M$ such that $\|y_2 - y_3\| < \frac{1}{2^2}$.

Proceeding like this, we choose $y_4, y_5, \ldots\ldots$, such that $\|y_n - y_{n+1}\| < \frac{1}{2^n}$.

Let $m < n$.

Then, $\|y_m - y_n\| = \|y_m - y_{m+1} + y_{m+1} - y_{m+2} + \ldots\ldots - y_n\|$.

$$\leq \|y_m - y_{m+1}\| + \ldots\ldots + \|y_{n-1} - y_n\|.$$

$$< \frac{1}{2^m} + \frac{1}{2^{m+1}} + \ldots\ldots + \frac{1}{2^{n-1}}.$$

$$= \frac{1}{2^m}\left[1 + \frac{1}{2} + \frac{1}{2^2} + \ldots\ldots + \frac{1}{2^{n-m-1}}\right].$$

$$< \frac{1}{2^m}\left[1 + \frac{1}{2} + \ldots\ldots + \frac{1}{2^{n-1-m}} + \frac{1}{2^{n-m}} + \ldots\ldots\right].$$

$$= \frac{1}{2^m}\left[\frac{1}{1-(1/2)}\right] = \frac{1}{2^{m-1}} \to 0 \text{ as } m \to \infty.$$

Therefore, $\|y_m - y_n\| \to 0$ as $m, n \to \infty$.

Hence, $\{y_n\}$ is a Cauchy sequence in N.

We know that, N is a Banach space and hence it is complete.

Therefore, $\{y_n\}$ is a convergent sequence.

Suppose $\{y_n\} \to y$.

Then, we have to prove that, the subsequence $\{(x_k + M)\} \to y + M$.

Now, $\|(x_k + M) - (y + M)\| = \|x_k - y + M\|$.

$$= \inf .\{\|x_k - y + m\|; m \in M\} \leq \|x_k - y + m\|, \quad \text{for all } m \in M .$$

We choose $y_k \in x_k + M$.

Therefore, $y_k = x_k + m'$, for some $m' \in M$.

Hence, by taking $m = m'$ and a known result, we have

$$\|(x_k + M) - (y + M)\| \leq \|x_k - y + m'\| = \|y_k - y\| .$$

Since $\{y_k\} \to y$, we have $\|y_k - y\| \to 0$.

Therefore, $\|(x_k + M) - (y + M)\| \to 0$.

Hence, $\{(x_k + M)\} \to y + M$.

Since, the Cauchy sequence $\{v_n + M\}$ converges, $\frac{N}{M}$ is complete.

Therefore, $\frac{N}{M}$ is a Banach space.

Hence the theorem.

Problem 4.1.15

Let B be a Banach space. Prove that $S = \{x; \|x\| = 1, x \in B\}$ is complete.

Solution

We have, S is the subset of B.

It is enough to prove that, S is closed in S.

Let $x \in \bar{S}$.

Therefore, there exists a sequence $\{x_n\}$ in S, which converges to x.

That is, $x = \lim_{n\to\infty} (x_n)$.

That implies, , $\|x\| = \left\| \lim_{n\to\infty} (x_n) \right\| = \lim_{n\to\infty} \|x_n\|$. [Since, $\|*\|$ is a continuous function].

Therefore, $\|x\| = 1$.

That is, $x \in S$.

That implies, S is closed in B.

Therefore, S is complete.

Hence proved.

4.2 Bounded Linear Functionals

Definition 4.2.1 (Continuous Linear transformation)

Let N and N' be two normed linear spaces with same scalars. Let $T : N \to N'$ be a linear transformation of N into N'. If T is a continuous function from the metric space N into the metric space N', we say that T is a continuous linear transformation. The equivalent condition for the above condition is, $(x_n) \to x$ in N implies $(T(x_n)) \to T(x)$ in N.

Theorem 4.2.2

Let N and N' be normed linear spaces and T be a linear transformation of N into N'. Then, the following are equivalent:

1) T is continuous.
2) T is continuous at the origin, in the sense that, $x_n \to 0 \Rightarrow T(x_n) \to 0$.
3) There exists a real number $k \geq 0$, with the property that $\|T(x)\| \leq k\|x\|,\ \forall x \in N$.
4) If $S = \{x; \|x\| < 1\}$ is a closed unit sphere in N, then its image $T(S)$ is a bounded set in N'.

Proof

To prove: (1) ⇒ (2)

Given that T is continuous.

That is, $x_n \to x \textit{ implies } T(x_n) \to T(x)$.

That implies, $x_n \to 0 \textit{ implies } T(x_n) \to T(0)$.

But, $T(0) = 0$.

Therefore, $x_n \to 0 \textit{ implies } T(x_n) \to 0$.

Hence, T is continuous at the origin.

To prove: (2) ⇒ (1)

Given that $x_n \to 0 \textit{ implies } T(x_n) \to 0$.

To prove that, $x_n \to x$ *implies* $T(x_n) \to T(x)$.
Now, $x_n \to x$ *implies* $(x_n - x) \to 0$.
By the hypothesis, we have $T(x_n - x) \to 0$, which implies $T(x_n) \to T(x)$.
Therefore, T is continuous.

To prove: (2) ⇒ (3)
Given that $x_n \to 0$ *implies* $T(x_n) \to 0$.
To prove that, there exists a real number $k \geq 0$, such that
$\|T(x)\| \leq k\|x\|, for\ all\ x \in \mathbb{N}$.
Suppose there doesn't exist such a k.
Then, for all positive integer n, there exists a vector $x_n \in \mathbb{N}$, such that $\frac{\|T(x_n)\|}{n\|x_n\|} > 1$.
Let us assume that $y_n = \frac{x_n}{n\|x_n\|}$.
That implies, $\|y_n\| = \frac{1}{n}$.
Therefore, $(y_n) \to 0$.
But, $T(y_n) = \frac{T(x_n)}{n\|x_n\|}$ and $\|T(y_n)\| > 1$.
Hence, $T(y_n)$ doesnot converge to zero.
Thus, we have exhibited a sequence (y_n) in $\mathbb{N}$, such that $(y_n) \to 0$, but $T(y_n)$ doesnot converge to zero.
This contradicts the hypothesis.
Therefore, there exists a real number $k \geq 0$, such that
$\|T(x)\| \leq k\|x\|, for\ all\ x \in \mathbb{N}$.

To prove: (3) ⇒ (2)
Given that, there exists a real number $k \geq 0$, such that
$\|T(x)\| \leq k\|x\|, for\ all\ x \in \mathbb{N}$.
To prove that, $x_n \to 0$ *implies* $T(x_n) \to 0$.
Consider a sequence $(x_n) \to 0$.
By hypothesis, there exists a real number $k \geq 0$, such that
$\|T(x_n)\| \leq k\|x_n\|$.

Now, (x_n) converging to zero means, there exists a positive integer m, such that

$\|x_n\| < \frac{\epsilon}{k+1}, \; for \; all \; n \geq m.$

Now, for all $n \geq m$, we get

$$\|T(x_n)\| \leq k\|x_n\| \leq k\frac{\epsilon}{k+1} = \epsilon.$$

That implies, $T(x_n)$ converges to zero.

To prove: (3) ⇒ (4)

Given that, there exists a real number $k \geq 0$, such that

$\|T(x)\| \leq k\|x\|, for \; all \; x \in \mathrm{N}.$

To prove that, $T(S)$ is bounded in N'.

Let y be an arbitrary vector in $T(S)$.

Then, $y = T(x)$, for some $x \in S$.

Therefore, $\|x\| \leq 1$.

Now, by hypothesis, $\|y\| = \|T(x)\| \leq k\|x\| = k, for \; all \; x \in \mathrm{N}$.

Hence, for all $y \in T(S)$, we have $\|y\| \leq k$.

Therefore, $T(S)$ is bounded.

To prove: (4) ⇒ (3)

Given that, $T(S)$ is bounded in N'.

To prove that, there exists a real number $k \geq 0$, such that

$\|T(x)\| \leq k\|x\|, for \; all \; x \in \mathrm{N}.$

Let $x \in \mathrm{N}$ arbitrarily and $x \neq 0$.

Then, $y = \frac{x}{\|x\|} \in S$.

Therefore, $T(y) \in T(S)$.

Hence, by hypothesis, there exists a real number

$k \geq 0$, such that $\|T(y)\| \leq k$.

That is, $\left\|T\left(\frac{x}{\|x\|}\right)\right\| \leq k$, which implies $\|T(x)\| \leq k\|x\|$.

If $x = 0$, then clearly, $\|T(x)\| = 0 = k\|x\|$.

For all $x \in \mathrm{N}$, there exists a real number $k \geq 0$, such that $\|T(x)\| \leq k\|x\|$.

Hence the theorem.

Note 4.2.3

If a linear transformation satisfies condition (3) of theorem 4.2.2, we say that T is a bounded linear transformation and k is said to be the bound of T. Hence, by the above theorem, boundedness implies continuity and continuity implies boundedness.

Definition 4.2.4 (Norm of T)

Suppose $T : N \to N'$ is a continuous linear transformation. Then, by theorem 4.2.2, T(S) is bounded. Therefore, the set $\{\|T(x)\|; \|x\| \leq 1\}$ is bounded. We define, $\|T\| = \sup.\{\|T(x)\|; \|x\| \leq 1\}$.

We also define norm of T as, $\|T\| = \inf.\{k; k \geq 0 \text{ and } \|T(x)\| \leq k\|x\|, \forall x\}$.

Note 4.2.5

The set of all continuous bounded linear transformation from N into N' is denoted by $\mathcal{B}(N, N')$.

A continuous linear transformation from N into itself is called an operator on N. $\mathcal{B}$(N) denotes the set of all operators on N.

Results 4.2.6

$\|T(x)\| \leq \|T\|\,\|x\|$, for all $x \in N$.

Proof

Let $x \in N$ arbitrarily and $x \neq 0$.

We define, $\|T\| = \sup.\{\|T(x)\|; x \in \mathrm{N}, \|x\| \leq 1\}$.

If x = 0, then T(x) = 0.

Therefore, $\|T(x)\| = 0 = \|T\|\,\|x\|$.

Suppose $x \neq 0$.

Let us take $y = \dfrac{x}{\|x\|}$.

Hence, $\|y\| = 1$.

By definition, $\|T(y)\| \leq \|T\|$.

That is, $\left\| T\left(\frac{x}{\|x\|}\right) \right\| \le \|T\|$.

$\Rightarrow \|T(x)\| \le \|T\| \|x\|$.

Hence proved.

Theorem 4.2.7

If N and N' are normed linear spaces, then the set $\mathcal{B}(\text{N}, N')$ of all continuous linear transformations of N into N' is itself a normed linear space with respect to the norm defined by

$\|T\| = sup\{\|T\|; x \in N \; and \; \|x\| \le 1\}$. Further, if N' is a Banach space, then $\mathcal{B}(\text{N}, N')$ is also a Banach space.

Proof

Let $T_1, \; T_2 \in \mathcal{B}(\text{N}, N')$ and let α be any scalar.

Now, $T_1 + T_2 \; and \; \alpha T_1$ are linear transformations.

We have to prove that, $T_1 + T_2 \; and \; \alpha T_1$ are continuous.

Now, $T_1 and \; T_2$ are linear transformations and hence, they are bounded.

Therefore, there exists real numbers $k_1 \ge 0 \;\; and \; k_2 \ge 0$, such that

$$\|T_1(x)\| \le k_1\|x\| \;\; and \; \|T_2(x)\| \le k_2\|x\|, for \; all \; x \in N.$$

Hence, $\|(T_1 + T_2)(x)\| = \|T_1(x) + T_2(x)\| \le \|T_1(x)\| + \|T_2(x)\|$

$$\le (k_1 + k_2)\|x\|.$$

That is, let us assume that, $\|(T_1 + T_2)(x)\| \le k\|x\|$, where $k = k_1 + k_2$.

This shows that, $T_1 + T_2$ is bounded and hence continuous.

Therefore, $T_1 + T_2 \in \mathcal{B}(\text{N}, N')$.

Again, $\|(\alpha T_1)(x)\| = \|\alpha T_1(x)\| \le |\alpha| k_1\|x\| = \lambda\|x\|$.

That implies, αT_1 is bounded and hence continuous.

Therefore, $\alpha T_1 \in \mathcal{B}(\text{N}, N')$.

Thus, $\mathcal{B}(\text{N}, N')$ is a linear space.

Now, for any $T \in \mathcal{B}(\text{N}, N')$, define

$$\|T\| = sup\{\|T(x)\|; x \in N \; and \; \|x\| \le 1\}.$$

We have to prove that, the above definition gives a norm in $\mathcal{B}(\text{N}, N')$.

i) For all $x \in N$, $\|T(x)\| \geq 0$.

Hence, $\|T\| \geq 0$.

ii) Now, $\|T\| = 0$ if and only if, $sup\{\|T(x)\|; x \in N \text{ and } \|x\| \leq 1\} = 0$.

If and only if, $\|T(x)\| = 0, for\ all\ x$.

If and only if, $T = 0$.

iii) Let $T_1, T_2 \in \mathcal{B}(\mathrm{N}, N')$.

Then, $\|(T_1 + T_2)(x)\| = sup\{\|(T_1 + T_2)(x)\|; x \in N \text{ and } \|x\| \leq 1\}$.

That is, $\|(T_1 + T_2)(x)\| \leq sup\{\|T_1(x)\| + \|T_2(x)\|; x \in N \text{ and } \|x\| \leq 1\}$.

That implies, $\|(T_1 + T_2)(x)\| \leq sup\{\|T_1(x)\|; x \in N \text{ and } \|x\| \leq 1\}$

$$+sup\{\|T_2(x)\|; x \in N \text{ and } \|x\| \leq 1\} = \|T_1(x)\| + \|T_2(x)\|.$$

iv) $\|\alpha T\| = sup\{\|(\alpha T)(x)\|; x \in N \text{ and } \|x\| \leq 1\}$

$$= |\alpha| sup\{\|T(x)\|; x \in N \text{ and } \|x\| \leq 1\}.$$

That is, $\|\alpha T\| = |\alpha|\|T\|$.

Thus, $\mathcal{B}(\mathrm{N}, N')$ is a normed linear space.

To prove the "further part".

Let us assume that, N' is a Banach space.

We have to prove that, $\mathcal{B}(\mathrm{N}, N')$ is a Banach space.

Consider a Cauchy sequence $\{T_n\}$ in $\mathcal{B}(\mathrm{N}, N')$.

We claim that, for all $x \in N$, $\{T_n(x)\}$ is a Cauchy sequence of vectors in N'.

Given that, $\{T_n\}$ is a Cauchy sequence.

Therefore, for given $\epsilon > 0$, there exists an integer $n_0 \geq 0$, such that

$$\|T_m - T_n\| < \frac{\epsilon}{\|x\|+1}, for\ all\ m, n \geq n_0 \qquad \text{.......... (4.2.7.1)}$$

Then, for all $m, n \geq n_0$, we have

$$\|T_m(x) - T_n(x)\| = \|(T_m - T_n)(x)\| \leq \|T_m - T_n\|\|x\| < \epsilon.$$

Thus, $\{T_n(x)\}$ is a Cauchy sequence of vectors in N'.

Since N' is a Banach space, this sequence converges to a vector $y_x \in N'$.

Let us define a linear transformation $T: N \to N'$ such that $T(x) = y_x$, so that $\lim_{n\to\infty}\{T_n(x)\} = T(x)$.

We have to prove that, (i) $T_n \to T$, ... (4.2.7.2)

(ii) $T \in \mathcal{B}(\mathrm{N}, N')$ .... (4.2.7.3)

Now, to prove equation (4.2.7.2);

Let $\epsilon > 0$ be given.

Then, $\|T_m - T_n\| < \epsilon,\ for\ all\ m, n \geq n_0$.

If $\|x\| \leq 1\ and\ m, n \geq n_0$, we have

$$\|T_m(x) - T_n(x)\| = \|(T_m - T_n)(x)\| \leq \|T_m - T_n\|\|x\| < \epsilon.$$

[Since $\|x\| \leq 1$]

Let us fix m and allow $n \to \infty$.

We see that, $\|T_m(x) - T_n(x)\| \to \|T_m(x) - T(x)\|$.

This shows that, $\|T_m(x) - T(x)\| \leq \epsilon, m \geq n_0\ and\ for\ all\ x$, with the condition $\|x\| \leq 1$.

That is, $\{T_n\} \to T$.

Next to prove equation (4.2.7.3);

We have to prove that, $T \in \mathcal{B}(\text{N}, N')$.

To prove this it is enough, if we prove that, T is continuous.

$$\|T(x)\| = \left\|\lim_{n\to\infty} T_n(x)\right\| \leq \lim_{n\to\infty} \|T_n(x)\| \leq sup\{\|T_n\|\|x\|\}$$
$$\leq (sup\{\|T_n\|\})\|x\| = k\|x\|$$

Let us say that, $\|T(x)\| = k\|x\|$.

That implies, T is bounded and hence continuous.

Therefore, $T \in \mathcal{B}(\text{N}, N')$.

That is, $\mathcal{B}(\text{N}, N')$ is a Banach space.

Hence the theorem.

Note 4.2.8

1. $\mathcal{B}$(N) is normed linear space. Hence, $\mathcal{B}$(N) is a Banach space, if N is a Banach space.
2. $\mathcal{B}$(N) is an algebra with identity.

We can define multiplication of vectors in $\mathcal{B}$(N) as follows;

If $T_1, T_2 \in \mathcal{B}(\text{N})$, we define $(T_1T_2)(x) = T_1(T_2(x)), for\ all\ x \in N$.

If α is any scalar, then $\alpha(T_1T_2) = (\alpha T_1)(T_2) = T_1(\alpha T_2)$.

Thus, $\mathcal{B}$(N) becomes an algebra.

If $N \neq \{0\}$, then $I \in \mathcal{B}$(N).

Now, $||I|| = sup\{||I(x)||; ||x|| \leq 1\} = sup\{||x||; ||x|| \leq 1\} = 1$.

Therefore, $\mathcal{B}$(N) is an algebra with identity.

Property 4.2.8

If $T_1, T_2 \in \mathcal{B}(N)$, then $\|T_1T_2\| \leq \|T_1\| \; \|T_2\|$.

Proof

$$\begin{aligned}\|T_1T_2\| &= \sup.\{\|(T_1T_2)(x)\|; \|x\| \leq 1\}. \\ &= \sup.\{\|T_1(T_2(x))\|; \|x\| \leq 1\}. \\ &\leq \sup.\{\|T_1\| \, \|T_2(x)\|; \|x\| \leq 1\}. \quad [\text{Since } \|T(x)\| \leq \|T\| \, \|x\|] \\ &= \|T_1\| \sup.\{\|T_2(x)\|; \|x\| \leq 1\}. \\ &= \|T_1\| \, \|T_2\|.\end{aligned}$$

Therefore, $\|T_1T_2\| \leq \|T_1\| \, \|T_2\|$.

Hence proved.

Definition 4.2.9

Let N and N' be two normed linear spaces. A one-to-one linear transformation T of N into N', such that $\|T(x)\| = \|x\|$, for all $x \in N$, is called an isometric isomorphism.

Problems 4.2.10

1. Let M be a closed linear space of Normed linear space N and T be a natural mapping of $N \to \frac{N}{M}$ defined by $T(x) = x + M$. Show that T is a continuous linear transformation for which $||T|| \leq 1$.

Solution

Given that, M is a closed linear subspace of N.

Therefore, $\frac{N}{M}$ is a linear space.

Also, $||T(x)|| = ||x + M|| = inf.\{||x + m||; m \in M\} \leq ||x + m||; m \in M$.

Now, $0 \in M$.

Therefore, $||T(x)|| \leq ||x + 0||$, is also true.

That implies, $\|T(x)\| \leq \|x\|,\ for\ all\ x.$

This shows that, T is bounded and hence continuous.

Now, $\|T\| = sup.\{\|T(x)\|; \|x\| \leq 1\} \leq sup.\{\|x\|; \|x\| \leq 1\} \leq 1.$

Hence proved.

T defined in this problem is called the natural linear transformation.

2. T is a continuous linear transformation from the normed linear space N to N' and M is its Null space. Show that T induces a natural linear transformation T' of $\frac{N}{M}$ into N' and $\|T'\| = \|T\|$.

Solution

Given that, M is the null space of T.

That is, $M = T^{-1}(\{0\})$.

Now, T is continuous and $\{0\}$ is closed in N'.

That implies, M is closed in N.

Therefore, $\frac{N}{M}$ is a normed linear space.

Hence, we have the natural linear transformation $T'': N \to \frac{N}{M}$ defined by $T''(x) = x + M.$

Also, we have, $\|T''\| \leq 1.$

Let us define $T': \frac{N}{M} \to N'$ by $T'(x + M) = T(x).$

We claim that, T' is the required linear transformation.

Now, we have to prove that, $\|T'\| = \|T\|.$

First we prove that, $\|T\| \leq \|T'\|.$

$$\begin{aligned} \text{We have, } \|T\| &= sup.\{\|T(x)\|; x \in N\ \ and\ \|x\| \leq 1\}. \\ &= sup.\{\|T'(T''(x))\|; x \in N\ \ and\ \|x\| \leq 1\}. \\ &\leq sup.\{\|T'\|\|T''(x)\|; x \in N\ \ and\ \|x\| \leq 1\}. \end{aligned}$$

That is, $\|T\| \leq \|T'\|\|T''\|.$

Since $\|T''\| \leq 1$, we have, $\|T\| \leq \|T'\|.$ .... (4.2.10.1)

Next we prove that, $\|T'\| \leq \|T\|.$

$$\begin{aligned} \text{We have, } \|T'\| &= sup.\{\|T'(x + m)\|; x \in N\ \ and\ \|x\| \leq 1\}. \\ &= sup.\{\|T(x)\|; x \in N\ \ and\ \|x\| \leq 1\}. \\ &\leq \|T\| sup.\{\|x\|; x \in N\ \ and\ \|x\| \leq 1\} = \|T\|. \end{aligned}$$

That is, $\|T'\| \leq \|T\|$. .... (4.2.10.2)

From equations (4.2.10.1) and (4.2.10.2), we get

$$\|T'\| = \|T\|.$$

Hence proved.

Definition 4.2.11

Let N be a normed linear space. A continuous linear transformation of N into $\mathbb{R}$ (or N into $\mathbb{C}$) is called a continuous linear functional or simply a functional.

Definition 4.2.12

The set of all such functionals on N is denoted by $\mathcal{B}(N, \mathbb{R})$ or $\mathcal{B}(N, \mathbb{C})$. This set is denoted by N^* and is called conjugate space of N. Clearly, N^* is a Banach space.

Lemma 4.2.13

Let M be a subspace of a normed linear space N. Let f be a functional defined on M. Let $x_0 \notin M$ and denote $M_0 = M + [x_0]$, the subspace of N, spanned by M and x_0. Then, f can be extended to a functional f_0 defined on M_0, such that $\|f_0\| = \|f\|$.

Proof

Case (i);

Let us assume that N is a real normed linear space.

Given that, $x_0 \notin M$.

Therefore, every element y in M_0 is uniquely expressible as $y = x + \alpha x_0$, for some $x \in M$.

Define f_0 on M_0 by $f_0(y) = f(x) + \alpha f_0(x_0) = f(x) + \alpha r_0$, for some real number r_0.

Therefore, above definition of f_0 extends the functional f to a linear functional f_0 on M_0, for every choice of the real number r_0.

We select the real number $f_0(x_0) = r_0$, such that $\|f_0\| = \|f\|$.

Now, $\|f_0\| = sup.\{|f_0(y)|; y \in M_0 \ and\ \|y\| \leq 1\}$.

Since $M_0 \supseteq M$, we have

$\|f_0\| \geq sup.\{|f_0(y)|; y \in M \ \ and \ \|y\| \leq 1\}$

$\geq sup.\{|f(y)|; y \in M \ \ and \ \|y\| \leq 1\}$

Hence, $\|f_0\| \geq \|f\|$.

Now, we have only to prove that, $\|f_0\| \leq \|f\|$.

For that, we have to prove that, $\|f_0(y)\| \leq \|f\|\|y\|, for\ all\ y \in M_0$.

This is proved by suitable choice of r_0. Here, r_0 is chosen in the following manner;

Let x_1, x_2 be two arbitrary vectors in M.

Then, $f(x_2) - f(x_1) = f(x_2 - x_1) \leq f|x_2 - x_1| \leq \|f\|\|x_2 - x_1\|$.

That is, $f(x_2) - f(x_1) \leq \|f\|\|x_2 + x_0 - x_0 - x_1\|$

$\leq \|f\|\|x_2 + x_0\| + \|f\|\|x_1 + x_0\|$.

Therefore, $-f(x_1) - \|f\|\|x_1 + x_0\| \leq -f(x_2) + \|f\|\|x_2 + x_0\|$.

This is true for any two vectors x_1, x_2 in M.

Hence,

$sup_{x \in M}\{-f(x) - \|f\|\|x + x_0\|\} \leq inf_{x \in M}\{-f(x) + \|f\|\|x + x_0\|\}$.

Choose r_0 such that

$sup_{x \in M}\{-f(x) - \|f\|\|x + x_0\|\} \leq r_0 \leq inf_{x \in M}\{-f(x) + \|f\|\|x + x_0\|\}$.

With this choice of r_0, we prove that, $\|f_0(y)\| \leq \|f\|\|y\|, for\ all\ y \in M_0$.

Let $y \in M_0$.

Then, $y = x + \alpha r_0$.

(i) Let $\alpha = 0$.

Therefore, $y = x$ and since $x \in M$, we have $f_0(y) = f(x) = f(y)$.

Hence, $|f_0(y)| = |f(y)| \leq \|f\|\|y\|$.

(ii) Next, let $\alpha \neq 0$ and $\alpha > 0$.

Now,

$r_0 \leq inf_{x \in M}\{-f(x) + \|f\|\|x + x_0\|\} \leq -f(x) + \|f\|\|x + x_0\|$, $for\ all\ x \in M$.

We know that, M is a linear space.

Therefore, $\frac{x}{\alpha} \in M$.

Replacing x by $\frac{x}{\alpha}$ in the above inequality, we get

$r_0 \leq \left\{-f\left(\frac{x}{\alpha}\right) + \|f\| \left\|\frac{x}{\alpha} + x_0\right\|\right\}$.

That implies, $\alpha r_0 \leq \{-f(x) + \|f\|\|x + \alpha x_0\|\}$.

That is, $f(x) + \alpha r_0 \leq \|f\|\|x + \alpha x_0\|$.

$$|f_0(y)| \leq \|f\|\|y\|.$$

(iii) Again, let $\alpha < 0$.

Now, $sup_{x\in M}\{-f(x) - \|f\|\|x + x_0\|\} \leq r_0$.

Replacing x by $\frac{x}{\alpha}$ in the above inequality, we get

$$\left\{-f\left(\frac{x}{\alpha}\right) - \|f\|\left\|\frac{x}{\alpha} + x_0\right\|\right\} \leq r_0.$$

That implies, $-\frac{1}{\alpha}f(x) - \|f\|\frac{\|x+\alpha x_0\|}{-\alpha} \leq r_0$.

That is, $f(x) + \alpha r_0 \leq \|f\|\|x + \alpha x_0\|$.

$$|f_0(y)| \leq \|f\|\|y\|.$$

Thus, $|f_0(y)| \leq \|f\|\|y\|, for\ all\ y \in M_0$.

Therefore, $\|f_0\| \leq \|f\|$.

Hence, $\|f_0\| = \|f\|$.

Case (ii);

Let N be a complex normed linear space.

Then, f is of the form $f(x) = g(x) + ih(x)$, where g and h are real functionals on M.

Now, $f(ix) = g(ix) + ih(ix)$. .... (4.2.13.1)

But, $f(ix) = if(x) = i[g(x) + ih(x)] = ig(x) - h(x)$ .... (4.2.13.2)

Comparing the above two equations (4.2.13.1) and (4.2.13.2), we get

$$h(x) = -g(ix).$$

Therefore, $f(x) = g(x) - ig(x)$.

Also, $\|g\| \leq |f(x)| \leq \|f\|\|x\|$.

That is, $\|g\| \leq \|f\|$.

Now, g is a real functional on M.

Therefore, by case (i), g can be extended to a functional g_0 on M_0, such that $\|g_0\| = \|g\|$.

Define $f_0: M_0 \to \mathbb{C}$ by $f_0(y) = g_0(y) - ig_0(iy)$, for all $y \in M_0$.

We claim that, f_0 is the required extension of f.

When $x \in M, g_0(x) = g(x)$.

Therefore, $f_0(x) = g_0(x) - ig_0(ix) = g(x) - ig(ix) = f(x)$.

Hence, f_0 is an extension of f to M.

Next, we prove that, f_0 is a linear functional.

Let $y_1, y_2 \in M_0$.

Now, $f_0(y_1 + y_2) = g_0(y_1 + y_2) - ig_0(i(y_1 + y_2))$.

$= [g_0(y_1) - ig_0(iy_1)] + [g_0(y_2) - ig_0(iy_2)]$.

$= f_0(y_1) + f_0(y_2)$.

Let c be any scalar.

Then, $f_0(cy) = f_0[(\alpha + i\beta)y] = f_0[\alpha y + i\beta y]$.

$= g_0(\alpha y + i\beta y) - ig_0(i\alpha y + i^2\beta y)$.

$= \alpha[g_0(y) - ig_0(iy)] + i\beta[g_0(y) - ig_0(iy)]$.

$= \alpha f_0(y) + i\beta f_0(y) = cf_0(y)$.

We have to prove that, $\|f_0\| = \|f\|$.

As in the first case, since $M_0 \supseteq M$, we have $\|f_0\| \geq \|f\|$.

Now, we have to prove that, $\|f_0\| \leq \|f\|$.

Suppose f_0 is a real number.

Let $y \in M_0$. Then, $f_0(y) = g_0(y) + 0$.

Hence, $|f_0(y)| = |g_0(y)| \leq \|g_0\|\|y\| = \|g\|\|y\| \leq \|f\|\|y\|$.

Therefore, $\|f_0\| \leq \|f\|$.

Otherwise, suppose, $f_0(y) = re^{i\theta}$, where r is real and $\theta > 0$.

Then, $|f_0(y)| = r = e^{-i\theta}(re^{i\theta}) = e^{-i\theta}f_0(y) = f_0(e^{-i\theta}y)$.

Since the above value is equal to r, it is a real value.

Therefore, $f_0(e^{-i\theta}y) = g_0(y)$.

Hence, $|f_0(y)| = |f_0(e^{-i\theta}y)| = |g_0(y)| \leq \|f\|\|y\|$.

That implies, $\|f_0\| \leq \|f\|$.

Therefore, $\|f_0\| = \|f\|$.

Hence proved.

Definition 4.2.14 (Partial Ordered Set – POSET)

$(R, \leq)$ is a poset. $x \leq y$ means "*x* is less than or equal to *y*". Let *X* be a non – empty set. Then, $(P(X), \leq)$ is a poset. Here, $A \leq B$, means "*A* is a subset of *B*".

Definition 4.2.15 (Comparable)

Two elements a and b in a poset $(P, \leq)$ are said to be *comparable*, if we can say either $a \leq b$ or $b \leq a$.

Definition 4.2.16 (Chain)

If every pair of elements in a poset are comparable, we say that the poset is a *chain* or *totally ordered*. In the above example $(\mathbb{R}, \leq)$ is a chain, but, $(P(X), \leq)$ is not a chain in itself. However, if $X = \{1,2,3,4\}$, then $\{\{1,2,3,4\}, \{1,2,3\}, \{1,2\}, \{2\}, \emptyset\}$ and $\{\{1,2,3,4\}, \{1,2,3\}, \{2,4\}, \{4\}, \emptyset\}$ are chains in *P*(*X*). Consider $\{\{1,2,3,4\}, \{1,2,3\}, \{2,3\}, \{3\}, \emptyset\}$, which is a subset of P(X), but not a chain. In a poset, we may have a number of chains.

Zorn's lemma 4.2.17

In a partially ordered set, if every chain has an upper bound, then the poset possesses a maximal element.

Theorem 4.2.18

This theorem is known is known as ***Hahn Banach Theorem***.

Let *M* be a linear subspace of a normed linear space. Let *f* be a functional defined on *M*. Then, *f* can be extended to a functional f_0 to the whole space *N*, such that $\|f_0\| = \|f\|$.

Proof

Consider the collection $P = \{(f_\lambda, M_\lambda)\}_{\lambda \in \Lambda'}$, where M_λ is a subspace of *N* containing *M* and f_λ is an extension of *f* to M_λ.

Clearly, by the lemma 4.2.11, $(f_0, M_0) \in P$. Hence, *P* is non-empty.

We define, $(f_\lambda, M_\lambda) \leq (f_\mu, M_\mu)$, if

i) $M_\lambda \subseteq M_\mu$ and

ii) f_μ coincides with f_λ on M_λ.

This is a partially ordered relation. P is a Poset with respect to the above partially ordered relation.

We will prove that, every chain in P has an upper bound.

Consider an arbitrary chain $K = \{(f_i, M_i)\}_{i\in A}$, where $A \subseteq \Lambda$.

Define $M' = \bigcup_{i\in A} M_i$,

Claim: M' is a subspace of N.

Let $x, y \in M'$ and α be any scalar.

Then, $x \in M_i$ and $y \in M_j$, for some $i, j \in A$.

Since K is a chain, $(f_i, M_i) \leq (f_j, M_j)$ or $(f_j, M_j) \leq (f_i, M_i)$.

That implies, $M_i \subseteq M_j$ or $M_j \subseteq M_i$.

Without loss of generality, we assume that $M_i \subseteq M_j$.

Now, $x, y \in M_j \Rightarrow x + y \in M_j$ and $\alpha x \in M_j$. [Since M_j is a subspace]\

$$\Rightarrow x + y \in M' \text{ and } \alpha x \in M'.$$

Thus, M' is a linear subspace of N containing M.

Define $\phi : M' \to C$ as follows;

Let $x \in M'$.

Then, that implies, $x \in M_i$, for some $i \in A$.

Therefore, we define $\phi(x) = f_i(x)$.

Clearly, ϕ is a well - defined linear functional on M'.

Hence, $(\phi, M') \in P$ and $(f_i, M_i) \leq (\phi, M')$, for all $i \in A$, and (ϕ, M') is an upper bound for the chain K.

Since K is arbitrary, we conclude that every chain in P has an upper bound.

Therefore, by Zorn's lemma, we get that P possesses a maximal element, say (g, H).

Claim: $H = N$.

Suppose $H \neq N$.

Then, there exists a vector x_0 in N, such that $x_0 \notin H$.

Let $H_0 = H + [x_0]$, the space generated by H and x_0.

Then, by the lemma 4.2.13, g can be extended to a functional g_0 on H_0, such that $\|g_0\| = \|g\|$.

Then, $(H_0, g_0) \in P$.

Also, $(H, g) \leq (H_0, g_0)$.

This contradicts the fact that (H, g) is the maximal element of P.

Therefore, we conclude that, $H = N$.

Hence, $f_0 = g$ is the required extension of f to the whole space N, such that $\|g\| = \|f\|$.

Hence the theorem.

Result 4.2.19

This is one of the applications of Hahn Banach theorem.

If N is a normed linear space and x_0 is a non – zero vector in N, then there exists $f_0 \in N^*$, such that $f_0(x_0) = \|x_0\|$ *and* $\|f_0\| = 1$.

Proof

Let $M = \{\alpha x_0\}$ be the space generated by x_0.

Then, M is a subspace of N.

Define $f: M \to C$ by $f(\alpha x_0) = \alpha \|x_0\|$.

We have to prove that, f is linear.

Let $\alpha x_0, \beta x_0 \in M$.

Now,

$$f(\alpha x_0 + \beta x_0) = f[(\alpha + \beta)x_0] = (\alpha + \beta)\|x_0\| = f(\alpha x_0) + f(\beta x_0).$$

Also, if c is any scalar, $f(c\alpha x_0) = cf(\alpha x_0)$.

Therefore, f is a linear functional on M.

Hence, by Hahn Banach theorem, f can be extended to a functional f_0 defined on whole space N, such that $\|f_0\| = \|f\| = 1$.

In other words, $f_0 \in N^*$ *and* $\|f_0\| = \|f\|$.

To prove: i) $f_0(x_0) = \|x_0\|$ and

ii) $\|f_0\| = 1$.

Let $y = \alpha x_0$.

When $\alpha = 1$, $y = x_0 \in M$.

Since f_0 is the extension of f, we have

$f_0(y) = f_0(x_0) = f(y) = f(x_0) = \|x_0\|$.

Also, $\|f\| = sup_{y \in M}\{|f(y)|,\ \|y\| \leq 1\} = sup_{y \in M}\{\|y\|,\ \|y\| \leq 1\} = 1$.

Therefore, $\|f_0\| = \|f\| = 1$.

Hence proved.

Theorem 4.2.20

If M is a closed linear subspace of a normed linear space N and x_0 is a vector not in M, then, there exists a functional $f_0 \in N^*$, such that $f_0(M) = 0$, $f_0(x_0) \neq 0$.

Proof

Given that, M is a closed linear subspace of a normed linear space N.

Therefore, $\frac{N}{M}$ is also a normed linear space.

Consider the natural mapping $T: N \to \frac{N}{M}$,

defined by $T(x) = x + M, for\ all\ x \in N$.

Since $x_0 \notin M$, we get that $x_0 + M$ is a non – zero vector in $\frac{N}{M}$.

Now, applying the previous theorem (4.2.19) to $\frac{N}{M}$,

There exists $f \in \left(\frac{N}{M}\right)^*$, such that $\|f\| = 1\ and\ f(x_0 + M) = \|x_0 + M\|$.

Let us define $f_0 \in N^*\ by\ f_0(x) = f\big(T(x)\big), for\ all\ x \in N$.

Then, $f_0(x_0) = f\big(T(x_0)\big) = f(x_0 + M) = \|x_0 + M\| \neq 0$.

Now, $f_0(M) = f\big(T(M)\big) = f(M) = \|0 + M\| = inf.\{\|0 + m\|; m \in M\}$.

Therefore, $f_0(M) = 0$.

Hence the theorem.

Properties 4.2.21

1. A proper closed subspace of a normed linear space is nowhere dense.

Proof

Let M be a proper closed subspace of a normed linear space N.

We have to prove that, M is nowhere dense.

That is , to prove that, $\bar{M}^0 = \emptyset$.

Since $\bar{M} = M$, we have to prove that, $M^0 = \emptyset$.

Let us assume that, $M^0 \neq \emptyset$.

Let $x \in M^0$.

That is, x is an interior point of M.

Then, there exists $r > 0$, such that $s(x, r) = \{y \in N;\ \|y - x\| < r\} \subseteq M$.

Let $y \in N$ arbitrarily.

Consider, $\left(x + \frac{ry}{2\|y\|}\right) - x$.

Now, $\left\|x + \frac{ry}{2\|y\|} - x\right\| < \frac{r}{2} < r$.

This shows that $x + \frac{ry}{\|y\|} \in s(x, r)$.

Since $x \in s(x, r) \subset M$, we get $\frac{ry}{\|y\|} \in M$ and again, since M is a subspace, $y \in M$.

Thus, $N = M$.

This contradicts that, M is a proper subspace of N.

This implies that, $M^0 = \emptyset$.

That is, M is nowhere dense.

Therefore, a Banach space cannot have a countable dense subset or a Banach space is not separable.

Hence proved.

2. Let N be a Banach space. Suppose $\{e_1, e_2, \dots\dots, e_n, \dots\dots\}$ is a countable base for N. Let M_n be the subspace of N, generated by $\{e_1, e_2, \dots\dots, e_n\}$, $for\ n = 1,2,3, \dots\dots$ Then, each M_n is proper and closed and $N = \bigcup_{n=1}^{\infty} M_n$ is the countable union of the closed subspaces $M_n{}'s$.

Solution

We know that, M_n is a nowhere dense subset.

Therefore, N is a countable union of nowhere dense subsets of N.

That implies, N is of first category.

This is a contradiction, because N being a complete metric space is of second category.

3. Prove that $\left(l_p^n\right)^* = l_q^n$, where $\frac{1}{p} + \frac{1}{q} = 1$.

Proof

We know that, l_p^n is the space of all n – tuples of scalars of $\mathbb{R}^n$.

For all $x = (x_1, x_2, \dots \dots, x_n) \in l_p^n$, the norm is defined by

$\|x\|_p = \left[\sum_{i=1}^n |x_i|^p\right]^{1/p}$.

Let $f \in \left(l_p^n\right)^*$.

Then, it is a linear functional $\left(l_p^n\right) \to R$.

Let $\{e_1, e_2, \dots \dots, e_n\}$ be the standard basis for l_p^n.

Let $y = (y_1, y_2, \dots \dots, y_n) = (f(e_1), f(e_2), \dots \dots, f(e_n))$ and $x = \sum x_i e_i$.

Then, $f(x) = \sum x_i f(e_i) = \sum x_i y_i$.

Therefore, if the n – tuple $(y_1, y_2, \dots \dots, y_n)$ are known, then the function f is uniquely determined.

Hence, for every $f \in \left(l_p^n\right)^*$, we can associate a n – tuple of scalars $(y_1, y_2, \dots \dots, y_n) \in \mathbb{R}^n$.

Consider, $F: \left(l_p^n\right)^* \to \mathbb{R}^n$ by $F(f) = y$.

Now, $|f(x)| = |\sum x_i y_i| \leq \sum |x_i y_i| \leq \|x\|_p \|y\|_q$.

That implies, $\|f\| \leq \|y\|_q$.

In fact, $\|f\| = \|y\|_q$.

This is seen by considering the vector x defined by $x_i = 0$, if $y_1 = 0$ and $x_i = \frac{|y_i|^q}{\|q\|}$, otherwise, where $|f(x)| \leq \|x\|_p \|y\|_q = \left(\sum |x_i|^p\right)^{1/p} \left(\sum |y_i|^q\right)^{1/q}$.

Thus, F is an isometric isomorphism of $\left(l_p^n\right)^*$ into l_q^n.

Therefore, $\left(l_p^n\right)^* = l_q^n$.

Hence proved.

4. Prove that $(l_1^n)^* = l_\infty^n$.

Proof

Let $x \in l_1^n$.

Now, $\|x\|_1 = \sum_{i=1}^n |x_i|$.

Let $F: (l_1^n)^* \to l_\infty^n$.

We have to prove that, F is an isometric isomorphism.

Now, proceeding like the previous problem 3, we have

$|f(x)| = |\sum_{i=1}^{n} x_i y_i| \leq \sum_{i=1}^{n} |x_i y_i| = \sum_{i=1}^{n} |x_i||y_i|$

$\leq \sum_{i=1}^{n} |x_i| . (Max.\{|y_i|\}) = \|y\|_\infty \|x\|_1.$

Therefore, $\|f\| \leq \|y\|_\infty$.

Now, by taking $x_i = 0$, if $y_i = 0$ and $x_i = \frac{|y_i|^q}{\|q\|}$, otherwise, we get that

$\|f\| = \|y\|_\infty$.

Thus, $F: (l_1^n)^* \to l_\infty^n$ is an isometric isomorphism.

Therefore, $(l_1^n)^* = l_\infty^n$.

Hence proved.

4.3 Elementary Topology

Definition 4.3.1

Let $\{X_\alpha\}_{\alpha \in \Lambda}$ be a family of topological spaces. Let $X = \prod_{\alpha \in \Lambda} X_\alpha$. Let $\Pi_\alpha : X \to X_\alpha$ be the projection of X on the αth component space X_α. The *product topology* is the weakest topology on X, with respect to which every projection Π_α is continuous.

Definition 4.3.2

Let N^* be a normed linear space. Hence, it is a metric space. The topology on N^* induced by this metric is called the *strong topology on* N^*. N^{**} is the set of all functional on N^*. The weakest topology on N^*, with respect to which all the functions in N^{**} are continuous is called the *weak topology on* N^*. Some of the functional of N^{**} are induced functionals of the form F_x, where $x \in N$. The weakest topology on N^*, with respect to which the functionals of the type F_x are continuous is called the *weak* topology on* N^*.

Hence, it is clear that $\text{weak}^*\ \text{topology} \subseteq \text{weak topology} \subseteq \text{strong topology}$.

Definition 4.3.3

Let $S(x, f_0, \varepsilon)$ be the collection of functions in N^*. That is,

$$S(x, f_0, \varepsilon) = \{f \in N^*; |F_x(f) - F_x(f_0)| < \varepsilon\}.$$

Let f_0 be an arbitrary functional in N^* and $\varepsilon > 0$ be given. Then,

$$S(x, f_0, \varepsilon) = \{f ; f \in N^* \text{ and } |f(x) - f_0(x)| < \varepsilon\}.$$

This is known as the *basic open neighbourhood of* f_0 in weak* topology.

Definition 4.3.4

The class of all sets of this kind of all x's, f_0's and ε's defines an *open sub basis for* N^* in the weak* topology. All finite intersection of members of sub basis will yield an *open basis*. Every *open set* in weak topology is an arbitrary union of members of above open basis.

Result 4.3.5

N^* is a Hausdorff space in the weak* topology.

Proof

Let f and g be two distinct elements in N^*.

Hence, $f(x) \neq g(x)$, for some $x \in N$.

Let $\dfrac{|f(x) - g(x)|}{3} = \varepsilon$.

Claim: $S(x, f, \varepsilon)$ and $S(x, g, \varepsilon)$ are disjoint neighbourhoods of f and g.

Let us assume that they are not disjoint.

Then, there exists some $h \in S(x, f, \varepsilon) \cap S(x, g, \varepsilon)$.

Now, $h \in S(x, f, \varepsilon) \Rightarrow |f(x) - h(x)| < \varepsilon$,

and $h \in S(x, g, \varepsilon) \Rightarrow |g(x) - h(x)| < \varepsilon$.

Therefore, $|f(x) - g(x)| \leq |f(x) - h(x)| + |h(x) - g(x)| < 2\varepsilon$.

That is, $3\varepsilon < 2\varepsilon$, which is a contradiction.

Therefore, N^* is a Hausdorff space in the weak* topology.

Theorem 4.3.6

If N is a normed linear space, then the closed unit sphere S^* in N^* is a compact Hausdorff space in the weak* topology.

Proof

Given that, $S^* = \{f \in N^*; \|f\| \leq 1\}$.

Since, N^* is a compact Hausdorff space in the weak* topology, we get that, S^* is also Hausdorff.

We have to prove that, , S^* is compact in the weak* topology.

For all $x \in N$, we define a compact set C_x as follows;

Define $C_x = [-\|x\|, \|x\|]$, if N is a real normed linear space.

$= \{z; |z| \le \|x\|\}$, if N is a complex normed linear space.

Let $C = \prod_{x \in N} C_x$.

Since each C_x is compact, by Tynchonoff theorem, C is also compact in the product topology.

Let $f \in S^*$. Then $\|f\| \le 1$.

Therefore, for all $x \in N$, $|f(x)| \le \|f\|\|x\| \le \|x\|$.

This shows that $f(x) \in C_x$.

Varying x in N, we can identify f as a string of elements in C_x's, or $f \in C = \prod_{x \in N} C_x$.

This is true for all $f \in S^*$.

Therefore, S^* can be imbedded in C or S^* can be regarded as a subspace of C.

We have to prove that, S^* is compact.

That is, we have to prove that, S^* is a closed subspace of C.

Thus, we have to prove that, $\overline{S^*} \subseteq S^*$.

Let $g \in \overline{S^*}$. Then, $g \in C = \prod_{x \in N} C_x$.

That implies, g is a function defined on the index set N.

Also, since $g \in C$, we have $|g(x)| \le \|x\|, for\ all\ x \in N$.

Now, $\|g(x)\| = sup.\{|g(x)|; \|x\| \le 1\} \le sup.\{\|x\|; \|x\| \le 1\}$.

Therefore, $\|g(x)\| \le 1$.

Since $|g(x)| \le \|x\|,\ for\ all\ x \in N$, g is bounded and hence continuous.

Thus, we have to prove that, g is linear.

Let x, y be two arbitrary elements in N.

We have to prove the following:

i) $g(x + y) = g(x) + g(y)$,

ii) $g(\alpha x) = \alpha g(x)$, for any scalar α.

Now, $g \in \overline{S^*}$ implies that every neighborhood of g intersects S^*.

Let $\epsilon > 0$ be given.

Then, there exists $f \in S^*$, such that $|g(x) - f(x)| < \epsilon/3$,

$|g(x) - f(y)| < \epsilon/3$, and $|g(x + y) - f(x + y)| < \epsilon/3$.

Now, $f \in S^*$, and hence f is linear.

Thus, $f(x + y) = f(x) + f(y)$.

Now,

$|g(x + y) - g(x) - g(y)|$

$= |g(x + y) - f(x + y) - g(x) + f(x) - g(y) + f(y)|$.

$\leq |g(x + y) - f(x + y)| + |g(x) - f(x)| + |g(y) - f(y)|$.

Therefore, $|g(x + y) - g(x) - g(y)| < \epsilon$, which is true for all $\epsilon > 0$.

That implies, $g(x + y) - g(x) - g(y) = 0$.

That is, $g(x + y) = g(x) + g(y)$.

Now, we have to prove that, $g(\alpha x) = \alpha g(x)$.

Let $\epsilon > 0$ be given.

Then, there exists $f \in S^*$, such that $|g(\alpha x) - f(\alpha x)| < \epsilon/2$.

That is, $|\alpha g(x) - \alpha f(x)| < \epsilon/2$,for all α.

Now, $f \in S^*$, and since f is linear, $f(\alpha x) = \alpha f(x)$.

Again, $|g(\alpha x) - \alpha g(x)| = |g(\alpha x) - f(\alpha x) + \alpha f(x) - \alpha g(x)|$

$$\leq |g(\alpha x) - f(\alpha x)| + \alpha|f(x) - g(x)|$$

$$< \epsilon/2 + \alpha(\epsilon/3).$$

This is true for any scalar α and every $\epsilon > 0$.

That implies, $g(\alpha x) = \alpha g(x)$.

Thus, g is linear.

Also, we have that, g is continuous and $||g|| \leq 1$.

That implies, $g \in S^*$.

Therefore, $\overline{S^*} \subseteq S^*$.

That is, S^* is closed in C.

Thus, S^* is compact.

Therefore, S^* is a compact Hausdorff space in weak* topology.

Hence the theorem.

Theorem 4.3.7

Let N be a normed linear space and S^* be the compact Hausdorff space in N^* with respect to the weak* topology. Then, the mapping $x \to F_x$, where F_x is defined as $F_x(f) = f(x)$ for all $f \in S^*$, is an isometric isomorphism of N into $C(S^*)$. If N is a Banach space, then this mapping is an isometric isomorphism of N onto a closed linear subspace of $C(S^*)$.

Proof

Let $f \in S^*$. Then, $\|f\| \leq 1$.

Now, for all $x \in N$, F_x is defined on S^* by $F_x(f) = f(x)$.

Therefore, $F_x: S^* \to R$.

We have to prove that, $F_x \in C(S^*)$.

Now, $|F_x(f)| = |f(x)| \leq \|f\|\|x\|$.

Since $\|f\| \leq 1$, $|F_x(f)| \leq \|x\|$, for all $f \in S^*$.

Therefore, F_x is bounded and hence continuous.

Thus, $F_x \in C(S^*)$.

Let $\emptyset: N \to C(S^*)$, defined by $\emptyset(x) = F_x$.

We know that, $\|F_x\| = \|x\|$.

Therefore, $\emptyset$ is an isometric isomorphism of N into $C(S^*)$.

Suppose N is a Banach space. Then, N is complete.

Hence, its image $\emptyset(N)$ is a complete subspace of $C(S^*)$.

Now, $C(S^*)$ is a metric space and $\emptyset(N)$ being a complete subspace of $C(S^*)$, is closed linear space.

Therefore, $\emptyset: N \to \emptyset(N)$ is an onto isometric isomorphism.

Hence the theorem.

Lemma 4.3.8

If B and B' are Banach spaces and T is a continuous linear transformation of B onto B', then the image of each open sphere centered on the origin in B contains an open sphere centered on the origin in B'.

Proof

Let S_r denote the open sphere with radius r, centered on the origin in B.

Then, $S_r = \{x \in B; \|x\| < r\}$.

Let $S_r{}'$ denote the open sphere with radius r, centered on the origin in B'.

Then, $S_r{}' = \{y \in B'; \|y\| < r\}$.

Now, we have to prove that, $S_r = rS_1$.

Let $x \in S_r$. Hence, we have $\|x\| < r$.

Therefore, $\left\|\frac{x}{r}\right\| < 1$, which implies $\frac{x}{r} \in S_1$.

That is, $x \in rS_1$.

Thus, $S_r \subseteq rS_1$.

Similarly, $rS_1 \subseteq S_r$.

Hence, we have $S_r = rS_1$.

That implies, $T(S_r) = T(rS_1) = rT(S_1)$.

Therefore, it sufficies to prove that, $T(S_1)$ contains some $S_\epsilon{}'$.

In order to prove this, first we prove that, $\overline{T(S_1)}$ contains some $S_\epsilon{}'$.

Let $y \in B'$.

Given that, T is onto. Hence, there exists $x \in B$, such that $T(x) = y$.

We can find a positive integer n, such that $\|x\| < n$.

This means that, $x \in S_n$, which implies $y = T(x) \in T(S_n)$.

Since y is arbitrary, we get $B' = \bigcup_{n=1}^{\infty} T(S_n)$.

We know that, B' is of second category and therefore, B' cannot be expressed as a countable union of nowhere dense sets.

Hence, $T(S_{n_0})$ is not nowhere dense for some n_0.

That is, $\overline{T(S_{n_0})}^{0} \neq \emptyset$.

Therefore, $\overline{T(S_{n_0})}$ has an interior point , say y.

Then, there exists an open set G, such that $G \subseteq \overline{T(S_{n_0})}$.

Thus, $y \in \overline{T(S_{n_0})}$ and G is a neighbourhood of y.

That implies, G intersects $T(S_{n_0})$.

Let $y_0 \in G \cap T(S_{n_0})$.

Then, $y_0 \in G \subseteq \overline{T(S_{n_0})}$. Thus, y_0 is an interior point of $\overline{T(S_{n_0})}$.

Therefore, there exists $x_0 \in S_{n_0}$ such that $T(x_0) = y_0$.

That implies, $\|x_0\| \leq n_0$.

Consider the function $f: B \to B'$ taking y to $y - y_0$.

This is just a translation. Hence, it is a homeomorphism of B' onto itself.

Now, the origin, that is, $y_0 - y_0$ is an interior point of $\overline{T(S_{n_0})} - y_0$.

Therefore, there exists some $\delta > 0$ such that $S_\delta{}' \subseteq \overline{T(S_{n_0})} - y_0$.

Next, we prove that, $T(S_{n_0}) - y_0 \subseteq T(S_{2n_0})$.

Let $y \in T(S_{n_0}) - y_0$.

That implies, $y \in T(x) - T(x_0)$, where $x \in S_{n_0}$ *and* $\|x\| < n_0$.

Thus, $y = T(x - x_0)$.

But, $\|x - x_0\| \leq \|x\| + \|x_0\| < n_0 + n_0 = 2n_0$.

Therefore, $x - x_0 \in S_{2n_0}$.

That is, $y = T(x - x_0) \in T(S_{2n_0})$.

That implies, $T(S_{n_0}) - y_0 \subseteq T(S_{2n_0})$.

Hence, $\overline{T(S_{n_0}) - y_0} \subseteq \overline{T(S_{2n_0})}$, which implies $\overline{T(S_{n_0})} - y_0 \subseteq \overline{T(S_{2n_0})}$.

We know that, $S_\delta{}' \subseteq \overline{T(S_{n_0})} - y_0$.

Thus, $S_\delta{}' \subseteq \overline{T(S_{2n_0})}$.

That is, $S_\delta{}' \subseteq 2n_0\overline{T(S_1)}$, which implies $\frac{1}{2n_0}S_\delta{}' \subseteq \overline{T(S_1)}$.

Therefore, $S_{\frac{\delta}{2n_0}}{}' \subseteq \overline{T(S_1)}$.

Hence, $S_\epsilon{}' \subseteq \overline{T(S_1)}$, where $\epsilon = \frac{\delta}{2n_0}$.

Second part,

We will prove that, $S_\epsilon{}' \subseteq T(S_3)$.

Let $y \in S_\epsilon{}'$.

Since $S_\epsilon{}' \subseteq \overline{T(S_1)}$, we get $y \in S_\epsilon{}' \subseteq \overline{T(S_1)}$ and so on.

Now, y is an interior point of $\overline{T(S_1)}$.

Hence, every neighbourhood of y intersects $T(S_1)$.

$S_{\frac{\epsilon}{2}}{}'$ is a neighbourhood of origin in B'.

That implies, $y + S_{\frac{\epsilon}{2}}{}'$ is a neighbourhood of origin of y in B'.

Therefore, $\left(y + S_{\frac{\epsilon}{2}}{}'\right) \cap T(S_1) \neq \emptyset$.

Hence, there exists a y_1 such that $y_1 \in \left(y + S_{\frac{\epsilon}{2}}{}'\right) \cap T(S_1)$.

Thus, $y_1 \in y + S_{\frac{\epsilon}{2}}{}'$ implies that $\|y - y_1\| < \epsilon/2$ and

$y_1 \in T(S_1)$ implies that $y_1 = T(x_1)$, where $\|x_1\| < 1$.

Now, we know that $y \in S_\epsilon{}'$.

Therefore, there exists $\|x_1\| < 1$, $y_1 = T(x_1)$ and $\|y - y_1\| < \epsilon/2$.

We observe that, $y - y_1 \in S_{\frac{\epsilon}{2}}{}' \subseteq \overline{T(S_1)}$.

Thus, there exists a vector $x_2 \in B$, such that $\|x_2\| < 1/2$ and

$\|(y - y_1) - y_2\| < \frac{\epsilon}{2^2}$, where $y_2 = T(x_2)$.

Continuing in this way, we obtain a sequence $\{x_n\}$ in B, such that

$$\|x_n\| < \frac{1}{2^{n-1}} \text{ and } \|y - (y_1 + \cdots + y_n)\| < \frac{\epsilon}{2^n}, \text{ where } y_n = T(x_n).$$

We claim that, $\{x_n\}$ is a Cauchy sequence in B.

Let $S_n = x_1 + x_2 + \cdots + x_n$.

Now, $\|S_n\| = \|x_1 + x_2 + \cdots + x_n\| \leq \|x_1\| + \|x_2\| + \cdots + \|x_n\|$

That is,

$$\|S_n\| < 1 + \frac{1}{2} + \cdots + \frac{1}{2^{n-1}} < 1 + \frac{1}{2} + \cdots + \frac{1}{2^{n-1}} + \frac{1}{2^n} + \cdots = \frac{1}{1 - {}^1\!/_2} = 2.$$

Further, if $m > n$, then

$$\|S_m - S_n\| = \|x_{n+1} + x_{n+2} + \cdots + x_m\| \leq \|x_{n+1}\| + \cdots + \|x_m\|.$$

Thus,

$$\|S_m - S_n\| < \frac{1}{2^n} + \frac{1}{2^{n+1}} + \cdots + \frac{1}{2^{m-1}}$$

$$= \frac{1}{2^n}\left[1 + \frac{1}{2} + \cdots + \frac{1}{2^{m-1-n}}\right] < \frac{1}{2^n}\left[1 + \frac{1}{2} + \cdots\right] < \frac{1}{2^{n-1}}.$$

Therefore, as $m, n \to \infty$, $\|S_m - S_n\| \to 0$.

This shows that, $\{x_n\}$ is a Cauchy sequence in B.

Since B is complete, $\{x_n\}$ converges to a vector, say x in B.

Now, we have, $x = lim. \{S_n\}$.

That implies, $\|x\| = \|lim. S_n\| \leq lim. \|s_n\| \leq 2 < 3$.

This shows that, $x \in S_3$.

Finally, we prove that, $y = T(x)$.

Now, $T(x) = T[lim.\{S_n\}] = lim.[T(S_n)] = lim.[T(x_1 + x_2 + \cdots + x_n)]$.

That is,

$$T(x) = lim.[T(x_1) + T(x_2) + \cdots + T(x_n)]$$
$$= lim.(y_1 + y_2 + \cdots + y_n) = y.$$

Since $x \in S_3$, we conclude that $y = T(x) = T(S_3)$.

That implies, $S_\epsilon{}' \subseteq T(S_3)$. Thus, $S_\epsilon{}' \subseteq 3T(S_1)$.

Therefore, $S_{\epsilon/3}{}' \subseteq T(S_1)$.

Hence the lemma.

Theorem 4.3.9

The following theorem is known as ***Open Mapping theorem***.

If *B* and *B′* are Banach spaces and if *T* is a continuous linear transformation of *B* onto *B′*, then *T* is an open mapping.

Proof

Let *G* be any open set in *B*.

We have to prove that, *T*(*G*) is open in *B′*.

Let *y* be any arbitrary vector in *T*(*G*).

Since *T* is onto, there exists a vector $x \in G$ such that $y = T(x)$.

Now, *G* is open and $x \in G$ implies that, there exists an open neighborhood of *x* in *B*, which is contained in *B*.

Hence, $x + S_r$ is such a neighborhood of *x*, with suitable choice of *r*.

Thus, $x \in x + S_r \subseteq G$.

Now, by the previous lemma 4.3.8, $T(S_r)$ contains some S_r.

Therefore, $y + S_r{}'$ is an open neighborhood of *y* in *B′*.

We claim that, $y \in y + S_r{}' \subseteq T(G)$.

Now, $y + S_r{}' \subseteq T(S_r) = T(x) + T(S_r) = T(x + S_r) \subseteq T(G)$.

Since *y* is arbitrary, we conclude that *T*(*G*) is open in *B′*.

Hence the theorem.

Theorem 4.3.10

A one to one continuous linear transformation of one Banach space onto another is a homeomorphism.

Proof

Let $T: B \to B'$ be such a linear transformation.

Given that, T is a bijection and continuous.

Thus, by Open mapping theorem, T is open.

That implies, T^{-1} is continuous.

Therefore, T is a homeomorphism.

Hence the theorem.

Definition 4.3.11

Let B be a Banach space. An idempotent linear operator P on B is called a *projection on B*.

Idempotent: $P^2 = P$ and $P: B \to B$ is a continuous linear transformation.

Theorem 4.3.12

Let P be a projection on B. Let M and N be its range and null space. Then, M and N are closed linear subspaces of B and $B = M \oplus N$.

Proof

Since M and N are range and null space, we have

Range of P is $M = \{P(z); z \in B\}$.

Null space of P is $N = \{z; P(z) = 0\}$.

We know that, M and N are subspaces of B.

Also, we have $N = P^{-1}(\{0\})$, $\{0\}$ is closed and P is continuous.

Therefore, N is closed.

Again, since P is a projection, we have,

$$M = \{P(x); x \in B\} = \{x; P^2(x) = P(x)\} = \{x; P(x) = x\}$$
$$= \{x; (I - P)(x) = x\}.$$

This shows that M is the null space of $I - P$.

We know that, $I - P$ is continuous and $M = (I - P)^{-1}\{0\}$.

Therefore, M is closed.

We have to prove that, $B = M \bigoplus N$.

Let z be an arbitrary vector in B.

Then, $z = P(z) + (I - P)(z)$.

Clearly, $P(z) \in M$.

Now, $P[(I - P)(z)] = P(I(z)) - P^2(z) = P(z) - P(z) = 0$.

Therefore, $(I - P)(z) \in N$.

Thus, every vector $z \in B$ can be expressed as $z = x + y$, where $x \in M$ and $y \in N$.

We have to prove that, $M \cap N = \{0\}$.

Now, any vector in M is of the form $P(z)$, for some $z \in B$.

Suppose, if $P(z) \in N$.

Then, $P\big(P(z)\big) = 0$ implies $P^2(z) = 0$.

That implies, $P(z) = 0$.

Therefore, 0 (zero) is the only vector common to both M and N.

Thus, $B = M \bigoplus N$.

Hence the theorem.

Theorem 4.3.13

Let B be a Banach space. Let M and N be closed linear subspaces of B such that $B = M \bigoplus N$. If $z = x + y$ is the unique representation of the vector in B as the sum of vectors in M and N, then the mapping P defined by $P(z) = x$ is a projection on B, whose range and null space are M and N.

Proof

Let $z \in B$.

Then, $z = x + y$, where $x \in M$ and $y \in N$ are unique.

Let us define $P: B \to B$ by $P(z) = x$.

We have to prove that,

i) P is a linear operator,

ii) P is idempotent,

iii) Range of P is M,

iv) Null space of P is N, and

v) P is continuous.

i) Let us prove that, P is linear.

Let $z, z' \in B$ and α be any scalar.

Then, there exists unique $x, x' \in M$ and $y, y' \in N$ such that $z = x + y$ and $z' = x' + y'$.

Then, $P(z + z') = P[(x + y) + (x' + y')] = P[(x + x') + (y + y')]$

$= x + x' = P(z) + P(z')$.

Again, $P(\alpha z) = P[\alpha(x + y)] = P(\alpha x + \alpha y) = \alpha x = \alpha P(z)$.

Therefore, P is linear.

ii) We have to prove that, P is idempotent.

That is, to prove, $P^2 = P$.

Let $z \in B$.

Then, there exists unique $x \in M$ and $y \in N$ such that $z = x + y$.

Now, $P(z) = x$.

Thus, $P^2(z) = P[P(z)] = P(x) = P(x + 0) = x$.

Therefore, for all $z \in B$, $P^2(z) = P(z)$.

That implies, $P^2 = P$.

That is, P is idempotent.

iii) To prove that, M is the range of P, that is, Range of $P = M$.

It is obvious that, range of $P \subseteq M$.

Let $x \in M$.

Then, $x = x + 0$ implies that $P(x) = x$.

But, $P(x)$ is in range of P.

Therefore, x belongs to the range of P.

That is, $M \subseteq$ Range of P.

That implies, Range of $P = M$.

iv) We have to prove that, Null space of $P = N$.

Let $y \in N$. Then, $y = 0 + y$ and $0 \in M$.

Thus, $P(y) = 0$.

That implies, $y \in$ Null space of P.

Therefore, $N \subseteq$ Null space of P.

Let $y' \in$ Null space of P.

That is, $P(y') = 0$.

Now, y' is of the form $y' = x + y$, where $x \in M$ and $y \in N$.

Then, $P(y') = x$. But, $P(y') = 0$.

Therefore, $x = 0$.

Thus, $y' = y \in N$.

Hence, Null space of $P \subseteq N$.

Therefore, Null space of $P = N$.

v) To prove that, P is continuous.

Let us define a new norm with vector space B, denoted by $||*||_1$ as follows;

For all $z \in B, ||z||_1 = ||x|| + ||y||$.

Clearly, B becomes a Banach space with respect to this norm, we denote this Banach space by B_1.

Now, $P: B_1 \to B$ and $||P(z)|| = ||x|| \leq ||x|| + ||y|| = ||z||_1$.

This shows that, P is a continuous map from B_1 into B.

If we prove that, B_1 and B have same topologies, then we can conclude that $P: B \to B$ is continuous.

In order to prove this, we have to prove that, B and B_1 are homeomorphic.

Now, consider the identity mapping T of B_1.

This T is 1-1 and onto and further

$$||T(z)|| = ||z|| = ||x + y|| \leq ||x|| + ||y|| = ||z||_1.$$

So, T is continuous from a Banach space B_1 onto another Banach space B.

Therefore, T is a homeomorphism.

Thus, the projection P is continuous.

Hence the theorem.

Note 4.3.14

1. Let B and B' be Banach spaces. Let us consider $B \times B'$. Define

$$d\big((x_1, y_1), (x_2, y_2)\big) = max.\{||x_1 - x_2||, ||y_1 - y_2||\}.$$

This gives rise to a topology on $B \times B'$, which is same as the product topology on $B \times B'$.

2. A sequence (x_n, y_n) in $B \times B'$ converges to (x, y), if and only if sequence (x_n) converges to x in B and sequence (y_n) converges to y in B'.

Definition 4.3.15

If T is a linear transformation of B into B', then $\{(x, T(x))/x \in B\}$ is called the *graph of T*. It is a subset of $B \times B'$.

Theorem 4.3.16

The following theorem is known as ***Closed Graph theorem***.

If B and B' are Banach spaces and if T is a linear transformation of B into B', then T is continuous if and only if Graph of T is closed.

Proof

Direct part,

Let us assume that, T is continuous.

Let $G =$ Graph of $T = \{(x, T(x)) : x \in B\} \subseteq B \times B'$.

We have to prove that, G is closed in $B \times B'$.

That is to prove that, $G = \bar{G}$.

Let $(x, y) \in \bar{G}$.

Then, we have to prove that, $(x, y) \in G$.

Then, there exists a sequence $\{(x_n, y_n)\}$ in G converging to (x, y).

This means that, there exists sequence $\{x_n\}$ converging to x in B and sequence $\{y_n\}$ converging to y in B'.

Therefore, each $(x_n, y_n) \in G$ implies that $y_n = T(x_n)$, for all n.

Since T is continuous, x_n converging to x implies $T(x_n)$ converges to $T(x)$.

That is, $\{y_n\}$ converges to $T(x)$.

Therefore, $T(x) = y$.

That implies, $(x, y) = (x, T(x)) \in G$.

Hence, $\bar{G} \subseteq G$.

Also, we know that, $G \subseteq \bar{G}$.

Therefore, $G \subseteq \bar{G}$.

Thus, G is closed.

Converse part,

Let us assume that, Graph of T is closed.

We have to prove that, T is continuous.

Let us denote the norm in B by $\|*\|$ and the norm in B' by $\|*\|'$.

In the linear space B_1, we define a new norm

$\|*\|_1$ by $\|x\|_1 = \|x\| + \|T(x)\|'$.

Let B_1 be the new normed linear space.

First, we prove that, $B_1$is a Banach space with respect to a base norm.

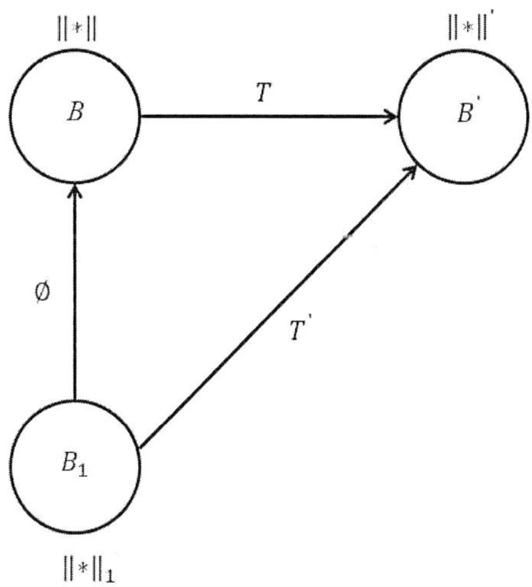

Let $\{x_n\}$ be a Cauchy sequence in B_1.

Then, $\|x_n\|_1 = \|x_n\| + \|T(x_n)\|'$, for all n.

Therefore, $\{x_n\}$ is a Cauchy sequence in B and $\{T(x_n)\}$ is a Cauchy sequence in B'.

But, both B and B' are complete.

Therefore, there exists vectors $x \in B$ and $y \in B'$ such that

$\|x_n - x\| \to 0$ and $\|T(x_n) - y\|' \to 0$.

Since, by hypothesis, T is closed, we get $(x, y) \in G$.

That implies, $T(x) = y$.

Now,

$\|x_n - x\|_1 = \|x_n - x\| + \|T(x_n - x)\|' = \|x_n - x\| + \|T(x_n) - y\|' \to 0.$

Thus, $\{x_n\} \to x$ in B_1.

This implies that, $B_1$is complete and hence $B_1$is a Banach space.

Next, we will prove the following:

i) $T: B_1 \to B'$ is continuous.

ii) B_1 *and* B' have same topology.

i) *To prove*:

$T: B_1 \to B'$ is continuous.

Let $x \in B_1$.

Now, $\|T(x)\|' \leq \|x\| + \|T(x)\|' = \|x\|_1$.

Thus, T is continuous as a mapping of B_1 into B'.

Let $\emptyset$ be the identity mapping of B_1 onto B.

Here, $\emptyset$ is one – to – one and onto.

Let $x \in B_1$.

Now, $\|\emptyset(x)\| = \|x\| + \|T(x)\|' = \|x\|_1$.

This shows that $\emptyset: B_1 \to B$ is continuous.

Then, as a consequence of open mapping theorem, we conclude that B_1 *and* B are homeomorphic.

Thus, B and B_1 have same topology.

Therefore, $T: B \to B'$ is continuous.

Hence the theorem.

Theorem 4.3.17

The following theorem is known as Banach Steinhauss theorem or ***Uniform Boundedness theorem.***

Let B be a Banach space and N be a normed linear space. Let T_i be a nonempty set of continuous linear transformation of B into N, such that $\{T_i(x)\}$ is a bounded subset of N, for all $x \in B$. Then, $\{\|T_i\|\}$ is a bounded set of numbers. In other words, $\{T_i\}$ is bounded as subset of $\mathcal{B}(B, N)$.

Proof

For every positive integer n, define

$$F_n = \{x; x \in B \text{ and } \|T_i(x)\| \leq n, \text{for all } i\}.$$

Let $x \in B$.

Then, by hypothesis, $\{T_i(x)\}$ is a bounded subset of N.

Therefore, there exists a positive integer m, such that

$\|T_i(x)\| \leq m$, for all i.

That implies, $x \in F_m$.

Thus, $B = \bigcup_{i=1}^{\infty} F_i$.

Also, each F_i is a closed subset of B.

Thus, B is a countable union of closed sets in B.

Now, B is of second category and so it cannot be expressed as a countable union of nowhere dense sets.

Therefore, for some n_0, the set F_{n_0} has nonempty interior.

Let x be an interior point of F_{n_0}.

Therefore, there exists an open set $S(x, r_0) = \{y \in B; \|y - x\| < r_0\}$ such that $x \in S(x, r_0) \subseteq F_{n_0}$.

Since F is closed, $x \in \overline{S(x, r_0)} \subseteq \overline{F_{n_0}} = F_{n_0}$.

That is, $S_0 = \overline{S(x, r_0)} = \{y \in B; \|y - x\| \leq r_0\} \subseteq F_{n_0}$.

That implies, $y \in S_0$ which implies $y \in F_{n_0}$.

That is, $\|T_i(x)\| \leq n_0$, for all i.

Thus,$\|T_i(S_0)\| \leq n_0$, for all i.

Now, $y \in S_0 - x \Rightarrow \|T_i(y)\| = \|T_i(S_0)\| + \|T_i(x)\| \leq n_0 + n_0 = 2n_0$.

That implies, $\|T_i(S_0 - x)\| \leq 2n_0$.

Since, S is a closed unit sphere, we have, $\left\|T_i\left(\frac{S_0 - x}{r_0}\right)\right\| \leq \frac{2n_0}{r_0}$.

That is, $\|T_i(S)\| \leq \frac{2n_0}{r_0}$, where S is the closed unit sphere centered at the origin.

Thus, $\|T_i\| \leq \frac{2n_0}{r_0}$, for all i.

Therefore, $\|T_i\|$ is a bounded set of numbers.

Hence the theorem.

Theorem 4.3.18

A nonempty subset X of a normed linear space N is bounded, if and only if $f(X)$ is a bounded set of numbers for each f in N^*.

Proof

Direct part,

Suppose X is bounded.

That is, $\|x\| \leq k$, for a real number $k \geq 0$.

Fix one $f \in N^*$.

Then, for all $x \in X, |f(x)| \leq \|f\|\|x\| \leq k\|f\|$.

That implies, $f(X)$ is bounded, for all f.

Converse part,

Suppose $f(X)$ is a bounded set of numbers.

We have to prove that, X is bounded.

We write, X in the form $X = \{x_i\}$.

We know that, for all $x_i \in X$, there exists $F_{x_i} \in N^{**}$ and the relation $x_i \to F_{x_i}$ is an isometric isomorphism of X into N^{**}.

Therefore, we can identify X as a subset of $\{F_{x_i}\}$ of N^{**}.

Now, $f(X)$ is bounded implies that $f\{(x_i)\}$ is bounded, for all $f \in N^*$.

This is equivalent to the fact that, $\{F_{x_i}(f)\}$ is bounded, for all $f \in N^*$.

Now, N^* is a Banach space and $\{F_{x_i}(f)\}$ is bounded, for all $f \in N^*$.

Therefore, by the previous theorem 4.3.17, $\|F_{x_i}\|$ is bounded.

But, $\|F_{x_i}\| = \|x_i\|$.

Thus, $\|x_i\|$ is bounded implies X is bounded.

Hence the theorem.

Definition 4.3.19

Given $T \in \mathcal{B}(N)$. Let us define a function $T^*: N^* \to N^*$ as follows:

$$T^*(f)(x) = f(T(x)), \text{ for all } x \in N \text{ and } f \in N^*.$$

Result 4.3.20

T^* is a continuous linear operator on N^*.

Proof

i) First, we will prove that, T^* is well defined.

Now, $f = g$ implies $f(x) = g(x)$, for all $x \in N$.

Since $T(x) \in N$, we have $f(T(x)) = g(T(x))$.

That implies, $T^*f(x) = T^*g(x)$, for all x.

Thus, $T^*f = T^*g$.

Therefore, $T^*: N^* \to N^*$ is a well – defined function.

ii) *To prove*: T^* is linear.

a) $T^*(f+g)(x) = (f+g)\big(T(x)\big) = f\big(T(x)\big) + g\big(T(x)\big)$

$= (T^*f)(x) + (T^*g)(x).$

That is, $T^*(f+g)(x) = (T^*f + T^*g)(x)$, for all $x \in N$.

Thus, $T^*(f+g) = T^*f + T^*g$.

b) $T^*(\alpha f)(x) = \big((\alpha f)(T)\big)(x) = \alpha\big[f\big(T(x)\big)\big] = \alpha T^*(f)(x)$, for all x.

Thus, $T^*(\alpha f) = \alpha T^*(f)$.

Therefore, $T^*: N^* \to N^*$ is linear.

iii) *To prove*: T^* is continuous.

Now,

$\|T^*\| = sup.\{\|T^*(f)\|; \|f\| \leq 1\} \leq sup.\{|T^*(f)(x)|; \|f\| \leq 1, \|x\| \leq 1\}$.

That is,

$\|T^*\| \leq sup.\{|f(T)(x)|; \|f\| \leq 1, \|x\| \leq 1\}$

$\leq sup.\{\|f\|\|T\|\|x\|; \|f\| \leq 1, \|x\| \leq 1\}$.

Thus, $\|T^*\| \leq \|T\|$.

Now, $T \in \mathcal{B}(N)$ implies T is continuous and bounded.

That implies, $T^*$is bounded and hence continuous.

Thus, T^* is a continuous linear operator on N^*.

Note 4.3.21

From the above result 4.3.20, we can write, $T^* \in \mathcal{B}(N^*)$. Thus, for all $T \in \mathcal{B}(N)$, there exists $T^* \in \mathcal{B}(N^*)$, which is termed as the *conjugate operator of T*.

Properties of Conjugate operator 4.3.22

i) $(\alpha T_1 + \beta T_2)^* = \alpha T_1^* + \beta T_2^*$.

ii) $(T_1 T_2)^* = T_2^* T_1^*$.

iii) $I^* = I$.

Proof

i) *To prove*: $(\alpha T_1 + \beta T_2)^* = \alpha T_1^* + \beta T_2^*$.

Let $x \in N$.

Now, $[(\alpha T_1 + \beta T_2)^*(f)](x) = f[(\alpha T_1 + \beta T_2)(x)] = f[\alpha T_1(x) + \beta T_2(x)]$.

Since f is linear, $[(\alpha T_1 + \beta T_2)^*(f)](x) = \alpha[f(T_1(x))] + \beta[f(T_2(x))]$.

That is,

$[(\alpha T_1 + \beta T_2)^*(f)](x) = \alpha T_1^*(f(x)) + \beta T_2^*(f(x)) = (\alpha T_1^* + \beta T_2^*)f(x)$.

Therefore, $(\alpha T_1 + \beta T_2)^*(f) = (\alpha T_1^* + \beta T_2^*)f$.

ii) *To prove*: $((T_1T_2)^*)f = (T_2^*T_1^*)f$, for all $f \in N^*$.

Now, $[(T_1T_2)^*f](x) = f[T_1(T_2(x))] = (T_1^*f)T_2(x) = (T_2^*T_1^*)f(x)$.

Therefore, $(T_1T_2)^*f = (T_2^*T_1^*)f$.

iii) *To prove*: $I^* = I$.

I is the identity operator in $\mathcal{B}(N)$.

Thus, $I.T = T.I = T$, for all $T \in \mathcal{B}(N)$.

That implies, $(I.T)^* = (T.I)^* = T^*$.

That is, $T^*I^* = I^*T^* = T^*$.

This shows that, I^* is the identity operator in $\mathcal{B}(N^*)$.

Thus, $I^* = I$.

Hence proved.

Problem 4.3.23

Let B be a Banach space and $T \in \mathcal{B}(B)$. Show that T has an inverse T^{-1}if and only if T^* has an inverse $(T^*)^{-1}$ and in that case $(T^*)^{-1} = (T^{-1})^*$.

Solution

T has an inverse i.e., T^{-1}, if and only if, $TT^{-1} = T^{-1}T = I$.

If and only if, $(TT^{-1})^* = (T^{-1}T)^* = I^*$.

If and only if, $(T^{-1})^*T^* = T^*(T^{-1})^* = I^*$.

If and only if, T^* has an inverse in $\mathcal{B}(N^*)$, and its inverse is $(T^{-1})^*$.

In other words, we can say that, $(T^*)^{-1} = (T^{-1})^*$.

Hence proved.

4.4 Hilbert Space

Definition 4.4.1

Let L be a complex normed linear space. The *inner product* of any two vectors x, y in L, denoted by (x, y) is a complex function which satisfies the following three conditions;

1) $(\alpha x+\beta y,z)=\alpha(x,z)+\beta(y,z)$.

2) $\overline{(x,y)}=(y,x)$.

3) $(x,x)=\|x\|^2$.

Note 4.4.2

$$(x,\alpha y+\beta z)=\overline{(\alpha y+\beta z,x)}=\overline{(\alpha y,x)+(\beta z,x)}=\overline{\alpha}\ \overline{(y,x)}+\overline{\beta}\ \overline{(z,x)}=\overline{\alpha}(x,y)+\overline{\beta}(x,z).$$

Definition 4.4.3

A *Hilbert space* is a complex Banach space in which the inner product of vectors are defined and which satisfies all the three conditions of inner product.

Example 4.4.4

The space of n-tuples of scalars, denoted by l_2^n is a Hilbert space.

Solution

Let $x=(x_1,x_2,\ldots\ldots,x_n)$ and $y=(y_1,y_2,\ldots\ldots,y_n)\in l_2^n$.

We know that, $\|x\|=\left[\sum_{i=1}^{n}|x_i|^2\right]^{1/2}$.

Therefore, l_2^n is a complex Banach space.

Define the inner product (x, y) in l_2^n by

$$(x,y)=\sum x_i\overline{y_i}=x_1\overline{y_1}+x_2\overline{y_2}+\ldots..+x_n\overline{y_n}.$$

1) $(\alpha x+\beta y, z)=$

$$\left(\alpha(x_1,x_2,\ldots\ldots,x_n)+\beta(y_1,y_2,\ldots\ldots,y_n),(z_1,z_2,\ldots\ldots,z_n)\right)=\sum_{i=1}^{n}(\alpha x_i+\beta y_i)\overline{z_i}.$$

$$=\alpha\sum_{i=1}^{n}x_i\overline{z_i}+\beta\sum_{i=1}^{n}y_i\overline{z_i}=\alpha(x,z)+\beta(y,z).$$

2) $\overline{(x,y)}=\overline{\left(x_1\overline{y_1}+x_2\overline{y_2}+\ldots\ldots+x_n\overline{y_n}\right)}=y_1\overline{x_1}+y_2\overline{x_2}+\ldots\ldots+y_n\overline{x_n}=(y,x)$.

3) $(x,x)=x_1\overline{x_1}+x_2\overline{x_2}+\ldots\ldots+x_n\overline{x_n}=\sum_{i=1}^{n}|x_i|^2=\|x\|^2$.

Therefore, l_2^n is a Hilbert space.

Hence proved.

Results 4.4.5

1) Schwarz inequality

If x and y are two vectors in Hilbert space, then $|(x,y)|\le\|x\|\,\|y\|$.

Proof

If $y = 0$, then $|(x,y)|=0=\|x\|\,\|y\|$.

Hence, the inequality is true.

Suppose $y\neq 0$.

To prove; $\dfrac{|(x,y)|}{\|y\|}\le\|x\|$.

That is to prove, $\left|\left(x,\dfrac{y}{\|y\|}\right)\right|\le\|x\|$.

If $\|y\|=1$, we have to prove that, $|(x,y)|\le\|x\|$.

Let us consider, $0\ge\|x-(x,y)x\|^2$.

Now, $0\le\|x-(x,y)x\|^2=\left(x-(x,y)y,x-(x,y)y\right)=\|x\|^2-|(x,y)|^2$.

Therefore, when $\|y\|=1$, we have $|(x,y)|\le\|x\|\Rightarrow|(x,y)|\le\|x\|\,\|y\|$.

When $\|y\| \neq 1$, we have $\left\|\frac{y}{\|y\|}\right\| = 1$.

Replacing y by $\frac{y}{\|y\|}$ in the inequality $|(x, y)| \leq \|x\|$, we get

$$\left|\left(x, \frac{y}{\|y\|}\right)\right| \leq \|x\| \Rightarrow |(x, y)| \leq \|x\| \|y\|.$$

Hence proved.

2) Parallelogram Law:

If x and y are any two vectors in a Hilbert space, then

$$\|x+y\|^2 + \|x-y\|^2 = 2\|x\|^2 + 2\|y\|^2.$$

Proof

Now, $\|x+y\|^2 + \|x-y\|^2 = (x+y, x+y) + (x-y, x-y) = 2\left[\|x\|^2 + \|y\|^2\right]$.

Hence proved.

Theorem 4.4.6

A closed convex subset C of a Hilbert space H contains a unique vector of smallest norm.

Proof

Since C is a convex subset of H, it is non – empty.

Also, for all $x, y \in C$, the vector $\frac{x+y}{2} \in C$.

Let us define, $d = inf.\{\|x\|; x \in C\}$.

Then, there exists a sequence $\{x_n\}$ of vectors in C, such that $\|x_n\| \to d$.

Now,

$$x_m, x_n \in C \Rightarrow \frac{x_m + x_n}{2} \in C \Rightarrow \left\|\frac{x_m + x_n}{2}\right\| \geq d \Rightarrow \|x_m + x_n\| \geq 2d.$$

.... (4.4.6.1)

By Parallelogram law of vectors, we have,

$\|x_m - x_n\|^2 = 2\|x_m\|^2 + 2\|x_n\|^2 - \|x_m + x_n\|^2$.

Therefore, by equation (4.4.6.1), we have

$\|x_m - x_n\|^2 \leq 2\|x_m\|^2 + 2\|x_n\|^2 - 4d^2 \to 2d^2 + 2d^2 - 4d^2 \to 0,$

as $m, n \to \infty$.

This means that, $\{x_n\}$ is a Cauchy sequence in C.

Since, C is a closed subspace of a complete space H, C is complete.

Thus, the Cauchy sequence $\{x_n\}$ in C converges to a vector $x \in C$.

We claim: i) $\|x\| = d$,

ii) x is unique.

i) $\|x\| = \|lim.\, x_n\| = lim.\, \|x_n\| = d.$

ii) *To prove*: x is unique

If possible, let us assume that, there exists another vector $x' \in C$, such that $\|x'\| = d$.

Then, $\frac{x+x'}{2} \in C$.

Thus, $\left\|\frac{x+x'}{2}\right\|^2 = \left\|\frac{x}{2} + \frac{x'}{2}\right\|^2 = 2\left\|\frac{x}{2}\right\|^2 + 2\left\|\frac{x'}{2}\right\|^2 - \left\|\frac{x}{2} - \frac{x'}{2}\right\|^2.$

That implies, $\left\|\frac{x+x'}{2}\right\|^2 < \left\|\frac{x}{2}\right\|^2 + \left\|\frac{x'}{2}\right\|^2 = d^2.$

That is, $\left\|\frac{x+x'}{2}\right\| < d$, which is a contradiction to the definition of d.

Therefore, x is unique.

Hence the theorem.

Theorem 4.4.7

Let B be a complex Banach space, whose norm satisfies the parallelogram law. Suppose the inner product in B is defined by $4(x, y) = \|x+y\|^2 - \|x-y\|^2 + i\|x+iy\|^2 - i\|x-iy\|^2$, for all $x, y \in B$, then B is a Hilbert space.

Proof

To prove the theorem, we have to prove the following three conditions:

i) $(\alpha x + \beta y, z) = \alpha(x, z) + \beta(y, z),$

ii) $(x, y) = \overline{(y, x)},$

iii) $(x, x) = \|x\|^2.$

i) *To prove*: $(\alpha x + \beta y, z) = \alpha(x, z) + \beta(y, z)$.

To prove this, we have to prove the following 2 conditions:

a) $(x + y, z) = (x, z) + (y, z)$,

b) $(\alpha x, y) = \alpha(x, y)$.

Now,

$$4(x + y, z) = \|x + y + z\|^2 - \|x + y - z\|^2 + i\|x + y + iz\|^2 + i\|x + y - iz\|^2.$$

By parallelogram law of vectors,

$$\|x + y + z\|^2 = \|(x + z) + y\|^2 = 2\|x + z\|^2 + 2\|y\|^2 - \|x + z - y\|^2. \qquad \text{.......... (4.4.7.1)}$$

Also, we have

$$\|z + x - y\|^2 = \|(z - y) + x\|^2 = 2\|z - y\|^2 + 2\|x\|^2 - \|z - y - x\|^2. \qquad \text{.......... (4.4.7.2)}$$

Using equation (4.4.7.2) in equation (4.4.7.1), we get

$$\|x + y + z\|^2 = 2\|x + z\|^2 + 2\|y\|^2 - 2\|z - y\|^2 - 2\|x\|^2 + \|z - y - x\|^2.$$

That implies,

$$\|x + y + z\|^2 - \|x + y - z\|^2 = 2\|x + z\|^2 + 2\|y\|^2 - 2\|z - y\|^2 - 2\|x\|^2 \qquad \text{.......... (4.4.7.3)}$$

Interchanging *x* and *y* in equation (4.4.7.3), we get

$$\|x + y + z\|^2 - \|x + y - z\|^2 = 2\|y + z\|^2 + 2\|x\|^2 - 2\|z - x\|^2 - 2\|y\|^2 \qquad \text{.......... (4.4.7.4)}$$

Adding equations (4.4.7.3) and (4.4.7.4), we get

$$2\{\|x + y + z\|^2 - \|x + y - z\|^2\} = 2\|x + z\|^2 + 2\|y + z\|^2 - 2\|z - y\|^2 - 2\|z - x\|^2.$$

That implies,

$$\|x + y + z\|^2 - \|x + y - z\|^2 = \|x + z\|^2 + \|y + z\|^2 - \|z - y\|^2 - \|z - x\|^2. \qquad \text{.......... (4.4.7.5)}$$

Replacing *z* by *iz* in equation (4.4.7.5), and multiplying throughout by *i*, we get

$$i\|x+y+iz\|^2 - i\|x+y-iz\|^2 = i\|x+iz\|^2 + i\|y+iz\|^2$$
$$-i\|y-iz\|^2 - i\|x-iz\|^2. \quad \ldots. (4.4.7.6)$$

Let us add equations (4.4.7.5) and (4.4.7.6).

The sum of the L.H.S. of equations (4.4.7.5) and (4.4.7.6) is

$$\|x+y+z\|^2 - \|x+y-z\|^2 + i\|x+y+iz\|^2 - i\|x+y-iz\|^2$$
$$= 4(x+y,z). \quad \ldots\ldots\ldots (4.4.7.7)$$

The sum of the R.H.S. of equations (4.4.7.5) and (4.4.7.6) is

$$\|x+z\|^2 + \|y+z\|^2 - \|z-y\|^2 - \|z-x\|^2 + i\|x+iz\|^2$$
$$+i\|y+iz\|^2 - i\|y-iz\|^2 - i\|x-iz\|^2 = 4(x,z) + 4(y,z) \quad \ldots\ldots (4.4.7.8)$$

Thus, from equations (4.4.7.7) and (4.4.7.8), we get

$$(x+y,z) = (x,z) + (y,z).$$

Hence part (a) is proved.

b) *To prove*: $(\alpha x, y) = \alpha(x,y)$.

Suppose α is any integer, then by the above part we get,

$$(\alpha x, y) = \alpha(x,y).$$

Suppose α is a rational number.

Let $\alpha = \frac{p}{q}$, where p and q are integers and $q \neq 0$.

Thus, $4(\alpha x, y) = \|\alpha x + y\|^2 - \|\alpha x - y\|^2 + i\|\alpha x + iy\|^2 - i\|\alpha x - iy\|^2$ implies

$$4\left(\frac{p}{q}x, y\right) = \left\|\frac{p}{q}x + y\right\|^2 - \left\|\frac{p}{q}x - y\right\|^2 + i\left\|\frac{p}{q}x + iy\right\|^2 - i\left\|\frac{p}{q}x - iy\right\|^2.$$

That is,

$$4\left(\frac{p}{q}x, y\right) = \left|\frac{1}{q}\right|^2 \{\|px+qy\|^2 - \|px-qy\|^2 + i\|px+iqy\|^2$$
$$- i\|px-iqy\|^2\}$$

That implies, $4\left(\frac{p}{q}x, y\right) = \frac{1}{|q|^2}4(px, qy)$.

Since p and q are integers, we have

$$4\left(\frac{p}{q}x, y\right) = \frac{4}{|q|^2}p(x,qy) = \frac{4p}{q\bar{q}}\bar{q}\overline{(y,x)} = \frac{4p}{q}(x,y) = 4\alpha(x,y).$$

Hence part (b) is proved.

Therefore, we conclude that, $(\alpha x + \beta y, z) = \alpha(x,z) + \beta(y,z)$.

Thus, part (i) is proved.

ii) *To prove*: $(x,y) = \overline{(y,x)}$.

Interchanging x and y in the given equation, we get

$4(y,x) = \|y+x\|^2 - \|y-x\|^2 + i\|y+ix\|^2 - i\|y-ix\|^2$.

That implies,

$4(y,x) = \|x+y\|^2 - \|x-y\|^2 + i\|i(x-iy)\|^2 - i\|-i(x+iy)\|^2$.

That is, $4(y,x) = \|x+y\|^2 - \|x-y\|^2 + i\|x-iy\|^2 - i\|x+iy\|^2$.

Thus, $4\overline{(y,x)} = \overline{\|x+y\|^2 - \|x-y\|^2 + \imath\|x-\imath y\|^2 - \imath\|x+\imath y\|^2}$.

That implies,

$4\overline{(y,x)} = \overline{\|x+y\|^2} + \overline{\|x-y\|^2} + \overline{\imath\|x-\imath y\|^2} - \overline{\imath\|x+\imath y\|^2} = 4(x,y)$.

Therefore, $\overline{(y,x)} = (x,y)$.

Hence, part (ii) is proved.

iii) *To prove*: $(x,x) = \|x\|^2$.

By taking $y = x$ in the given equation, we get

$4(x,x) = \|x+x\|^2 - \|x-x\|^2 + i\|x+ix\|^2 - i\|x-ix\|^2$.

That is, $4(x,x) = 4\|x\|^2 + i\|x\|^2\|1+i\|^2 - i\|x\|^2\|1-i\|^2$.

That implies, $4(x,x) = 4\|x\|^2 + i\|x\|^2\|1+i\|^2 - i\|x\|^2\|1-i\|^2$.

Since, $\|1+i\| = \|1-i\|$, we get $(x,x) = \|x\|^2$.

Hence, part (iii) is proved.

Hence the theorem.

Definition 4.4.8

Let $x, y \in H$. If $(x, y) = 0$, we say x is orthogonal to y. It is written as $x \perp y$.

Note 4.4.9

1) x is orthogonal to y implies $(x, y) = 0$.

   $\Rightarrow (y,x) = \overline{(x,y)} = 0 \Rightarrow y \perp x$.

2) Zero is orthogonal to every vector in H.
3) Zero is the only vector orthogonal to itself.

Definition 4.4.10

Let S be a non empty subset of a Hilbert space H. $x \perp S$ means *x is orthogonal to every vector in S*. The set of vector in H, each of which is orthogonal to every vector in S is called *orthogonal complement of S*. It is denoted by $S^{\perp}$.

Properties 4.4.11

1) $\{0\}^{\perp} = H$.

Every vector in H is orthogonal to zero vector.

Therefore, $\{0\}^{\perp} = H$.

2) $H^{\perp} = \{0\}$.

Zero vector alone is orthogonal to every vector in H.

Therefore, $H^{\perp} = \{0\}$.

3) $S \cap S^{\perp} \subseteq \{0\}$.

Proof

Suppose $x \in S \cap S^{\perp} \Rightarrow x \in S$ and $x \in S^{\perp} \Rightarrow x \perp x \Rightarrow x = 0 \Rightarrow x \in \{0\}$.

Therefore, $S \cap S^{\perp} \subseteq \{0\}$.

Hence proved.

4) $S_1 \subseteq S_2 \Rightarrow S_1^{\perp} \supseteq S_2^{\perp}$.

Proof

Given $S_1 \subseteq S_2$.

Let $x \in S_2^{\perp}$ (arbitrarily)

$\Rightarrow x \perp S_2 \Rightarrow x \perp S_1 \Rightarrow x \in S_1^{\perp}$.

Therefore, $S_2^{\perp} \subseteq S_1^{\perp}$.

Hence proved.

5) $S^{\perp}$ is a closed linear subspace of H.

Proof

i) To prove, $S^{\perp}$ is a linear subspace.

Let $x, y \in S^{\perp}$ and α be any scalar.

Claim a) $x+y\in S^{\perp}$.

b) $\alpha x\in S^{\perp}$.

Let $x\in S^{\perp}\Rightarrow x\perp z$, for all $z\in S$.

$\Rightarrow (x,z)=0$.

Similarly, $y\in S^{\perp}\Rightarrow (y,z)=0$, for all $z\in S$.

Therefore, $(x+y,z)=(x,z)+(y,z)=0$, for all $z\in S$.

Hence, $(x+y)\perp S\Rightarrow (x+y)\in S^{\perp}$.

Again, $x\in S^{\perp}\Rightarrow (x,z)=0$, for all $z\in S$.

Therefore, $(\alpha x,z)=\alpha(x,z)=0\Rightarrow \alpha x\perp S\Rightarrow \alpha x\in S^{\perp}$.

Hence, $S^{\perp}$ is a linear subspace.

ii) To prove; $S^{\perp}$ is closed.

That is, to prove; $\overline{S^{\perp}}=S^{\perp}$.

Let $x\in \overline{S^{\perp}}$.

Then, there exists a sequence $\{x_n\}$ of vectors in $S^{\perp}$, which converge to x.

Hence, $x_n\in S^{\perp}\Rightarrow (x_n,y)=0$, for all $y\in S$.

This is true for all n.

Therefore, the sequence $\{(x_n, y)\}$ of complex numbers converges to zero.

That is, $\lim\limits_{n\to\infty}(x_n,y)=0\Rightarrow (\lim\limits_{n\to\infty}x_n,y)=0\Rightarrow (x,y)=0$, for all $y\in S$.

$\Rightarrow x\in S^{\perp}$.

Hence, $\overline{S^{\perp}}\subseteq S^{\perp}$.

It is obvious that, $S^{\perp}\subseteq \overline{S^{\perp}}$.

Therefore, $\overline{S^{\perp}}=S^{\perp}$.

Hence, $S^{\perp}$ is closed.

That implies, $S^{\perp}$ is a closed linear subspace of H.

Hence proved.

6) If S is a non - empty subset of Hilbert space H, then $S \subseteq S^{\perp\perp}$.

Proof

Every vector in S is orthogonal to every vector in $S^{\perp}$.

Now, $(S^{\perp})^{\perp}$ is the collection of vectors which are orthogonal to every vector in $S^{\perp}$.

Therefore, $S \subseteq (S^{\perp})^{\perp}$.

Hence proved.

Unit

5 Lp SPACES AND SOME INEQUALITIES

5.1 Introduction

In this chapter, we discuss about the fundamental concepts of L^p spaces of functions. The norms of L^p spaces are defined in terms of integrals. We also discuss some of the important inequalities like Young's inequality, Holder's inequality and Minkowski's inequality.

5.2 Fundamental concepts of L^p spaces

Definition 5.2.1

Let $(X, \mathcal{A}, \mu)$ be a measurable space and $1 \leq p < \infty$. Then, $\mathcal{L}^p(X,\mu)$ is the set of all measurable functions $f : X \to \overline{\mathbb{R}}$ such that $|f|^p$ is integrable, that is

$$\mathcal{L}^p(X,\mu) = \left\{ f : X \to \overline{\mathbb{R}} : f \text{ is measurable and } \int_X |f|^p \, d\mu < \infty \right\}.$$

If $\alpha \in \mathbb{R}$ and $f \in \mathcal{L}^p(X,\mu)$,

then αf is measurable and $\int_X |\alpha f|^p \, d\mu = |\alpha|^p \int_X |f|^p \, d\mu < \infty$,

that is, $\alpha f \in \mathcal{L}^p(X,\mu)$.

If $f, g \in \mathcal{L}^p(X,\mu)$, then

$f + g$ is measurable, and since $|f+g|^p \leq 2^{p-1}\left(|f|^p |g|^p\right)$, it follows that

$$\int_X |f+g|^p \, d\mu \leq \int_X 2^{p-1}\left(|f|^p + |g|^p\right) d\mu = 2^{p-1}\left(\int_X |f|^p \, d\mu + \int_X |g|^p \, d\mu \right) < \infty.$$

and so $f + g \in \mathcal{L}^p(X,\mu)$.

Definition 5.2.3

Let $(X, \mathcal{A}, \mu)$ be a measure space. A measurable function $f : X \to \overline{\mathbb{R}}$ is said to be *essentially bounded* (with respect to μ), if there is a constant $M > 0$ such that $|f(x)| \leq M$ a.e. on X. .... (5.2.3.1)

The smallest constant M such that (5.2.3.1) holds is called the *essential supremum of* $|f|$ and is denoted by $\|f\|_\infty$, that is,

$$\|f\|_\infty = \text{ess.}\ \underset{X}{\text{sup.}}|f| = \inf\{M \in \mathbb{R} : |f| \leq M \text{ a.e. on } X\}.$$

Note that, f is essentially bounded if there is a constant $M > 0$ such that $\mu(\{x \in X : |f(x)| > M\}) = 0$, that is, the set of points in X where f fails to be bounded is a null set.

Let $\mathcal{L}^\infty(X, \mu)$ be the set of all essentially bounded functions on a measure space $(X, \mathcal{A}, \mu)$.

Definition 5.2.4

A function ϕ defined on an open interval (a, b) is said to be *convex*, if for each $x, y \in (a,b)$ and each λ, $0 < \lambda < 1$, $\phi(\lambda x + (1-\lambda)y) \leq \lambda\phi(x) + (1-\lambda)\phi(y)$.

5.3 Some important inequalities

Definition 5.3.1

Let p and q be positive real numbers. If $1 < p < \infty$ and $\frac{1}{p} + \frac{1}{q} = 1$ or if $p = 1$ and $q = \infty$ or if $p = \infty$ and $q = 1$, then we say that p and q are *conjugate exponents*.

Lemma 5.3.2

The following inequality is known as ***Young's inequality***.

Let p and q be conjugate exponents, with $1 < p, q < \infty$, $\alpha \geq 0$ and $\beta \geq 0$.

Then, $\alpha\beta < \frac{\alpha^p}{p} + \frac{\beta^q}{q}$.

Proof

If $p = 2 = q$, then the inequality follows from the fact that $(\alpha-\beta)^2 \geq 0$.

Consider the function $f:[0,\infty)\to\mathbb{R}$ given by $f(\alpha)=\frac{\alpha^p}{p}+\frac{\beta^q}{q}-\alpha\beta$, for fixed $\beta > 0$.

Then, $f(0)=\frac{\beta^q}{q}$, $f(\beta^{q/p})=0$ and $\lim\limits_{\alpha\to+\infty} f(\alpha)=+\infty$.

Hence, f has a global minimum on $[0,\infty)$, that is, there is an $\alpha_0\in[0,\infty)$ such that

$$f(\alpha_0)\leq f(\alpha)\text{, for all } \alpha\in[0,\infty).$$

Now, since $f'(\alpha_0)=0$, it follows that

$$0=f'(\alpha_0)=\alpha_0^{p-1}-\beta \;\Leftrightarrow\; \beta=\alpha_0^{p\ 1} \;\Leftrightarrow \alpha_0=\beta^{\frac{1}{p-1}}=\beta^{q/p}.$$

Hence, for all $\alpha\in[0,\infty)$,

$$0=f\left(\beta^{q/p}\right)\leq f(\alpha)=\frac{\alpha^p}{p}+\frac{\beta^q}{q}-\alpha\beta \;\Leftrightarrow\; \alpha\beta\leq\frac{\alpha^p}{p}+\frac{\beta^q}{q}.$$

Hence proved.

Theorem 5.3.3

The following inequality is known as ***Holder's inequality***.

Let $1\leq p,q\leq\infty$ be conjugate exponents, $(X,\mathcal{A},\mu)$ be a measure space, $f\in\mathcal{L}^p(X,\mu)$ and $g\in\mathcal{L}^p(X,\mu)$. Then,

$$fg\in\mathcal{L}^1(X,\mu) \text{ and } \int_X |fg|\,d\mu\leq\|f\|_p\|g\|_q.$$

Proof

Firstly, we consider that $1<p<\infty$.

If $\|f\|_p=0$ or $\|g\|_q=0$, then the result follows trivially.

Therefore, we assume that, $\|f\|_p>0$ and $\|g\|_q>0$.

Let $F=\frac{f}{\|f\|_p}$ and $G=\frac{g}{\|g\|_q}$.

Then, $F \in \mathcal{L}^p(X,\mu)$ and $G \in \mathcal{L}^p(X,\mu)$ and $\|F\|_p = 1.\|G\|_q$.

By Young's inequality (Lemma 5.3.2), we have that

$$|FG| \le \frac{1}{p}|F|^p + \frac{1}{q}|G|^q.$$

That implies, $\int_X |FG| d\mu \le \frac{1}{p}\int_X |F|^p d\mu + \frac{1}{q}\int_X |G|^q d\mu = \frac{1}{p} + \frac{1}{q} = 1$.

Hence, $\int_X |fg| d\mu \le \|f\|_p \|g\|_q$.

Now, let us assume that $p = 1$ and $q = \infty$.

Let $M = \|g\|_\infty$.

Then, $|fg| \le M|f|$ a.e. on X and so,

$$\int_X |fg| d\mu \le \int_X M|f| d\mu \le M \int_X |f| d\mu = \|g\|_\infty \|f\|_1.$$

Therefore, $\int_X |fg| d\mu \le \|f\|_p \|g\|_q$.

Hence proved.

Theorem 5.3.4

Let $(X, \mathcal{A}, \mu)$ be a finite measure space and $1 \le r < p \le \infty$. Then, $\mathcal{L}^p(X,\mu) \subseteq \mathcal{L}^r(X,\mu)$.

Proof

Let $t = \frac{p}{r}$ and $s = \frac{p}{p-r}$.

Then, $\frac{1}{t} + \frac{1}{s} = 1$, that is, s and t are conjugate exponents.

Let $f \in \mathcal{L}^p(X,\mu)$.

Then, by Holder's inequality (Theorem 5.3.3),

$$\|f\|_r^r = \int_X |f|^r d\mu \le \left(\int_X \left(|f|^r\right)^t d\mu\right)^{1/t} \left(\int_X 1^s d\mu\right)^{1/s}.$$

$$= \left(\int_X \left(|f|^r\right)^{p/r} d\mu \right)^{r/p} \left(\int_X 1^s \, d\mu \right)^{1/s}.$$

$$= \|f\|_p^r [\mu(X)]^{1/s}.$$

Hence, $\|f\|_r \le \|f\|_p [\mu(X)] \frac{1}{sr} = \|f\|_p [\mu(X)]^{\frac{1}{r} - \frac{1}{p}} < \infty$,

and therefore $f \in \mathcal{L}^r(X, \mu)$.

Hence the theorem.

Theorem 5.3.5

The following inequality is known as the ***Minkowski Inequality***.

If f and g are in $\mathcal{L}^p(X,\mu)$ with $1 \le p \le \infty$, then, $f+g \in \mathcal{L}^p(X,\mu)$ and $\|f+g\|_p \le \|f\|_p + \|g\|_p$.

Proof

Already, we have shown that $f+g \in \mathcal{L}^p(X,\mu)$.

Let $q = \dfrac{p}{p-1}$.

If $\int_X |f+g|^p \, d\mu = 0$, then the result is obvious.

Let us assume that, $\int_X |f+g|^p \, d\mu \ne 0$, then

$$\int_X |f+g|^p \, d\mu = \int_X |f+g| |f+g|^{p-1} \, d\mu.$$

$$\le \int_X |f| |f+g|^{p-1} \, d\mu + \int_X |g| |f+g|^{p-1} \, d\mu.$$

$$\le \left(\int_X |f+g|^{(p-1)q} \right)^{1/q} \left[\left(\int_X |f|^p \, d\mu \right)^{1/p} + \left(\int_X |g|^p \, d\mu \right)^{1/p} \right].$$

$$= \left(\int_X |f+g|^p \, d\mu \right)^{1/q} \left[\|f\|_p + \|g\|_p \right].$$

Dividing both sides by $\left(\int_X |f+g|^p \, d\mu\right)^{1/q}$, we get

$$\left(\int_X |f+g|^p \, d\mu\right)^{1/p} = \left(\int_X |f+g|^p \, d\mu\right)^{1-\frac{1}{q}} \le \|f\|_p + \|g\|_q \Leftrightarrow \|f+g\|_p \le \|f\|_p + \|g\|_p ..$$

If $p = \infty$, then for each $x \in X$,

$$|f(x)+g(x)| \le |f(x)| + |g(x)| \le \|f\|_\infty + \|g\|_\infty .$$

Thus, $f+g \in \mathcal{L}^\infty(X,\mu)$ and $\|f+g\|_\infty \le \|f\|_\infty + \|g\|_\infty$.

Hence proved.

Note 5.3.6

Let $(X, \mathcal{A}, \mu)$ be a measure space and $1 \le p < \infty$. Define a real valued function $\|\cdot\|_p$ on $\mathcal{L}^p(X,\mu)$ by

$$\|f\|_p = \left(\int_X |f|^p \, d\mu\right), \quad \text{for } f \in \mathcal{L}^p(X,\mu).$$

Then, $\|\cdot\|_p$ does not define a norm on $\mathcal{L}^p(X,\mu)$.

Solution

If $f \in \mathcal{L}^p(X,\mu)$, then

$$\|f\|_p = 0 \text{ if and only if } \int_X |f|^p \, d\mu = 0.$$

if and only if $|f| = 0$ a. e. on X.

if and only if $f = 0$ a.e. on X.

This shows that $\|\cdot\|_p$ does not define a norm on $\mathcal{L}^p(X,\mu)$.

The way we deal with this, is we define a relation $\sim$ on $\mathcal{L}^p(X,\mu)$ as follows:

For $f, g \in \mathcal{L}^p(X,\mu)$,

$f \sim g$ if and only if $f = g$ a.e. on X.

We can show that ~ defines an equivalence relation on $\mathcal{L}^p(X,\mu)$ that differ only on a null set. We denote the quotient space of $\mathcal{L}^p(X,\mu)$ by $\mathcal{L}^p(X,\mu)/\sim$. That is,

$$\mathcal{L}^p(X,\mu) = \mathcal{L}^p(X,\mu)/\mathcal{N}.$$

where $\mathcal{N} = \{f \in \mathcal{L}^p(X,\mu) : f = 0 \text{ a.e.on } X\}$. Also, $\mathcal{L}^p(X,\mu)$ is a set of equivalence classes of functions. For $f \in \mathcal{L}^p(X,\mu)$, let us denote the equivalence class of f by $[f]$. Here, $[f]$ is the set of all functions in $\mathcal{L}^p(X,\mu)$ that differ from f on a null set.

Similarly, let us denote by $\mathcal{L}^\infty(X,\mu)$, the quotient space obtained by identifying functions in $\mathcal{L}^\infty(X,\mu)$ that coincide almost everywhere.

Theorem 5.3.7

Let $(X,\mathcal{A},\mu)$ be a measure space and $1 \le p \le \infty$. Let us define addition and scalar multiplication in $\mathcal{L}^p(X,\mu)$ as follows;

$[f]+[g]=[f+g]$ and $\alpha[f]=[\alpha f]$, where $f,g \in \mathcal{L}^p(X,\mu)$ and $\alpha \in \mathbb{R}$.

Then, $\mathcal{L}^p(X,\mu)$ is a real vector space.

Note 5.3.8

$\mathcal{L}^p(X,\mu)$ is a linear space. Suppose that $1 \le p < \infty$ and $f \in \mathcal{L}^p(X,\mu)$, let us define the norm $\|\cdot\|_p : \mathcal{L}^p(X,\mu) \to [0,\infty)$ by

$$\|[f]\|_p = \|f\|_p = \left(\int_X |f|^p \, d\mu\right)^{1/p}$$

and for $p = \infty$, define

$$\|[f]\|_p = \|f\|_\infty = ess\sup_X |f|.$$

It is important to note that the definition of $\|\cdot\|_p$ (or $\|\cdot\|_\infty$) is independent of the choice of a representative of the equivalence class [f], for $f \in \mathcal{L}^p(X,\mu)$(or $f \in \mathcal{L}^\infty(X,\mu)$).

Let $f,g \in \mathcal{L}^p(X,\mu)$ such that $g \in [f]$.

Then, $[f]=[g]$ and $f=g$ a.e. on X.

Therefore, $\int_X f d\mu = \int_X g d\mu$.

Theorem 5.3.9

Let $(X, \mathcal{A}, \mu)$ be a measure space. Then, $\left(\mathcal{L}^p(X,\mu), \|\cdot\|_p\right)$ and $\left(\mathcal{L}^\infty(X,\mu), \|\cdot\|_\infty\right)$ are normed linear spaces.

5.4 Convergence and completeness

Definition 5.4.1

A sequence in a normed linear space is said to *converge to an element f* in the space, if given $\varepsilon > 0$, there is a number N such that for all $n > N$,

$$\|f - f_n\| < \varepsilon.$$

When f_n converges to f, it can be written as

$$f = \lim f_n \text{ or } f_n \to f.$$

Definition 5.4.2

A sequence of functions $\{f_n\}$ is said to *converge pointwise to f* if for each x,

$$f(x) = \lim f_n(x).$$

Definition 5.4.3

A sequence of functions $\{f_n\}$ is said to *converge to f almost everywhere,* if there is a set of measure zero such that for each x in $\overline{E}$,

$$f(x) = \lim f_n(x).$$

Definition 5.4.4

A sequence $\{f_n\}$ in a normed linear space is said to be a *Cauchy sequence*, if for given $\varepsilon > 0$, there exist an N such that for all $m, n \geq N$,

$$\|f_n - f_m\| < \varepsilon.$$

Definition 5.4.5

A normed linear space is said to be *complete*, if every Cauchy sequence is convergent.

That is, for each Cauchy sequence $\{f_n\}$ in the space, there is an element f in the space such that

$$f_n \to f .$$

Definition 5.4.6

A normed linear space which is complete is said to be a *Banach space.*

Definition 5.4.7

A series $\{f_n\}$ in a normed linear space is said to be *summable to a sum s*, if s is in the space and the sequence of partial sum of the series converges to s. That is,

$$\left\| s - \sum_{i=1}^{n} f_i \right\| \to 0 .$$

We write this as $s = \sum_{i=1}^{\infty} f_i$.

Definition 5.4.8

The series $\{f_n\}$ is said to be *absolutely summable*, if $\sum_{n=1}^{\infty} \|f_n\| < \infty$.

Note 5.4.9

Absolute summability of a series of real numbers implies that the series is summable. But in general, this is not true for series of elements in a normed linear space. The result becomes true, when the space is complete.

Theorem 5.4.10

A normed linear space is X complete if and only if every absolutely summable series is summable.

Proof

Let X be a complete space.

To prove that every absolutely summable series is summable.

Let $\{f_n\}$ be an absolutely summable series of elements of *X*.

That is, $\|f_n\| = M < \infty$.

Hence, for each $\varepsilon > 0$, there is an *N* such that $\sum_{n=N}^{\infty} \|f_n\| < \varepsilon$.

Let $s_n = \sum_{i=1}^{n} f_i$ be the partial sum of the series $\{f_n\}$.

Then, for $n \geq m > N$, $\|s_n - s_m\| = \left\| \sum_{i=m}^{n} f_i \right\| \leq \sum_{i=m}^{\infty} \|f_i\| \leq \sum_{n=N}^{\infty} \|f_n\| < \varepsilon$.

Hence, the sequence of partial sums is a Cauchy sequence in *X*.

Since *X* is complete, $\{s_n\}$ converges to an element *s* in *X*.

Hence $\{f_n\}$ is summable.

Conversely,

Assume that every absolutely summable series is summable.

To prove that *X* is complete.

Let $\{f_n\}$ be a Cauchy sequence in *X*.

Then, by definition, for each integer *k*, there is an integer n_k such that

$$\|f_n - f_m\| < 2^{-k}, \qquad \text{for all } n, m \geq n_k .$$

Here, the n_k's may be chosen such that $n_{k+1} > n_k$.

Hence, $\{f_{n_k}\}_{k=1}^{\infty}$ is a subsequence of $\{f_n\}$.

Let $g_1 = f_{n_1}$, and $g_k = f_{n_k} - f_{n_{k-1}}$, for $k > 1$.

Then, $\sum_{i=1}^{k} g_i = \sum_{i=1}^{k} \left(f_{n_i} - f_{n_{i-1}}\right) = f_{n_k}$.

Hence, $\{g_k\}$ is a series whose *k*-th partial sum is f_{n_k}.

But, $\|g_k\| = \left\|f_{n_k} - f_{n_{k-1}}\right\| < 2^{-k+1}$, if $k > 1$.

Therefore, $\|g_k\| \leq \|g_1\| + 2^{-k+1} = \|g_1\| + 1 < \infty$.

Hence the series $\{g_k\}$ is absolutely summable.

Therefore, by assumption, $\{g_k\}$ is summable.

Thus, there exist an element $f \in X$ to which the partial sums of the series converge.

Hence, the subsequence $\{f_{n_k}\}$ converges to *f*.

Claim: $f = \lim f_n$.

Since $\{f_n\}$ is a Cauchy sequence,

for given $\varepsilon > 0$, there is an integer N such that for all $n, m \geq N$, $\|f_n - f_m\| < \varepsilon / 2$.

Since $f_n \to f$,

for the same $\varepsilon > 0$, there is a *K* such that for all $k \geq K$, $\|f_{n_k} - f\| < \varepsilon / 2$.

Choose *k* large such that $k > K$ and $n_k \geq N$.

Then for $n > N$,

$$\|f_n - f\| = \|f_n - f_{n_k} + f_{n_k} - f\| \leq \|f_n - f_{n_k}\| + \|f_{n_k} - f\| < \varepsilon / 2 + \varepsilon / 2 = \varepsilon .$$

Thus, $f_n \to f$.

That is, every Cauchy sequence of points of *X* converges to an element in *X*. Therefore, *X* is complete.

Hence the theorem.

Theorem 5.4.11

This theorem is known as ***Riesz – Fischer theorem***.

The L^p spaces are complete.

Proof

Let us assume that $1 \leq p < \infty$.

By the previous theorem 5.4.10, we need only to show that every absolutely summable series is summable in L^p.

Let $\{f_n\}$ be an absolutely summable series in L^p.

Let $\sum_{n=1}^{\infty} \|f_n\| = M < \infty$.

Define the functions g_n as $g_n(x)=\sum_{k=1}^{n}|f_k(x)|$.

Hence, by Minkowski's inequality, we have

$$\|g_n\|\le\sum_{k=1}^{n}\|f_k\|\le\sum_{n=1}^{\infty}\|f_n\|=M\ .$$

That is, $\|g_n\|\le M$.

Hence, $\int(g_n)^p\le M^p$.

For each x, $\{g_n(x)\}$ is an increasing sequence of extended real numbers and hence, $\{g_n(x)\}$ must converge to an extended real number.

Let it be $g(x)$.

Thus, the function g so defined is measurable and since $g_n\ge 0$, by Fatou's lemma, we have

$$\int g^p\le\underline{\lim}\int(g_n)^p\le M^p.$$

Hence, g^p is integrable.

Therefore, $g(x)$ is finite for all x.

Now, for each x such that $g(x)$ is finite, the series $\sum_{k=1}^{\infty}f_k(x)$ is an absolutely summable series of real numbers.

Hence, it must be summable to a real number and let us define this number as $s(x)$.

Let us define $s(x)=0$ for those x, where $g(x)=0$.

Hence, the function s defined above is the limit of the partial sums

$s_n=\sum_{k=1}^{n}f_k$ almost everywhere.

Thus, s is measurable.

Since $|s_n(x)|\le g(x)$, we have $|s(x)|\le g(x)$.

Therefore, s is in L^p and

$$|s_n(x)\quad s(x)|^p\le(|s_n(x)|\quad|s(x)|)^p\le(2g(x))^p=2^p[g(x)]^p.$$

Since $2^p g^p$ is integrable and $|s_n(x) - s(x)|^p$ converges to 0 for almost all x.

By Lebesgue convergence theorem, we have $\int |s_n - s|^p \to 0$.

Hence, $\|s_n - s\|^p \to 0$ and therefore $\|s_n - s\| \to 0$.

Thus, the series $\{f_n\}$ has the sum s in L^p.

Hence, every absolutely summable series is summable in L^p.

This implies that, the L^p spaces are complete.

Hence the theorem.

Unit

6

FUNDAMENTAL THEOREMS OF VECTOR CALCULUS

6.1 K – surfaces and K - forms

In this chapter, we discuss about the k – surfaces, k – forms, simplexes and chain and their properties. We also discuss some important theorems like Stoke's theorem, Fundamental theorem of Calculus, Green's theorem, and Divergence theorem of Gauss.

Definition 6.1.1

Let D be a compact subset ofR^k. We say that, f is a $\mathscr{C}'$ mapping on D into R^n, if there is a $\mathscr{C}'$ mapping of an open set $W \subset R^k$, such that $D \subset W$ *and* $g(x) = f(x)$, for all $x \in D$.[Restriction of g to D is f].

Definition 6.1.2

Suppose E is an open set in R^n. A k – surface in E is a $\mathscr{C}'$ mapping $\emptyset$ from a compact set $D \subset R^k$ into E. The domain D of $\emptyset$ is called the parameter domain. Usually, a point in D is denoted by $(u_1, \dots, u_k)$.

Note 6.1.3

1) The 1 – surface are just differentiable curves.
2) Usually, we take $D = [a,b]^k = I^k$ or D as the k – simplex Q^k.

Examples 6.1.4

1) Let $D = [0,2\pi] \subset R^1$. Here, D is a compact subset of R^1. Let us define $\emptyset: D \to R^2$ by $\emptyset(t) = (acost, asint), t \in D$. $\emptyset$ is a $\mathscr{C}'$ mapping of D into E. Therefore, $\emptyset$ is called the 1 – surface. We notice that, $\emptyset$ is a circle in R^2.

2) Let $D = [0,\pi] \times [0,2\pi]$ be a compact subset of R^2.

Let $U = (u,v) \in D$. Let us define $\emptyset: D \to R^3$ by

$\emptyset(u) = (asinucosv, asinusinv, acosu), u \in D$. $\emptyset$ is a $\mathscr{C}'$ mapping of D into R^3. Therefore, $\emptyset$ is called the 2 – surface in R^3. We observe that, $\emptyset$ is the external surface of a sphere.

3) Let $D = [0, a] \times [0, \pi] \times [0,2\pi]$ be a compact subset of R^3. Let us define $\emptyset: D \to R^3$ by $\emptyset(r, \theta, \emptyset) = (rsin\theta cos\emptyset, rsin\theta sin\emptyset, rcos\theta)$. $\emptyset$ is a $\mathscr{C}'$ mapping of D into R^3. Therefore, $\emptyset$ is called the 3 – surface in R^3. We observe that, $\emptyset$ is the solid sphere of radius a.

Note 6.1.5

1) The 1 – surfaces are curves.
2) The 2 – surfaces are surfaces of solids.
3) The 3 – surfaces are volumes and so on.

Definition 6.1.6

Suppose E is an open subset in R^n. A differential form of order k, $k \geq 1$, in E, that is, a k – form in E, is a function w, symbolically represented by the sum, $w = \sum a_{i_1,\dots,i_k} dx_{i_1} \wedge \dots \wedge dx_{i_k}$, where the indices $i_1, \dots, i_k$ range independently from 1 to n, which assigns to each k – surface $\emptyset$ in E, a number denoted by $w(\emptyset)$ or $\int_{\emptyset} w$, which is defined by the rule

$$\int_{\emptyset} w = \int \sum a_{i_1,\dots,i_k}(\emptyset(u)) \frac{\partial(x_{i_1},\dots,x_{i_k})}{\partial(u_1,\dots,u_k)} du,$$

where D is the parameter domain of $\emptyset$.

The functions $a_{i_1,\dots,i_k}(x)$ are real and continuous functions on E.

Examples 6.1.7

1) Let $(x_1, x_2, x_3, x_4) \in R^4$.

Now, $w = a_{12}(x)dx_1 \wedge dx_2 + a_{24}(x)dx_2 \wedge dx_4 + a_{31}(x)dx_3 \wedge dx_1$.

$$= (2x_1^2 + 5x_1 + 7x_3)dx_1 \wedge dx_2 + (x_1 + x_4)dx_2 \wedge dx_4 + (x_2 + e^{x_4})dx_3 \wedge dx_1.$$

This is a 2 – form in R^4.

2) $w = x_1 dx_2 \wedge dx_4 + (x_1 + x_3)dx_1 \wedge dx_3$ is a 2 – form in R^4.

3) 1 – form in R^2, is $Adx + Bdy$. This is a general 1 – form in R^2, $(x, y) \in R^2$, A, B are real and continuous functions on R^2.

4) $(x^2 + y)dx + (x + y)dy$ is a 1 – form in R^2.

5) $dx + dy$ is a 1 – form in R^2.

6) Let $(x_1, x_2, x_3) \in R^3$.

Now, $w = a_{13}(x)dx_1 \wedge dx_3 + a_{23}(x)dx_2 \wedge dx_3 + a_{12}(x)dx_1 \wedge dx_2$.

This is a general 2 – form in R^3.

7) Let $(x_1, x_2, x_3) \in R^3$.

Now, $w = cdx \wedge dy \wedge dz$ is a general form in R^3.

Thus, $w = a_{231}(x)dx_2 \wedge dx_3 \wedge dx_1 + a_{123}(x)dx_1 \wedge dx_2 \wedge dx_3$

$$+ a_{312}(x)dx_3 \wedge dx_1 \wedge dx_2.$$

This is a general 2 – form in R^3.

Definition 6.1.8

A k – form in E is of the form $w = \sum a_{i_1,\dots,i_k} dx_{i_1} \wedge \dots \wedge dx_{i_k}$, where the indices $i_1, \dots, i_k$ vary independently from 1 to n. The above k – form is said to be of class $\mathscr{C}'$, if the functions $a_{i_1,\dots,i_k}$ are all of class $\mathscr{C}'$. A 0 – form in E is defined to be a continuous function in E.

Examples 6.1.9

Here, we will see some examples of integral of a k – form over a k – surface.

1) Consider the form $w = xydx - y^2dy$ in R^2. Evaluate $\int_\emptyset w$, where $\emptyset$ is a 1 – surface in E, such that $\emptyset: [0,1] \to E$, defined by $\emptyset(t) = (3t^2, t^3)$.

Solution

Now, $\int_\emptyset w = \int [3t^2 t^3 6t - t^6 3t^2]dt$ (integral over $D = [0,1]$)

Thus, $w(\emptyset) = \frac{47}{21}$.

We notice that, integral of a 1 – form over a 1 – surface is simply a line integral.

Similarly, integral of a 2 – form over a 2 – surface is a surface integral or a double integral.

2) Consider the 1 – form $w = xdy + ydx$ in R^2. Evaluate $\int_\gamma w$, where γ is a 1 – surface in R^2, defined by $\gamma(t) = (acost, bsint), t \in [0,2\pi], a, b > 0$.

Solution

Now, $\int_0^{2\pi}[acost.bcost + bsint(-asint)]dt = ab\int_0^{2\pi} cos2tdt = 0.$

3) Consider the 2 – form $w = dx\wedge dy$ in R^2. Evaluate $\int_{\emptyset} w$, where $\emptyset$ is a 2 – surface in R^2, such that $\emptyset: D \to R^2$ defined by $\emptyset(r,\theta) = (rcos\theta, rsin\theta) \in R^2, D = [0,a] \times [0,2\pi]$.

Solution

$$\text{Now,} \quad \int_{\emptyset} w = \int dx\wedge dy, (integral\ over\ \emptyset),$$

$$= \int \frac{\partial(x,y)}{\partial(r,\theta)} drd\theta, (integral\ over\ D).$$

$$= \int_0^a \int_0^{2\pi} rdrd\theta = \frac{a^2}{2}\int_0^{2\pi} d\theta = \pi a^2.$$

4) Let D be the 3 cell defined by $0 \le r \le 1, 0 \le \theta \le \pi, 0 \le \emptyset \le 2\pi$. Define $\underline{\overline{\emptyset}}(r,\theta,\emptyset) = (x,y,z)$, where $x = rsin\theta cos\emptyset, y = rsin\theta sin\emptyset$, $z = rcos\theta$. Consider the 3 – form $w = dx\wedge dy\wedge dz$ in R^3. Evaluate $\int_{\underline{\overline{\emptyset}}} w$.

Solution

Consider the 3 – form $w = dx\wedge dy\wedge dz$ in R^3.

$$\text{Now,} \quad \int_{\underline{\overline{\emptyset}}} w = \int dx\wedge dy\wedge dz \ (integral\ over\ \emptyset)$$

$$= \int \frac{\partial(x,y,z)}{\partial(r,\theta,\emptyset)} drd\theta d\emptyset, (integral\ over\ D)$$

$$\int_0^{2\pi}\int_0^{\pi}\int_0^1 r^2 sin\theta drd\theta d\emptyset = \frac{1}{3}\int_0^{2\pi}\int_0^{\pi} sin\theta d\theta d\emptyset = \frac{2}{3}\int_0^{2\pi} d\emptyset = \frac{4\pi}{3}.$$

Definition 6.1.10

Let w_1, w_2 be two k – forms in E. We say that, w_1 and w_2 are equal and write $w_1 = w_2$ if and only if $w_1(\emptyset) = w_2(\emptyset)$, for every k – surface $\emptyset$ in E. In particular, a k – form w is said to be equal to zero or $w = 0$, if and only if $w(\emptyset) = 0$, for all k – surface $\emptyset$ in E.

The above concept will be clear, if we regard a k – form w as a function acting on the set of k – surfaces.

Properties 6.1.11

1) If c is a real number, then cw is also a k – form defined by $\int_{\emptyset} cw = c\int_{\emptyset} w$, for every k – surface $\emptyset$.

2) Let w_1, w_2 be two k – forms in E. If $w = w_1 + w_2$, then w is a k – form defined by
$\int_{\emptyset} w = \int_{\emptyset} w_1 + \int_{\emptyset} w_2$.

3) Again, $-w$ is defined by $\int_{\emptyset}(-w) = -\int_{\emptyset} w$.

Example 6.1.12

Consider $w = A(x)dx_1 \wedge dx_2 \wedge dx_4$ is a 3 – form in R^4.

Now, $\overline{w} = Adx_2 \wedge dx_1 \wedge dx_4$ and $\emptyset: D \to R^4$ is 3 – surface.

Let $u = (u_1, u_2, u_3)$.

Let us assume that, $\int_{\emptyset} w = \int A(\emptyset(u))\frac{\partial(x_1,x_2,x_4)}{\partial(u_1,u_2,u_3)}du = \emptyset$, and .....(6.1.12.1)

$$\int_{\emptyset} \overline{w} = \int A(\emptyset(u))\frac{\partial(x_2,x_1,x_4)}{\partial(u_1,u_2,u_3)}du = -\emptyset. \quad \text{..........} (6.1.12.2)$$

The above equation (6.1.12.2) is true, because, two rows of a Jacobian are interchanged.

Thus, $\int_{\emptyset}(-w) = -\int_{\emptyset} w$, for every 3 - surface in R^4.

Therefore, $w = -\overline{w}$.

Property 6.1.13

Consider a k – form $w = A(x)dx_{i_1} \wedge \dots \wedge dx_{i_k}$. Let $\overline{w}$ be the k – form obtained from w, by interchanging some pair of subscripts in w.

Then, we notice that, $\int_{\emptyset}(-w) = -\int_{\emptyset} w$, for every k - surface $\emptyset$ in E, because the Jacobian changes sign, when two rows are interchanged.

Therefore, $\overline{w} = -w$.

In particular, $dx_i \wedge dx_j = -(dx_j \wedge dx_i)$ holds for all i, j.

Also, $dx_i \wedge dx_i = 0$.

General Property 6.1.14

Consider $w = A(x)dx_{i_1}\wedge ...\wedge dx_{i_k}$. If $i_r = i_s$, for some $r \neq s$, then if these two subscripts are interchanged, then $\bar{w} = w$. Hence, $w = 0$.

In other words, if two subscripts i_r *and* i_s are identical, then $w = 0$.

Basic forms 6.1.15

If I is the ordered k – tuple, $\{j_1, j_2, ..., j_k\}$ such that $1 \leq j_1 \leq j_2 \leq \cdots \leq j_k \leq n$, then I is called an increasing k – index. Then, the k – form $dx_{j_1}\wedge ...\wedge dx_{j_k}$ is called a basic k – form. It is written as dx_I.

Examples 6.1.16

In R^5, let $w = dx_1\wedge dx_2\wedge dx_3$ be a basic 3 – form in R^3.

1) Given that, $w = dx_1\wedge dx_2\wedge dx_3$ implies that $w = dx_I$,

where $I = \{1,2,3\}$ is an increasing 3 – index.

2) Let $dx_J = dx_2\wedge dx_4\wedge dx_5$ be another basic 3 – form in R^5.

Here, $J = \{2,4,5\}$ is an increasing 3 – index.

3) Let $w = dx_3\wedge dx_1\wedge dx_2$ be a basic 3 – form in R^5, but, it is not a basic 3- form.

Now, $w = dx_3\wedge dx_1\wedge dx_2 = -dx_1\wedge dx_3\wedge dx_2 = dx_1\wedge dx_2\wedge dx_3$.

This is a basic 3 – form.

Note 6.1.17

Every k – form in R^n, can be converted into a basic k – form.

Let $w = dx_{j_1}\wedge ...\wedge dx_{j_k}$ be a k – form in R^n.

Consider the set of k – integers $\{j_1, ..., j_k\}$. This set can be changed into an increasing k – index J, by a finite number of interchanges of pairs.

Each interchange amounts to multiplication by (-1).

Therefore, $dx_{j_1}\wedge ...\wedge dx_{j_k} = \in (j_1, ..., j_k)dx_J$, where

$\in (j_1, ..., j_k) = 1$ *or* (-1), depending upon the number of interchanges required. Here, $\in (j_1, ..., j_k)$ is same as $s(j_1, ..., j_k)$.

Example 6.1.18

Let $w = dx_3\wedge dx_1\wedge dx_2\wedge dx_4$, be a 4 – form in R^5. Change this into a basic 4 – form.

Solution

Given that, $w = dx_3 \wedge dx_1 \wedge dx_2 \wedge dx_4 = s(3,1,2,4)dx_J$,

where $J = \{1,2,3,4\} = 1dx_J = dx_1 \wedge dx_2 \wedge dx_3 \wedge dx_4$.

Definition 6.1.19

Standard presentation of a k – form

Consider the general form of a k – form in R^n,

$w = \sum a_{i_1,\ldots,i_k}(x)dx_{i_1} \wedge \ldots \wedge dx_{i_k}$.

If every k – tuple $\{i_1, \ldots, i_k\}$ in each term is converted into an increasing k – index, then the k – form is called standard presentation of w. It can be written in the form $w = \sum b_I(x)dx_I$, where I is an increasing k – index chosen from $\{1,2, \ldots, n\}$.

Examples 6.1.20

1) Consider the 3 – form in R^4,

$w = x_1^2 dx_1 \wedge dx_3 \wedge dx_2 + (x_2 + x_3)dx_2 \wedge dx_4 \wedge dx_1 - dx_1 \wedge dx_2 \wedge dx_3$
$+(1 + x_4)dx_2 \wedge dx_1 \wedge dx_4$. Change this into standard presentation.

Solution

Given that,

$w = -x_1^2 dx_1 \wedge dx_2 \wedge dx_3 + (x_2 + x_3)dx_1 \wedge dx_2 \wedge dx_4 - dx_1 \wedge dx_2 \wedge dx_3$
$-(1 + x_4)dx_1 \wedge dx_2 \wedge dx_4$.

$= (1-x_1^2)dx_1 \wedge dx_2 \wedge dx_3 + (x_2 + x_3 - 1 - x_4)dx_1 \wedge dx_2 \wedge dx_4$.

$= (1-x_1^2)dx_I + (x_2 + x_3 - 1 - x_4)dx_J$,

where $I = \{1,2,3\}, J = \{1,2,4\}$ are increasing 3 – indices.

2) Convert the following 2 – form into standard presentation;

$x_1 dx_2 \wedge dx_1 - x_2 dx_3 \wedge dx_2 + x_3 dx_2 \wedge dx_3 + dx_1 \wedge dx_2$.

Solution

$w = x_1 dx_2 \wedge dx_1 - x_2 dx_3 \wedge dx_2 + x_3 dx_2 \wedge dx_3 + dx_1 \wedge dx_2$.

$= -x_1 dx_1 \wedge dx_2 + x_2 dx_2 \wedge dx_3 + x_3 dx_2 \wedge dx_3 + dx_1 \wedge dx_2$.

$= (-x_1 + 1)dx_1 \wedge dx_2 + (x_2 + x_3)dx_2 \wedge dx_3$.

$= (-x_1 + 1)dx_I + (x_2 + x_3)dx_J$,

where $I = \{1,2\}, J = \{2,3\}$ are increasing 3 – indices.

3) Consider the 3 – form

$w = (1 + x)dx_1 \wedge dx_2 \wedge dx_3 + xdx_1 \wedge dx_3 \wedge dx_2 + dx_2 \wedge dx_1 \wedge dx_3.$

Show that this cannot be converted into standard presentation.

Solution

Given that,

$w = (1 + x)dx_1 \wedge dx_2 \wedge dx_3 + xdx_1 \wedge dx_3 \wedge dx_2 + dx_2 \wedge dx_1 \wedge dx_3.$

$= (1 + x)dx_1 \wedge dx_2 \wedge dx_3 - xdx_1 \wedge dx_2 \wedge dx_3 - dx_1 \wedge dx_2 \wedge dx_3 = 0.$

Therefore, the above 3 – form is not in standard presentation.

Note 6.1.21

The number of increasing 3 – indices from {1,2,3,4} are

$I_1 = \{1,2,3,4\}, I_2 = \{1,2,4\}, I_3 = \{1,3,4\}, I_4 = \{2,3,4\}.$

Theorem 6.1.22

Suppose $w = \sum_I b_I(x)dx_I$ is the standard presentation of a k – form w in an open set $E \subset R^n$. If $w = 0$ in E, then $b_I(x) = 0$, for every increasing k – index I and for every $x \in E$.

Proof

Assume that $b_J(v) \neq 0$, for some increasing k – index $J = \{j_1, \dots, j_k\}$ and for some $v \in E$.

We will prove the result which contradicts $w = 0$.

In other words, we will be exhibiting a k – surface ∅ in E, for which $w(\emptyset) = \int_{\emptyset} w \neq 0.$

By assumption, $b_J(v) > 0$.

Therefore, there exists a $\epsilon > 0$, such that $b_J(v) > \epsilon > 0$.

That is, $b_J(v) - \epsilon > 0$. .... (6.1.22.1)

Now, b_J is continuous at $v(= (v_1, \dots, v_n)) \in E$.

Therefore, there exists a real number $h > 0$, such that $|x_i - v_i| < h$, $i = 1,2, \dots, n$.

That implies, $|b_J(x) - b_J(v)| < \epsilon$.

That is, $b_J(x) > b_J(v) - \epsilon$.

Thus, by equation (6.1.22.1), we have,$b_J(v) > 0$.

Thus, we have proved, $b_J(v) > 0$, whenever $|x_i - v_i| < h, i = 1,2, \dots, n$. .... (6.1.22.2)

Let us define, $D = [-h, h]^k \subset R^k$.

Here, D is the compact subset of R^k.

Then, $u = (u_1, \dots, u_k) \in D implies\, |u_r| \leq h, r = 1,2, \dots, k$.

Let us define, $\emptyset: D \to E$ by $\emptyset(u) = v + \sum_{r=1}^{k} u_r e_{jr}$.

That implies, $\emptyset(u) = (x_1, \dots, x_n)(say)$

Thus, $\emptyset$ is a k – surface in E.

Now, $x_i = \begin{cases} v_i + u_k e_i, & i = j_k, for\ some\ j_k \in J \\ v_i, & otherwise \end{cases}$

Then, $|x_i - v_i| < h, i = 1,2, \dots, n$.

Therefore, by equation (6.1.22.2), we get, $b_J(x) > 0$ or $b_J(\emptyset(u)) > 0$.

Claim: $w(\emptyset) \neq 0$.

Now, $\int_{\emptyset} w = \int b_J(\emptyset(u)) \frac{\partial(x_{j_1}, \dots, x_{j_k})}{\partial(u_1, \dots, u_k)} du$.

We observe that, $\frac{\partial(x_{j_1}, \dots, x_{j_k})}{\partial(u_1, \dots, u_k)} = \begin{vmatrix} 1 & 0 & \cdots & 0 \\ 0 & 1 & \cdots & 0 \\ \cdots & \cdots & \cdots & \cdots \\ 0 & 0 & \cdots & 1 \end{vmatrix}$.

Also, since $b_J(\emptyset(u)) > 0$, we get, $w(\emptyset) > 0$.

That is, $w(\emptyset) \neq 0$.

This contradicts the hypothesis that, $w = 0$.

Therefore, we conclude that, $b_I(x) = 0$, for all $x \in E$ and for all increasing k – index I.

Hence the theorem.

Product of two basic forms 6.1.23

Let $I = \{i_1, \dots, i_p\}$ be an increasing p – index and $J = \{j_1, \dots, j_q\}$ be an increasing q – index. Then, $dx_I = dx_{i_1} \wedge dx_{i_2} \wedge \dots \wedge dx_{i_p}$.

$$dx_J = dx_{j_1} \wedge dx_{j_2} \wedge \dots \wedge dx_{j_q}.$$

Thus, the product of these two forms is a $p + q$ form written by

$w = dx_I \wedge dx_J = dx_{i_1} \wedge dx_{i_2} \wedge \dots \wedge dx_{i_p} \wedge dx_{j_1} \wedge dx_{j_2} \wedge \dots \wedge dx_{j_q}$.

The above definition is valid, if $I \cap J = \emptyset$.

If there are subscripts common to I and J, then $w = 0$.

Example 6.1.24

Let $p = 3, I = (2,3,7), dx_I = dx_2 \wedge dx_3 \wedge dx_7$ and

Let $q = 4, J = (1,4,5,8), dx_J = dx_1 \wedge dx_4 \wedge dx_5 \wedge dx_8$.

Then, the product is

$w = dx_I \wedge dx_J = dx_2 \wedge dx_3 \wedge dx_7 \wedge dx_1 \wedge dx_4 \wedge dx_5 \wedge dx_8$.

$= \pm dx_{[I,J]}$, where $[I,J] = \{1,2,3,4,5,7,8\}$.

Here, $[I,J]$ is an increasing $3 + 4$ index.

Therefore, $w = -dx_2 \wedge dx_3 \wedge dx_1 \wedge dx_7 \wedge dx_4 \wedge dx_5 \wedge dx_8$.

$= dx_2 \wedge dx_3 \wedge dx_1 \wedge dx_4 \wedge dx_7 \wedge dx_5 \wedge dx_8$.

$= -dx_2 \wedge dx_3 \wedge dx_1 \wedge dx_4 \wedge dx_5 \wedge dx_7 \wedge dx_8$.

$= dx_2 \wedge dx_1 \wedge dx_3 \wedge dx_4 \wedge dx_5 \wedge dx_7 \wedge dx_8$.

$= -dx_1 \wedge dx_2 \wedge dx_3 \wedge dx_4 \wedge dx_5 \wedge dx_7 \wedge dx_8$.

Thus, $w = -dx_{[I,J]}$.

6.2 Simplexes and Chain

Definition 6.2.1

Let f be a mapping of a vector space X into a vector space Y. Then, f is said to be an affine map, if $f - f(0)$ is linear. That is, if there exists a linear transformation $A \in L(X,Y)$, such that

$$f(x) = f(0) + Ax.$$

Note 6.2.2

An affine mapping of R^k into R^n, will be determined completely, if we know f(0) and f(e_i), $1 \le i \le k$, where $\{e_1, e_2, \ldots\ldots, e_k\}$ is the standard basis for R^k.

We know that, Q^k is the standard simplex or k-simplex and $Q^k \subseteq R^k$.

If $u = (u_1, u_2, \ldots\ldots, u_k) \in Q^k$, then

i) $u_i \ge 0$,

ii) $u_1 + u_2 + \ldots\ldots + u_k \le 1$.

Q^k is a compact subset of R^k.

We will define a k-surface in R^n with Q^k as its parameter domain.

Define 6.2.3 Oriented Affine k-Simplex

Let $P_0, P_1, \ldots\ldots, P_k$ be the k + 1 fixed points of R^n. Define $\sigma: Q^k \to R^n$ by

$\sigma(u) = \sigma(\alpha_1, \alpha_2, \ldots\ldots, \alpha_k) = P_0 + \sum_{i=1}^{k} \alpha_i (P_i - P_0)$. Clearly, σ is a k-surface in R^n.

This k-surface is called Oriented affine k-Simplex in R^n. This is denoted by $\sigma = [P_0, P_1, \ldots\ldots, P_k]$.

Note 6.2.4

σ is a i) k - surface

ii) Affine map

iii) Oriented

σ is oriented, because the order of vectors $[P_0, P_1, \ldots\ldots, P_k]$ is taken into account.

If we write, $\sigma' = [P_1, P_0, P_2, \ldots\ldots, P_k]$, then this is a different oriented affine k-simplex in R^n.

Properties 6.2.5

$\sigma(0) = 0$.

$\sigma(e_1) = P_1$.

....

$\sigma(e_k) = P_k$.

Therefore, there exists $A \in L(Q^k, R^n)$, such that $\sigma(u) = \sigma(0) + Au$,

for all $u \in Q^k$ .... (6.2.5.1)

To determine A:

Now, (1) becomes, $\sigma(u) = P_0 + A(u)$.

When $u = e_1$, then $\sigma(e_1) = P_0 + A(e_1)$.

Therefore, $A(e_1) = P_1 - P_0$.

$A(e_2) = P_2 - P_0$.

....

$A(e_k) = P_k - P_0$.

Thus, A is completely determined.

Therefore, $[A]=\begin{bmatrix} P_1-P_0 & 0 & \ldots\ldots & 0 \\ 0 & P_2-P_0 & \ldots\ldots & 0 \\ \ldots\ldots & \ldots\ldots & \ldots\ldots & \ldots\ldots \\ 0 & 0 & \ldots\ldots & P_k-P_0 \end{bmatrix}$.

That is, A is a n × k matrix and the jth column of A is $P_j - P_0$.

Therefore, $[A] = [P_1 - P_0, P_2 - P_0, \ldots\ldots, P_j - P_0, \ldots\ldots, P_k - P_0]$.

$P_j - P_0$ is a column vector [n × 1] and there are k columns and n rows.

Note 6.2.6

1) Let n = k.

Therefore, $\sigma : Q^k \to R^k$.

Now, $\sigma = [0, e_1, e_2, \ldots\ldots, e_k]$.

Here, e_i's are unit vectors in R^k.

$$\sigma(u) = \sigma(\alpha_1, \alpha_2, \ldots\ldots, \alpha_k)$$

$$= P_0 + \sum_{i=1}^{k} \alpha_i (P_i - P_0)$$

$$= \sum_{i=1}^{k} \alpha_i e_i \text{ [Since } P_0 = 0].$$

= u.

Thus, σ is the identity map.

2) Consider, $\sigma = [P_0, P_1, \ldots\ldots, P_k]$.

If $\overline{\sigma} = \{P_{i_0}, P_{i_1}, \ldots\ldots, P_{i_k}\}$, where $\{i_0, i_1, \ldots, i_k\}$ is a permutation of the ordered set {0, 1, 2, …., k}, then $\overline{\sigma} = s(i_0, i_1, \ldots\ldots, i_k).\sigma$, where s is the function which assigns +1 or -1.

Thus, $\overline{\sigma} = \pm\sigma$, depending upon s = 1 or s = -1,

If $\overline{\sigma} = \sigma$, we say both σ and $\overline{\sigma}$ have same orientation.

If $\overline{\sigma} = -\sigma$, we say both σ and $\overline{\sigma}$ have opposite orientation.

Definition 6.2.7

Consider the oriented affine k-simplex $\sigma = [P_0, P_1, \ldots.., P_k]$ in $E \subset R^n$. Then, $\sigma(u) = \sigma(0) + Au$, where $A \in L(R^k, R^n)$, for all $u \in Q^k$. Then, the matrix $[A]_{n\times k}$ has $[P_1 - P_0, \ldots.., P_k - P_0]$ as its k-columns. If det.[A] is positive, we say σ is positively oriented. If det.[A] is negative, we say σ is negatively oriented.

Problems 6.2.8

Consider the oriented affine 3-simplex $\sigma = [0, e_1, e_1 + e_2, e_1 + e_2 + e_3]$ in R^3, show that σ is positively oriented.

Solution

$\sigma = [P_0, P_1, P_2, P_3]$.

$\sigma(u) = \sigma(0) + Au$, where $A \in L(Q^3, R^3)$.

Then, $A(e_1) = P_1 - P_0 = e_1 - 0 = e_1$.

$A(e_2) = P_2 - P_0 = e_1 + e_2$.

$A(e_3) = P_3 - P_0 = e_1 + e_2 + e_3$.

Therefore, the column of matrix [A] are

$P_1 - P_0 = (1, 0, 0)$

$P_2 - P_0 = (1, 1, 0)$

$P_3 - P_0 = (1, 1, 1)$

Therefore, $[A] = \begin{bmatrix} 1 & 1 & 1 \\ 0 & 1 & 1 \\ 0 & 0 & 1 \end{bmatrix}$

$$|A| = \begin{vmatrix} 1 & 1 & 1 \\ 0 & 1 & 1 \\ 0 & 0 & 1 \end{vmatrix} = 1$$

Therefore, σ is positively oriented.

Definition 6.2.9 An Oriented O-simplex

An oriented O-simplex in $E \subset R^n$ is defined to be a point P_0 with the sign attached

We write, σ = +P0 or σ = -P0. [Note: σ is basically a O-surface]. In general, $\sigma = \varepsilon P_0$, where $\varepsilon = \pm 1$. Suppose f is a O-form in E. We know that f is a real valued function acting on E.

We define, $\int_\sigma f = \varepsilon f(P_0)$.

Theorem 6.2.10

If σ is an oriented rectilinear *k*-simplex in an open set $E \subset R^n$ and if $\overline{\sigma} = \varepsilon\sigma$, then $\int_{\overline{\sigma}} w = \varepsilon \int_\sigma w$, for every *k*-form *w* in *E*.

Proof

When k = 0, σ is a O-simplex.

If σ = P_0, then $\overline{\sigma} = \varepsilon P_0$.

w is a O-form, say *f*.

$$\int_{\overline{\sigma}} f = \varepsilon f(P_0) = \varepsilon \int_\sigma f .$$

Therefore, the theorem is true for $k = 0$.

Suppose $k > 1$.

Let σ = $[P_0, P_1, \ldots\ldots, P_j, \ldots\ldots, P_k]$.

$\sigma(u) = \sigma(0) + Au$, where $A \in L(Q^k, R^n)$.

The columns of matrix $[A]_{n\times k}$ are

$$[P_1 - P_0, P_2 - P_0, \ldots\ldots, P_j - P_0, \ldots\ldots, P_k - P_0].$$

Denote them by $[x_1, x_2, \ldots\ldots, x_k]$.

Case i):

Let $1 \le j \le k$.

Suppose $\overline{\sigma}$ is obtained from σ, by interchanging P_0 and P_j.

That is, $\overline{\sigma} = [P_j, P_2, \ldots\ldots, P_{j-1}, P_0, P_{j+1}, \ldots\ldots, P_k]$.

If $\sigma(u) = \sigma(0) + Bu$, for all $u \in Q^k$, then $B \in L(Q^k, R^n)$ and the columns of $[B]_{n\times k}$ are $[P_1 - P_j, P_2 - P_j, \ldots\ldots, P_{j-1} - P_j, P_0 - P_j, P_{j+1} - P_j, \ldots\ldots, P_k - P_j]$

That is,

$$[x_1 - x_j, x_2 - x_j, \ldots\ldots, x_{j-1} - x_j, -x_j, x_{j+1} - x_j, \ldots\ldots, x_k - x_j].$$

If we subtract the jth column from each of the others, then the determinants $\frac{\partial(x_{i_1}, x_{i_2}, \ldots\ldots, x_{i_k})}{\partial(u_1, u_2, \ldots\ldots, u_k)}$ involved in the evaluation of $\int_{\bar{\sigma}} w$ are affected and we get the columns $(x_1, \ldots\ldots, x_{j-1}, -x_j, x_{j+1}, \ldots\ldots, x_k)$. These differ from those of [A], only in the sign of jth column.

Therefore,

$$\int_{\bar{\sigma}} w = \varepsilon \int_{\sigma} w.$$

Case ii):

Let $0 \le i \le j \le k$.

Suppose $\bar{\sigma}$ is obtained from σ by interchanging P_i and P_j. Then,

$$\bar{\sigma} = P_0 + c(u), \text{ where } c \in L(R^k, R^m).$$

Now, c has same columns as those of A, except that the ith and j^{th} columns have been interchanged.

Therefore, $t = -1$.

In this case also, $\int_{\bar{\sigma}} w = \varepsilon \int_{\sigma} w$.

Lastly, consider a general form of $\bar{\sigma}$, as $\bar{\sigma} = [P_{i_0}, P_{i_1}, \ldots\ldots, P_{i_k}]$, where $i_0, i_1, \ldots\ldots, i_k$ is a permutation of $(0, 1, 2, \ldots\ldots, k)$.

But, this arises as a result of (finite number) composition of transformations of the type mentioned in case (i) and case (ii).

Therefore, the result is true for this $\bar{\sigma}$ also.

Hence, $\int_{\bar{\sigma}} w = \varepsilon \int_{\sigma} w$.

Hence the theorem.

Definition 6.2.11 An Affine chain

A finite collection of oriented affine K-simplexes, say $\sigma_1, \sigma_2, \ldots\ldots, \sigma_r$ in an open set $E \subset R^n$ is called an affine k-chain in E. This is denoted by Γ.

Note 6.2.12

1) For any k-form w in E, we define

$$\int_{\Gamma} w = \sum_{i=1}^{r} \int_{\sigma_i} w .$$

Consequently, we write $\Gamma = \sigma_1 + \sigma_2 + \ldots\ldots + \sigma_r$.

2) Suppose ϕ is a k-surface in $E \subset R^n$. Then, we can view as two different functions.

i) $\phi : D \to E$, where D is a compact subset of R^k. D is called the parameter domain. For every $u \in D$, ϕ associates a vector $\phi(u) \in E$.

ii) φ can be regarded as a real valued function acting on a domain, which is the set of k-forms in E, because, for all k-forms w, ϕ associates the real number $\int_{\phi} w$.

Note 6.2.13

$\Gamma = \sigma_1 + \sigma_2 + \ldots\ldots + \sigma_r$ based on the second above meaning of ϕ.

Example 6.2.14

Suppose σ_1 and σ_2 are two oriented affine k-simplexes in E, which have opposite orientations.

Then, $\sigma_1 = -\sigma_2$.

If Γ is a k-chain in E and if $\Gamma = \sigma_1 + \sigma_2$, then

$$\int_{\Gamma} w = \int_{\sigma_1} w + \int_{\sigma_2} w = 0, \text{ for all } k\text{-forms in } E.$$

Note 6.2.15

It is not true that $\Gamma(u) = (\sigma_1 + \sigma_2)(u) = 0$, for all $u \in Q^k$.

Definition 6.2.16 Boundary of k-simplex

Let $\sigma = [P_0, P_1, \ldots\ldots, P_k]$ be an oriented affine k-simplex in an open set $E \subset R^n$. The affine $k - 1$ chain $\{\sigma_1, \sigma_2, \ldots\ldots, \sigma_k\}$, where $\sigma_j = [P_0, P_1, \ldots\ldots, P_{j-1}, P_{j+1}, \ldots\ldots, P_k]$, $j = 0, 1, \ldots\ldots, k$ and $\partial\sigma = \sum_{j=0}^{k} (-1)^j \sigma_j$ is called the boundary of σ.

Example 6.2.17

If $\sigma = [P_0, P_1, P_2, P_3]$ is a 3-simplex, find $\partial\sigma$.

Solution

We have,

$$\sigma_0 = [P_1, P_2, P_3],\ \sigma_1 = [P_0, P_2, P_3],\ \sigma_2 = [P_0, P_1, P_3],\ \sigma_3 = [P_0, P_1, P_2,].$$

Therefore, $\partial\sigma = \sum_{j=0}^{k}(-1)^j \sigma_j = \sigma_0 - \sigma_1 + \sigma_2 - \sigma_3$.

Note 6.2.18

Each σ_j, $j = 0, 1, \ldots\ldots, k$, is a k-1 simplex, having Q^{k-1} as its parameter domain.

Consider σ_0, where $\sigma_0 = [P_1, P_2, \ldots\ldots, P_k]$.

$\sigma_0(u) = P_1 + B(u)$, for all $u \in Q^{k-1}$, where

$B(e_1) = P_2 - P_1$.

$B(e_2) = P_3 - P_1$.

....

$B(e_i) = P_{i+1} - P_1$.

....

$B(e_{k-1}) = P_k - P_1$.

Consider $\sigma_j = [P_0, \ldots\ldots, P_{j-1}, P_{j+1}, \ldots\ldots, P_k]$.

This is a k-1 simplex.

$\sigma_j = P_0 + C(u)$, for all $u \in Q^{k-1}$, $C \in L(R^{k-1}, R^n)$.

$C(e_i) = P_i - P_0$, $i = 1, 2, \ldots\ldots, j - 1$.

That is, $C(e_i) = P_{i+1} - P_0$, $i = j, j+1, \ldots\ldots, k - 1$.

Problems 6.2.19

1. Put $\tau^2 = \tau_1 + \tau_2$, where $\tau_1 = [0, e_1, e_1 + e_2]$ and $\tau_2 = [0, e_2, e_2 + e_1]$. Show that $\partial\,\tau^2$ is the sum of 4 oriented 1-simplexes. Find them. What is $\partial(\tau_1 - \tau_2)$?

Solution

Given $\tau^2 = \tau_1 + \tau_2$, where $\tau_1 = [0, e_1, e_1 + e_2]$ and $\tau_2 = [0, e_2, e_2 + e_1]$.

Now, $\tau^2 = [0, e_1 - e_2, 0]$.

$\partial\tau^2 = [0, e_1 - e_2]$.

Again, $\partial\tau^2 = \partial\tau_1 + \partial\tau_2$,

where $\partial\tau_1 = [e_1, e_1 + e_2] - [0, e_1 + e_2] + [0, e_1]$.

$\partial\tau_2 = -[e_2, e_2 + e_1] + [0, e_2 + e_1] - [0, e_2]$.

Therefore,

$$\partial\tau^2 = \partial\tau_1 + \partial\tau_2$$
$$= [e_1, e_1 + e_2] + [0, e_1] + [e_2, 0] + [e_2 + e_1, e_2].$$

Hence, $\partial\tau^2$ is the sum of 4 oriented 1-simplexes.

2. Prove that the unit square I^2 is the union of $\sigma_1(Q^2)$ and $\sigma_2(Q^2)$, where $\sigma_1(u) = u$, $\sigma_2(u) = e_1 + e_2 - u$. Prove that boundary of I^2 is equal to $\partial I^2 = \partial\sigma_1 + \partial\sigma_2$, is a positively oriented boundary of I^2?

Solution

σ_1, σ_2 are two simplexes in R^2.

Parameter domain of σ_1 and σ_2 is Q^2.

σ_1 is just the identity map.

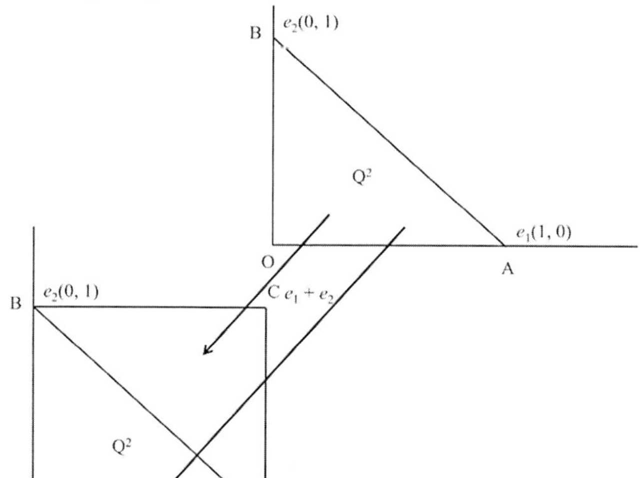

Range of σ_1 in Q^2, is itself, that is, the triangular area OAB.

$\sigma_2(0) = e_1 + e_2 = C$.

$\sigma_2(e_1) = e_2 = B$.

$\sigma_2(e_2) = e_1 = A$.

$$\sigma_2\left(\frac{1}{2}, \frac{1}{2}\right) = e_1 + e_2 - \left(\frac{1}{2}, \frac{1}{2}\right)$$

$= (1, 0) + (0, 1) - (½, ½) = (½, ½) = D$.

Range of σ_2 is the triangular area ACB.

Thus, I^2 is got as the range of $\sigma_1 + \sigma_2$.

Now, $\sigma = [P_0, P_1, P_2]$.

Also, $\sigma_1(u) = u$.

Therefore, σ_1 is the identity map.

Hence, $\sigma_1 = [P_0, P_1, P_2] = [0, e_1, e_2]$.

Therefore, $\partial\sigma_1 = [e_1, e_2] - [0, e_2] + [0, e_1]$

Next, $\sigma_2(u) = e_1 + e_2 - u$.

Hence, $\sigma_2 = [P_0, P_1, P_2] = [e_1 + e_2, e_2, e_1]$.

Therefore, $\partial\sigma_2 = [e_2, e_1] - [e_1 + e_2, e_1] + [e_1 + e_2, e_2]$.

Hence, $\partial I^2 = \partial\sigma_1 + \partial\sigma_2$,

$$= [0, e_1] + [e_1, e_1 + e_2] + [e_1 + e_2, e_2] + [e_2, 0].$$

It is the sum of 4 one simplexes.

They are OA, AC, CB, BO in order.

Therefore, ∂I^2 is the positively oriented boundary of I^2.

3) For $k \geq 2$, $\sigma = [P_0, P_1, P_2, \ldots\ldots]$ is an oriented affine k-simplex. Prove that $\partial^2\sigma = 0$.

Proof

Let $k = 2$.

Then, $\sigma = [P_0, P_1, P_2]$.

Now, $\partial\sigma = [P_1, P_2] - [P_0, P_2] + [P_0, P_1]$.

$$\partial(\partial\sigma) = [P_2] - [P_1] - [P_2] + [P_0] + [P_1] - [P_0] = 0.$$

Therefore, the result is true for $k = 2$.

Let $k = 3$.

Then, $\sigma = [P_0, P_1, P_2, P_3]$.

Therefore, $\partial\sigma = [P_1, P_2, P_3] - [P_0, P_2, P_3] + [P_0, P_1, P_3] - [P_0, P_1, P_2]$.

$$\Rightarrow \partial(\partial\sigma) = [P_2, P_3] - [P_1, P_3] + [P_1, P_2] - [P_2, P_3] + [P_0, P_3] - [P_0, P_2] + [P_1, P_3] - [P_0, P_3] + [P_0, P_1] - [P_1, P_2] + [P_0, P_2] - [P_0, P_1].$$

$$= 0.$$

Therefore, the result is true for $k = 3$.

Suppose, assume that the result is true for $k = m - 1$.

That is, $\sigma = [P_0, P_1, \ldots\ldots, P_{m-1}]$.

$\Rightarrow \partial^2\sigma = 0$.

To prove: It is true for $k = m$.
Let $\sigma = [P_0, P_1, \ldots\ldots, P_m]$.
$\sigma = [P_0, P_1, \ldots\ldots, P_{m-1}, P_m]$.
Therefore, $\partial\sigma = [P_1, \ldots., P_m] - [P_0, P_2, \ldots., P_m] + \ldots. + [P_0, \ldots., P_{m-2}, P_m]$
$- [P_0, \ldots., P_{m-2}, P_{m-1}]$.

$\Rightarrow \partial(\partial\sigma) = 0$.
Hence proved.

6.3 Stoke's theorem

Theorem 6.3.1 (Stoke's theorem)

If ψ is a k-chain of class $\mathscr{C}'$ in an open set $V \subset R^m$ and if w is a $(k-1)$ form of $\mathscr{C}'$ in V, then $\int_{\psi} dw = \int_{\partial\psi} w$.

Proof
Given that, ψ is a k-chain of class $\mathscr{C}'$ in V.

$\Rightarrow$ ψ is a finite collection of oriented affine k-simplexes, say $\phi_1, \phi_2, \ldots\ldots, \phi_r$ in V each is of class $\mathscr{C}'$.

Also, $\psi = \sum_{i=1}^{r} \phi_i$ and

$$\partial\psi = \sum_{i=1}^{r} \partial\phi_i .$$

Therefore, we have to prove that, $\int_{\sum_{i=1}^{r}\phi_i} dw = \int_{\sum_{i=1}^{r}\partial\phi_i} w$.

Therefore, it is enough to prove that, $\int_{\phi} dw = \int_{\partial\phi} w$. ....(6.3.1.1)

for every oriented affine k-simplex ϕ in V of class $\mathscr{C}'$, and w is a $(k-1)$ form in V of class $\mathscr{C}'$.
Fix one such ϕ and put $\sigma = [0, e_1, e_2, \ldots\ldots, e_k]$.
Then, σ is the oriented affine k-simplex with parameter domain Q^k and which denotes the identity mapping.

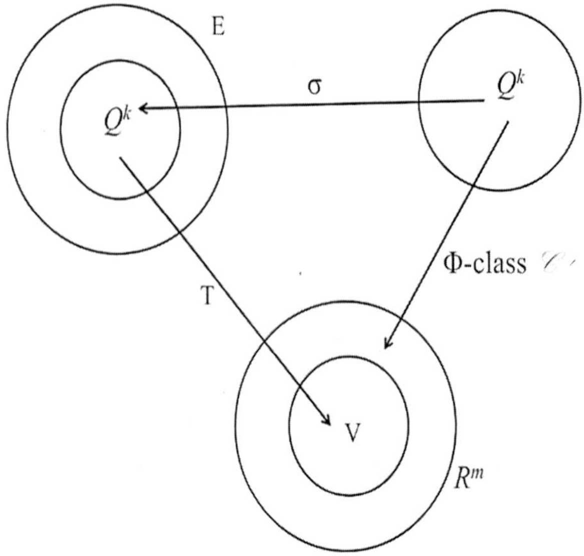

ϕ is defined on Q^k, a compact subset of R^k and since ϕ is of class $\mathscr{C}'$, we get that there exist an open set $E \subset R^k$ containing Q^k, and there is a $\mathscr{C}'$ mapping T of E to V, such that $\phi = T \circ \sigma = T\sigma$.

Then, $\int\limits_{\phi} dw = \int\limits_{T\sigma} dw = \int\limits_{\sigma} (dw)_T = \int\limits_{\sigma} d(w_T)$ .... (6.3.1.2)

$$\int\limits_{\partial\phi} w = \int\limits_{\partial(T\sigma)} w = \int\limits_{T(\partial\sigma)} w = \int\limits_{\sigma} w_T \qquad \text{.......... (6.3.1.3)}$$

Therefore, in order to prove equation (6.3.1.1), we have to prove that, the right hand sides of (6.3.1.2) and (6.3.1.3) are equal.

That is, to prove $\int\limits_{\sigma} d(w_T) = \int\limits_{\partial\sigma} w_T$.

Put $w_T = \lambda$.

Then, we have to prove, $\int\limits_{\sigma} d\lambda = \int\limits_{\partial\sigma} \lambda$ .... (6.3.1.4)

for every $(k\text{-}1)$ form $\lambda = w_T$ in E and for the special k-simplex

$\sigma = [0, e_1, e_2, \ldots\ldots, e_k]$.

Case (i): Let $k = 1$.

Then, λ is a 0-form, say f.

Hence, $f \in \mathscr{C}''(E)$ and df is a 1-form.

Therefore, σ = [0, 1] is a 1-simplex on *E*.

Now, $\sigma : Q^1 \to [0,1]$.

Then, ∂σ = [e_1] – [0] = $\sigma_1 + \sigma_2$, where σ_1 and σ_2 are 0-simplexes.

Now, left hand side of (6.3.1.4) becomes,

$$\int_\sigma d\lambda = \int_\sigma df = \int_0^1 f'(u)du = f(1) - f(0).$$

The right hand side of (6.3.1.4) becomes,

$$\int_{\partial\sigma} \lambda = \int_{\partial\sigma} f = \int_{\sigma_1+\sigma_2} f = \int_{\sigma_1} f + \int_{\sigma_2} f = f(\sigma_1) + f(\sigma_2) = f(1) - f(0).$$

Thus, equation (6.3.1.4) is true for $k = 1$.

Next, assume $k > 1$.

Fix an integer r ($1 \le r \le k$) and choose $f \in \mathscr{C}'(E)$.

It is enough to prove equation (6.3.1.4) for the case $\lambda = f(x)dx_1 \wedge dx_2 \wedge \ldots\ldots \wedge dx_{r-1} \wedge dx_{r+1} \wedge \ldots\ldots \wedge dx_k$, because every ($k$-1) form is a sum of these special ones for $r = 1, 2, \ldots\ldots, k$.

We have, $\sigma = [0, e_1, e_2, \ldots\ldots, e_k]$.

Then, $$\partial\sigma = \sum_{i=0}^{k} (-1)^i [0, e_1, \ldots., e_{i-1}, e_{i+1}, \ldots\ldots, e_k].$$

$$= [e_1, e_2, \ldots., e_k] + \sum_{i=1}^{k} (-1)^i [0, e_1, \ldots., e_{i-1}, e_{i+1}, \ldots\ldots, e_k].$$

$$= [e_1, e_2, \ldots., e_k] + \sum_{i=1}^{k} (-1)^i \tau_i, \text{ where } \tau_i = [0, e_1, \ldots., e_{i-1}, e_{i+1}, \ldots\ldots, e_k].$$

Consider, $\tau_0 = [e_r, e_1, \ldots., e_{r-1}, e_{r+1}, \ldots\ldots, e_k]$.

Then, $$[e_1, \ldots., e_k] = (-1)^{r-1} \tau_0.$$

Thus, $$\partial\sigma = (-1)^{r-1}\tau_0 + \sum_{i=1}^{k} (-1)^i \tau_i. \quad \ldots\ldots\ldots (6.3.1.5)$$

Here, $\tau_0, \tau_1, \ldots\ldots, \tau_k$ are (k-1) simplexes in *E*.

Each has Q^{k-1} as its parameter domain.

Consider τ_0

$u = (u_1, \ldots\ldots, u_{k-1}) \in Q^{k-1}$.

Let $\tau_0(u) = x = (x_1, x_2, ..., x_k)$.

$\tau_0 = [e_r, e_1, ..., e_{r-1}, e_{r+1}, ..., e_k]$.

$= [P_0, P_1, ..., P_{r-1}, P_r, ..., P_{k-1}]$.

Then, $\tau_0(u) = P_0 + u_1(P_1 - P_0) + ... + u_{k-1}(P_{k-1} - P_0)$.

$= e_r + u_1(e_1 - e_r) + ... + u_{r-1}(e_{r-1} - e_r) + u_r(e_{r+1} - e_r) + ...+ u_{k-1}(e_k - e_r)$.

$= (u_1, u_2, ..., u_{r-1}, (1 - u_1 - u_2 - ...... - u_{k-1}), u_r, u_{r+1}, ..., u_{k-1})$.

$$x_j = \begin{cases} u_j & \text{if } j = 1, 2, ..., r-1 \\ 1 - (u_1 + ... + u_{k-1}), & \text{if } j = r \\ u_{j-1}, & \text{if } j = r+1, ,....., k \end{cases} \quad .... (6.3.1.6)$$

If $1 \le i \le k$, $u \in Q^{k-1}$, $x = \tau_i(u)$ and if we work as we did above, we get

$$x_j = \begin{cases} u_j, & 1 \le j < i \\ u_j, & j = i \\ u_{j-1}, & i < j \le k \end{cases} \quad .... (6.3.1.7)$$

For $0 \le i \le k$, let J_i denote the Jacobian of the mapping

$(u_1, u_2, ..., u_{k-1}) \to (x_1, x_2, ..., x_{r-1}, x_{r+1}, ..., x_k)$ induced by τ_i.

When we take $i = 0$ in (6.3.1.6), we get

$x_r = 1 - (u_1 + u_2 + ...+ u_{k-1})$.

But we consider, $(u_1, u_2, ..., u_{k-1}) \to (x_1, x_2, ..., x_{r-1}, x_{r+1}, ..., x_k)$.

$$J_0 = \frac{\partial(x_1, ..., x_{r-1}, x_{r+1}, ..., x_k)}{\partial(u_1, ..., u_{k-1})} = 1.$$

Similarly, when $i = r$, $\tau_r = 1$.

For all other I's, we get $\tau_i = 0$, because $x_i = 0$, in that case and hence τ_i has a row of zeros.

Thus, $\tau_i = 0$, if $i \ne 0 \text{ and } i \ne r$.

Therefore, $\int\limits_{\tau_i} \lambda = 0$, if $i \ne 0 \text{ and } i \ne r$.

Therefore, $\int\limits_{\partial\sigma} \lambda = \int\limits_{(-1)^{r-1}\tau_0 + \sum_{i=1}^{k}(-1)^i \tau_i} \lambda$ reduces to $(-1)^{r-1} \int\limits_{\tau_0} \lambda + (-1)^r \int\limits_{\tau_r} \lambda$

$$= (-1)^{r-1} \int\limits_{Q^{k-1}} f(\tau_0(u))\tau_0 du + (-1)^r \int\limits_{Q^{k-1}} f(\tau_r(u))\tau_r du.$$

$$= (-1)^{r-1} \int_{Q^{k-1}} [f(\tau_0(u)) - f(\tau_r(u))] du. \qquad \text{..........} (6.3.1.8)$$

Next, we evaluate $\int_\sigma d\lambda$

$$\lambda = f(x) dx_1 \wedge dx_2 \wedge \ldots\ldots \wedge dx_{r-1} \wedge dx_{r+1} \wedge \ldots\ldots \wedge dx_k.$$

$$\Rightarrow d\lambda = \left[\sum_{i=1}^{k} D_i f(x) dx_i \right] \wedge dx_1 \wedge \ldots\ldots \wedge dx_{r-1} \wedge dx_{r+1} \wedge \ldots\ldots \wedge dx_k.$$

$$= D_r f(x) dx_r \wedge dx_1 \wedge \ldots\ldots \wedge dx_{r-1} \wedge dx_{r+1} \wedge \ldots\ldots \wedge dx_k.$$

$$= (-1)^{r-1} D_r f(x).dx_1 \wedge \ldots\ldots\ldots \wedge dx_k.$$

$$= (-1)^{r-1} D_r f(x).dx.$$

Therefore, $\int_\sigma d\lambda = (-1)^{r-1} \int_{Q^k} D_r f(x) dx.$ .... (6.3.1.9)

We evaluate the right hand side of (6.3.1.9), by first integrating with respect to x, over the intervel $[0, 1 - (x_1 + x_2 + \ldots\ldots + x_{r-1} + x_{r+1} + \ldots\ldots + x_k)]$.

Then, we put $(x_1, x_2, \ldots\ldots, x_{r-1}, x_{r+1}, \ldots\ldots, x_k) = (u_1, u_2, \ldots\ldots, u_{k-1})$ and with the help of (6.3.1.6), we notice that the integral of (6.3.1.9) over Q^k is equal to the integral of (6.3.1.8), over Q^{k-1}.

Thus, equation (6.3.1.4) is proved.

Hence the theorem.

Note 6.3.2

1. When $k = m = 1$ in Stoke's theorem, we get the Fundamental theorem of Calculus.
2. When $k = m = 2$ in Stoke's theorem, we get the Green's theorem.
3. When $k = m = 3$ in Stoke's theorem, we get the Divergence theorem of Gauss.

Definition 6.3.3

Exact form

A k – form w in an open set $E \subset R^n$ is said to be *exact*, if there exists a $k - 1$ form say λ of class C' in E, such that $w = d\lambda$.

Definition 6.3.4

Closed form

A k – form w of class $\mathscr{C}'$ in an open set $E \subset R^n$ is said to be *closed*, if $dw = 0$.

Note 6.3.5

Every exact form is closed.

Proof

Let w be an exact k – form in E.

Then, there exists a $k - 1$ form in E, such that $w = d\lambda$.

We have to prove that, w is closed.

That is, we have to prove that, $dw = 0$.

By problem 6.2.19 (3), we have $dw = d(d\lambda) = d^2\lambda = 0$.

Therefore, every exact form is closed.

Hence proved.

Problems 6.3.6

1) Let $E = R^2 - \{0\}$. Consider the 1 – form $\eta = \frac{xdy - ydx}{x^2+y^2}$. Prove that

i) η is closed in $R^2 - \{0\}$,

ii) η is not exact in E.

Solution

i) Given $\eta = \frac{xdy-ydx}{x^2+y^2} = \frac{x}{x^2+y^2}dy - \frac{y}{x^2+y^2}dx$.

That implies, $d\eta = \left[\frac{\partial}{\partial x}\left(\frac{x}{x^2+y^2}\right)dx + \frac{\partial}{\partial y}\left(\frac{x}{x^2+y^2}\right)dy\right]dy$

$$-\left[\frac{\partial}{\partial x}\left(\frac{y}{x^2+y^2}\right)dx + \frac{\partial}{\partial y}\left(\frac{y}{x^2+y^2}\right)dy\right]dx.$$

That is, $d\eta = \frac{(x^2+y^2+2x^2)}{(x^2+y^2)^2}dx\wedge dy - \frac{(x^2+y^2+2y^2)}{(x^2+y^2)^2}dx\wedge dy = 0$.

Therefore, η is closed in $R^2 - \{0\}$.

Hence part (i) is proved.

ii) Let D be the closed interval, say, $[0,2\pi]$.

Let $\sigma: D \to E$ be the function defined by $\sigma(t) = (acost, asint)$, $a > 0$.

Then, σ is a 1 – simplex.

Now, $\sigma(0) = \sigma(2\pi)$.

Thus, $\partial\sigma = 0$.

But, $\int\limits_{\sigma}\eta = \int\frac{xdy-ydx}{x^2+y^2} = \int_0^{2\pi}\frac{acost.acost+asint.asint}{a^2cos^2t+a^2sin^2t}dt = \int_0^{2\pi}dt = 2\pi \neq 0.$

Therefore, η is not exact.

Hence proved.

2) Consider the open set $E = R^3 - \{0\}$, the 3 – space with origin removed. If $w = \frac{xdy\wedge dz+ydz\wedge dx+zdx\wedge dy}{(x^2+y^2+z^2)^{3/2}}$ is a closed 2 – form in E, then prove that, w is not exact.

Solution

Let us choose $D = [0,\pi] \times [0,2\pi]$.

Now, let us define $\sigma: D \to R^3$ by $\sigma(uv) = (sinu.cosv, sinu.sinv, cosu)$.

Clearly, σ is a 2 – surface in E.

Already, we have proved that, $\partial\sigma = 0$.

Claim: $\int w \neq 0$, over σ.

The following integral is taken over σ.

$$\text{Now,}\int w = \int\frac{xdy\wedge dz+ydz\wedge dx+zdx\wedge dy}{(x^2+y^2+z^2)^{\frac{3}{2}}} = \int\frac{xdy\wedge dz}{(x^2+y^2+z^2)^{\frac{3}{2}}} + \int\frac{ydz\wedge dx}{(x^2+y^2+z^2)^{\frac{3}{2}}} + \int\frac{zdx\wedge dy}{(x^2+y^2+z^2)^{3/2}}.$$

$$\text{Let us assume that, }\int w = \int\frac{xdy\wedge dz}{(x^2+y^2+z^2)^{\frac{3}{2}}} + \int\frac{ydz\wedge dx}{(x^2+y^2+z^2)^{\frac{3}{2}}} + \int\frac{zdx\wedge dy}{(x^2+y^2+z^2)^{3/2}} = I_1 + I_2 + I_3.$$

Now,

$$I_1 = \int\frac{xdy\wedge dz}{(x^2+y^2+z^2)^{\frac{3}{2}}}(integral\ over\ \sigma)$$

$$= \int sinu.cosv\frac{\partial(y,z)}{\partial(u,v)}dudv(integral\ over\ D).$$

$$\text{Again, }\frac{\partial(y,z)}{\partial(u,v)} = \begin{vmatrix} cosu.sinv & sinu.cosv \\ -sinu & 0 \end{vmatrix} = sin^2u.cosv.$$

Therefore,

$$I_1 = \int_0^{\pi}\int_0^{2\pi} sinu.cosv[sin^2u.cosv]dudv = \int_0^{\pi}\int_0^{2\pi} sin^3u.cos^2vdudv.$$

That is, $I_1 = \int_0^{\pi} sin^3 udu \int_0^{2\pi} cos^2 vdv = \int_0^{\pi} sin^3 udu \int_0^{2\pi} \left(\frac{1+cos2v}{2}\right) dv$

$= \pi \int_0^{\pi} sin^3 udu.$

That implies, $I_1 = \frac{\pi}{4} \int_0^{\pi} (3sinu - sin3u) du$

$= \frac{4\pi}{3}.$

Now, $I_2 = \int_0^{\pi} \int_0^{2\pi} sinu. sinv[sin^2 u. sinv] dudv$

$= \int_0^{\pi} \int_0^{2\pi} sin^3 u. sin^2 vdudv.$

That is, $I_2 = \int_0^{\pi} sin^3 udu \int_0^{2\pi} sin^2 vdv = \int_0^{\pi} sin^3 udu \int_0^{2\pi} \left(\frac{1-cos2v}{2}\right) dv$

$= \pi \int_0^{\pi} sin^3 udu.$

Thus, $I_2 = \frac{4\pi}{3}.$

Now, $I_3 = \int_0^{\pi} \int_0^{2\pi} cosu \frac{\partial(y,z)}{\partial(u,v)} dudv$, where

$\frac{\partial(x,y)}{\partial(u,v)} = \begin{vmatrix} cosu. cosv & -sinu. sinv \\ cosu. sinv & sinu. cosv \end{vmatrix} = sinu. cosu.$

Therefore, $I_3 = \int_0^{\pi} \int_0^{2\pi} cosu(sinu. cosu) dudv = \int_0^{\pi} \int_0^{2\pi} sinu. cos^2 ududv.$

That is, $I_3 = \int_0^{\pi} sinu. cos^2 udu \int_0^{2\pi} dv = \frac{4\pi}{3}.$

Thus, we get, $\int w\,(integral\ over\ \sigma) = I_1 + I_2 + I_3 = 4\pi \neq 0.$

Therefore, w is not exact.

Hence the theorem.

Note 6.3.7

1. ***Condition for a 1 – form to be closed:***

Let w be a 1 – form in an open set $E \subset R^n$.

Then, $w = f_1(x)dx_1 + \cdots + f_n(x)dx_n$.

This implies, $w = \sum_{i=1}^{n} f_i(x)dx_i$.

Then, $dw = \sum_{i=1}^{n}\left[\sum_{j=1}^{n} D_j f_i(x)dx_j\right] \wedge dx_i = \sum_{i,j=1}^{n} D_j f_i(x)dx_j \wedge dx_i$.

Since $dx_j \wedge dx_i = -dx_i \wedge dx_j$, we get that, the right hand side of above equation vanishes, if

$D_j f_i(x) = D_i f_j(x)$, for all i, j, where $1 \leq i, j \leq n$.

Therefore, a 1 – form $\sum f_i(x)dx_i$ becomes a closed form, if $D_j f_i(x) = D_i f_j(x)$, for all i, j, where $1 \leq i, j \leq n$.

2. *Verification of the above condition for* $\mathbf{n = 3}$:

Now, $w = f_1(x)dx_1 + f_2(x)dx_2 + f_3(x)dx_3$

Therefore,
$$\begin{aligned} dw &= [D_1 f_1(x)dx_1 + D_2 f_1(x)dx_2 + D_3 f_1(x)dx_3] \wedge dx_1 \\ &\quad + [D_1 f_2(x)dx_1 + D_2 f_2(x)dx_2 + D_3 f_2(x)dx_3] \wedge dx_2 \\ &\quad + [D_1 f_3(x)dx_1 + D_2 f_3(x)dx_2 + D_3 f_3(x)dx_3] \wedge dx_3. \\ &= D_2 f_1(x)dx_2 \wedge dx_1 + D_3 f_1(x)dx_3 \wedge dx_1 \\ &\quad + D_1 f_2(x)dx_1 \wedge dx_2 + D_3 f_2(x)dx_3 \wedge dx_2 \\ &\quad + D_1 f_3(x)dx_1 \wedge dx_3 + D_2 f_3(x)dx_2 \wedge dx_3. \\ &= 0, \text{ if } D_2 f_1 = D_1 f_2,\ D_3 f_2 = D_2 f_3 \text{ and } D_1 f_3 = D_3 f_1. \end{aligned}$$

Result 6.3.8

If w is an exact k – form in E, and if σ is any k – chain whose boundary is zero, then $\int_{\sigma} w = 0$.

Proof

Let w be an exact k – form in E.

Then, there exists a $k - 1$ form, say, λ in E, such that $w = d\lambda$. .... (6.3.8.1)

Let Ψ be any k – chain of class $\mathscr{C}'$ in E.

Then, by equation (6.3.8.1), we have

$\int_{\Psi} w = \int_{\Psi} d\lambda$.

By Stoke's theorem, we have, $\int_{\Psi} w = \int_{\partial\Psi} \lambda$.

Suppose Ψ_1 and Ψ_2 are two such k – chains in E, which have same boundaries.

That is, $\partial\Psi_1 = \partial\Psi_2$.

Thus, we get, $\int_{\Psi_1} w = \int_{\Psi_2} w$.

That implies, $\int_{\Psi_1 - \Psi_2} w = 0$.

That is, the integral of an exact form over a k – chain (whose boundary is zero) is always zero.

Thus, the integral of an exact form is always 0, over a k – chain, whose boundary is zero or if w is an exact k – form in E and if σ is any k – chain whose boundary is zero, then $\int_{\sigma} w = 0$.

Properties 6.3.9

1) Let w be a closed k – form in E. Then, $dw = 0$.

Therefore, by Stoke's theorem, $\int_{\partial\Psi} w = \int_{\Psi} dw = 0$.

Here, Ψ is a k+1 – chain of class $\mathscr{C}''$ in E.

The above result is stated as "Integrals of closed k – forms in E are 0, when integrated over k – chains which are boundaries of $(k + 1)$ chains in E.

2) Boundary of a boundary is zero.

Proof

Let Ψ be a $(k + 1)$ chain in E and λ be a (k – 1) form in E of class $\mathscr{C}''$.

We know that, $d^2\lambda = 0$.

Thus, by Stoke's theorem, $\int_{\partial^2\Psi} \lambda = \int_{\partial(\partial\Psi)} \lambda = \int_{\partial\Psi} \mathrm{d}\lambda = \int_{\Psi} \mathrm{d}^2\lambda = 0$.

That implies, $\partial^2\Psi = 0$.

That is, boundary of a boundary is zero.

Hence proved.

Problem 6.3.10

Fix $b > a > 0$. Define $\Phi(r, \theta) = (rcos\theta, rsin\theta)$. For $a \leq r \leq b$, $0 \leq \theta \leq 2\pi$. Put $w = x^3 dy$. Verify Stoke's theorem.

Solution

We know that, $D = [a, b] \times [0,2\pi]$.

Given that, $w = x^3 dy$.

That implies, $dw = 3x^2 dx\wedge dy$.

Then, $\int_{\emptyset} dw - \int 3x^2 dx\wedge dy$ (integral over $\emptyset$).

Now, $dx \wedge dy = rdrd\theta$.

Thus, $\int_{\emptyset} dw = \int_a^b \int_0^{2\pi} 3r^2 cos^2\theta . rdr. d\theta = \int_a^b 3r^3 \int_0^{2\pi} cos^2\theta . d\theta$

$$= 3\left(\frac{b^4 - a^4}{4}\right) \int_0^{2\pi} \left(\frac{1 + cos2\theta}{2}\right) d\theta.$$

Therefore, $\int_{\emptyset} dw = \frac{3\pi}{4}(b^4 - a^4)$. .... (6.3.10.1)

To find: $\int_{\partial\emptyset} w$

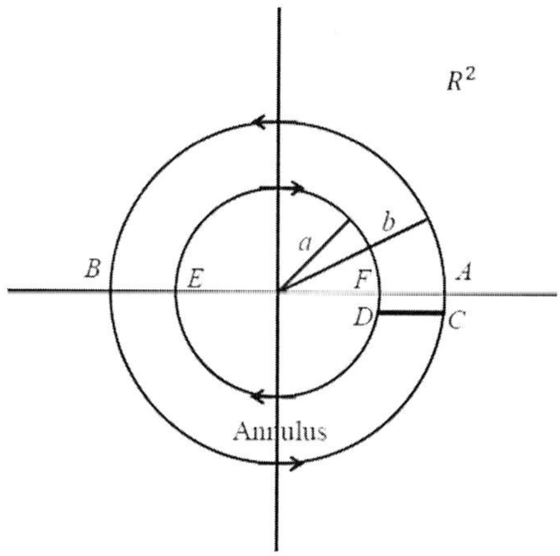

The boundary $\partial\emptyset$ consists of four 1 – surfaces ABC + CD + DEF + FA = $\gamma_1 + \gamma_2 + \gamma_3 + \gamma_4$.

For γ_1, *r* is fixed as *b* and θ varies from 0 to 2π.

For γ_2, $\theta = 0$, *r* varies from $b \to a$.

For γ_3, $\theta = 0$, *r* varies from $a \to b$.

For γ_4, *r* is fixed as *a* and θ varies from 2π to 0.

Thus, $\int_{\partial\emptyset} w = \int_{\gamma_1} w + \int_{\gamma_2} w + \int_{\gamma_3} w + \int_{\gamma_4} w$.

It is clear that, $\int_{\gamma_2} w + \int_{\gamma_3} w + \int_{CD} w + \int_{FA} w = 0$.

Let us evaluate:

$$\int_{\gamma_1} w + \int_{\gamma_4} w = \int_{\gamma_1} x^3 dy + \int_{\gamma_4} x^3 dy$$

$$= \int_0^{2\pi} (b\cos\theta)^3 b\cos\theta d\theta + \int_{2\pi}^0 (a\cos\theta)^3 a\cos\theta d\theta.$$

$$= (b^4 - a^4) \int_0^{2\pi} \cos^4\theta d\theta = (b^4 - a^4) \int_0^{2\pi} \left(\frac{1+\cos2\theta}{2}\right)^2 d\theta.$$

$$= (b^4 - a^4) \int_0^{2\pi} \left[\frac{1+2\cos2\theta+\cos^2 2\theta}{4}\right] d\theta.$$

$$= (b^4 - a^4) \int_0^{2\pi} \frac{1}{4}\left[1 + 2\cos2\theta + \frac{1+\cos4\theta}{2}\right] d\theta.$$

$$= \left(\frac{b^4-a^4}{32}\right)(24\pi) = \frac{3\pi}{4}(b^4 - a^4).$$

Thus, $\int_{\gamma_1} w + \int_{\gamma_4} w = \frac{3\pi}{4}(b^4 - a^4)$. .... (6.3.10.2)

From equations (6.3.10.1) and (6.3.10.2), we get

$$\int_{\emptyset} dw = \int_{\partial\emptyset} w.$$

Hence, Stoke's theorem is verified.

Theorem 6.3.11

Suppose E is a convex open set in R^n, $f \in \mathscr{C}'(E)$, p is an integer such that $1 \le p \le n$ and $D_j f(x) = 0$, for $j = p+1, \dots, n$; $x \in E$. Then, there exists another function $F \in \mathscr{C}'(E)$, such that $(D_p F)(x) = f(x)$ and $(D_j F)(x) = 0$, $j = p+1, \dots, n$.

Proof

We write, $x = (x_1, x_2, \dots, x_{p-1}, x_p, x_{p+1}, \dots, x_n) = (x', x_p, x'')$,

where $x' = (x_1, x_2, \dots, x_{p-1})$ and $x'' = (x_{p+1}, \dots, x_n)$.

Then, if $p = 1$, x' is absent and if $p = n$, x'' is absent.

Let V be the set of all $(x', x_p) \in R^p$, such that $(x', x_p, x'') \in E$, for some x''.

Then, the mapping $E \to V$ is a projection.

Therefore, V is also convex and open in R^p.

Now, $D_j f(x) = 0$, for $j = p+1, \dots, n$, means that f contains only the coordinates $(x_1, x_2, \dots, x_{p-1}, x_p)$.

That is, f does not depend on x''.

Hence, there is a function $\emptyset$ defined on V, such that $f(x) = \emptyset(x', x_p)$, for all $x \in E$.

Case (i):

Let $p = 1$.

Then, x' is absent and V is a segment of R.

Then, there exists a function $\emptyset$ defined on V, such that $f(x) = \emptyset(x_1)$, for all $x \in E$.

Pick $c \in V$ and define $F(x) = \int_c^{x_1} \emptyset(t)dt$.

Then, $D_1F(x) = f(x)$ and $D_jf(x) = 0$, for $j = 2,3, \dots, n$.

That is, F satisfies the required condition (2).

Thus, the theorem is true for $p = 1$.

Case (ii):

Let $p > 1$.

Let U be the set of all $x' \in R^{p-1}$, such that $(x', x_p) \in V$, for some x_p.

Being a projection of V onto U, we get that, U is also convex and an open set in R^{p-1} and there is a function $\alpha \in \mathscr{C}'(U)$, such that $\alpha x' = x_p$.

In other words, $(x', \alpha(x')) \in V$, for all $x' \in U$.

Define, $F(x) = \int_{\alpha(x')}^{x_p} \emptyset(x', t)dt$, $(x \in E)$.

Then, it is clear that, $(D_pF)(x) = f(x)$ and $(D_jF)(x) = 0, j = p + 1, \dots, n$.

That is, F satisfies condition (2).

Hence the theorem.

Lemma 6.3.12

This lemma is known as ***Poincare's lemma****.*

Closed forms on convex open sets are exact.

It can also be stated as, If $E \subset R^n$ is convex and open, if $k \geq 1$, if w is a k – form of class $\mathscr{C}'$ in E and if $dw = 0$, then there is a $k - 1$ form λ in E, such that $w = d\lambda$.

Proof

For $p = 1,2, \dots, n$, let Y_p denote the set of all k – forms w of class $\mathscr{C}'$ in E, with standard presentation $w = \sum_I f_I(x)\, dx_I$, which does not involve $dx_{p+1}, \dots, dx_n$.

In other words, $I \subset \{1,2, \dots, p\}$, if $f_I(x) \neq 0$, for some $x \in E$.

We proceed by induction on p.

Let $p = 1$. Let $w \in Y_1$.

Then, $w = f(x)dx_1$, where $f \in \mathscr{C}'(E)$.

Let w be closed. Then, $dw = 0$.

That is, $\left[\sum_{j=1}^{n} D_j f(x) dx_j\right] \wedge dx_1 = 0$.

That implies, $\sum_{j=2}^{n} D_j f(x) dx_j \wedge dx_1 = 0$.

By a known theorem, we get that, each coefficient $D_j f(x) = 0$, for $j = 2, \dots, n$.

Then, by theorem 6.3.10, there exists a function $F \in \mathscr{C}'(E)$, such that $D_1 F(x) = f(x)$ and $D_j f(x) = 0$, for $j = 2, \dots, n$. .... (6.3.12.1)

Claim: $w = dF$.

Now, $dF = \sum_{j=1}^{n} D_j F(x)\, dx_j = D_1 F(x) dx_1 + \sum_{j=2}^{n} D_j F(x)\, dx_j$.

Then, by equation (6.3.11), we get, $dF = f(x)dx_1 = w$.

Next, let us take $p > 1$.

Let us assume the induction hypothesis that, "Every closed k – form in Y_{p-1} is exact".

We have to prove that, every closed k – form in Y_p is exact.

Let us choose $w \in Y_p$, which is closed, that is, $dw = 0$.

Now, w is of the form $w = \sum_I f_I(x) dx_I$.

Then, $dw = 0$ gives $\sum_I \left[\sum_j D_j f_I(x) dx_j\right] \wedge dx_I = 0$. .... (6.3.12.2)

Consider a fixed j, with $p < j \leq n$.

Each I which occurs in equation (6.3.12.2), lies within $\{1,2, \dots, p\}$.

If I_1, I_2 are two of these increasing k – indices and if $I_1 \neq I_2$, then the two increasing $k + 1$ indices (I_1, j) and (I_2, j) are also distinct.

Therefore, there is no cancellation of terms in equation (6.3.12.2).

As a result, we have

$$\sum D_j f_I(x) = 0, \text{ for } j = p+1, \dots, n,\ x \in E. \qquad \text{.......... (6.3.12.3)}$$

Therefore, by theorem 6.3.10, there exist functions $F_I \in \mathscr{C}'(E)$, such that

$$D_p F_I(x) = f_I(x),\ D_j F_I(x) = 0, \text{ for } j = p+1, \dots, n. \qquad \text{.......... (6.3.12.4)}$$

We have, $w = \sum_I f_I(x) dx_I$.

Let us gather those terms in w, which contain dx_p separately and rewrite them as follows:

$$w = \alpha + \sum_{I_0} f_I(x) dx_{I_0} \wedge dx_p,$$

where $\alpha \in Y_{p-1}$ and each I_0 is an increasing $k-1$ index, which take values in $\{1,2,\dots,p-1\}$ and $I = (I_0, p)$.

Define $\beta = \sum_{I_0} F_I(x) dx_{I_0}$, where F_I is the function defined in equation (6.3.12.4).

Then, β is a $k-1$ form in E and $d\beta$ is a $k-$ form.

Let us define, $\gamma = w - (-1)^{k-1} d\beta$. Then, γ is a $k-$ form.

We claim that, (i) $\gamma \in Y_{p-1}$, (ii) γ is closed.

Now, $\gamma = w - (-1)^{k-1} \sum_{I_0} \left[\sum_{j=1}^{n} D_j F_I(x) dx_j\right] \wedge dx_{I_0}$.

That is, $\gamma = w - (-1)^{k-1} \sum_{I_0} \left[\sum_{j=1}^{p-1} D_j F_I(x) dx_j + D_p F_I(x) dx_p + \sum_{j=p+1}^{n} D_j F_I(x) dx_j\right] \wedge dx_{I_0}$.

Then, by equation (6.3.11.4), we have

$$\gamma = w - (-1)^{k-1} \sum_{I_0} \left[\sum_{j=1}^{p-1} D_j F_I(x) dx_j + f_I(x) dx_p\right] \wedge dx_{I_0}.$$

$$= w - (-1)^{k-1} \sum_{I_0} \sum_{j=1}^{p-1} D_j F_I(x) dx_j \wedge dx_{I_0}$$

$$-(-1)^{k-1} \sum_{I_0} f_I(x) dx_{I_0} \wedge dx_p.$$

That implies,

$$\gamma = \alpha - \sum_{I_0} \sum_{j=1}^{p-1} D_j F_I(x) dx_{I_0} \wedge dx_j.$$

This shows that γ is a $k-$ form, which belongs to Y_{p-1}.

Now, $\gamma = w - (-1)^{k-1} d\beta$.

Thus, $d\gamma = dw - (-1)^{k-1} d^2\beta$.

Since $dw = 0$ and $d^2\beta = 0$, we get that, $d\gamma = 0$.

That implies, γ is closed.

Therefore, by induction hypothesis, we get that, γ is exact.

That is, $\gamma = d\mu$, for some k – 1 form μ in *E*.

Let us take, $\lambda = \mu + (-1)^{k-1}\beta$, which is a *k* – 1 form in *E*.

Claim: $w = d\lambda$.

Now, $d\lambda = d\mu + (-1)^{k-1}d\beta = \gamma + (-1)^{k-1}d\beta$.

That is, $d\lambda = w - (-1)^{k-1}d\beta + (-1)^{k-1}d\beta = w$.

Thus, $w = d\lambda$.

Therefore, *w* is exact.

Hence the lemma is proved.

Definition 6.3.12

Let *E* and *U* be two open sets in R^n. If there exists a 1 – 1 $\mathscr{C}'$ mapping of *E* onto *U*, we say that *E* and *U* are $\mathscr{C}'$ equivalent.

Theorem 6.3.13

Fix *k*, $1 \leq k \leq n$. Let $E \subset R^n$ be an open set in which every closed *k* – form is exact. Let *T* be a 1 – 1 $\mathscr{C}''$ mapping of E onto an open set $U \subset R^n$, whose inverse *S* is also of class $\mathscr{C}''$, then every closed *k* – form in *U* is also exact in *U*.

The theorem can also be stated as, "Every closed form is exact in any set which is $\mathscr{C}''$ equivalent to a convex open set".

Proof

Let *w* be a closed *k* – form in *U*.

Then, $dw = 0$.

Now, w_T is the transformed *k* – form in *E*.

Thus, $d(w_T) = (dw)_T = 0$.

Therefore, w_T is a closed *k* – form in *E*. Also, *E* is convex and open.

Then, by Poincare's lemma, w_T is exact.

That is, there exists a *k* – 1 form λ in *E*, such that $w_T = d\lambda$.

Now, $w = (w_T)_S = (d\lambda)_S = d(\lambda_S)$ and λ_S is a k – 1 form in U.

Thus, we have found out a *k* – 1 form λ_S is *U*, such that $w = d(\lambda_S)$.

Therefore, *w* is exact in *U*.

Hence the theorem.

6.4 Vector field

Definition 6.4.1

Let E be an open set in R^3. Let $F_1, F_2, F_3 \in \mathscr{C}'$(E). Let us define

$\vec{F} = F_1 e_1 + F_2 e_2 + F_3 e_3$.

$\vec{F}$ associates a vector in R^3, with every point in E. $\vec{F}$ is a continuous mapping of E into R^3. $\vec{F}$ is called a *vector field in E*. F_1, F_2, F_3 are called a *scalar valued functions*.

Note 6.4.2

Forms associated with the vector field are discussed here.

Let $F_1 e_1 + F_2 e_2 + F_3 e_3$ be a vector field in E. We associate a 1 – form and 2 – form with this vector field.

The 1 – form $\lambda_F = F_1 dx + F_2 dy + F_3 dz$ and

The 2 – form $w_F = F_1 dy \wedge dz + F_2 dz \wedge dx + F_3 dx \wedge dy$.

Thus, every vector field $\vec{F}$ in E, will give rise to a 1 – form $\lambda_{\vec{F}}$ and 2 – form $w_{\vec{F}}$ as defined above.

Conversely, a 1 – form E will yield a vector field in E. That is, if λ is a 1 – form in E, there exists a vector field $\vec{F}$ in E, such that $\lambda = \lambda_{\vec{F}}$.

Examples 6.4.3

1) Let $\lambda = 2x^2 dx - 3(x^2 + y^2)dy + 7xyzdz$ and

$\vec{F} = 2x^2 e_1 - 3(x^2 + y^2)e_2 + 7xyze_3$. Then, $\lambda = \lambda_{\vec{F}}$. Similarly, for any given 2 – form w in E, there exists a vector field $\vec{F}$ in E, such that $w = w_{\vec{F}}$.

2) Let $w = (5x^3 + y)dx \wedge dy + (3x^2 y)dy \wedge dz$. Define

$\vec{F} = (3x^2 y)e_1 + (5x^3 + y)e_3$. Then, $w = w_{\vec{F}}$.

Definition 6.4.4

Let $u \in \mathscr{C}'(E)$. The vector field $(D_1 u)e_1 + (D_2 u)e_2 + (D_3 u)e_3$ is called the *gradient of u* and it is denoted by ∇u.

Definition 6.4.5

Let $\vec{F} = F_1 e_1 + F_2 e_2 + F_3 e_3$ be a vector field in E.

Then, $\nabla . \vec{F} = D_1 F_1 + D_2 F_2 + D_3 F_3$.

$$\nabla \times \vec{F} = \begin{vmatrix} e_1 & e_2 & e_3 \\ D_1 & D_2 & D_3 \\ F_1 & F_2 & F_3 \end{vmatrix} = (D_2 F_3 - D_3 F_2) e_1 + (D_3 F_1 - D_1 F_3) e_2 + (D_1 F_2 - D_2 F_1) e_3.$$

Theorem 6.4.6

Suppose E is an open set in R^3. $u \in \mathscr{C}''(E)$ and G is a vector field in E of class $\mathscr{C}''$.

a) If $F = \nabla u$, then $\nabla \times \vec{F} = 0$.

b) If $F = \nabla \times G$, then $\nabla \cdot \vec{F} = 0$.

Proof

Let $\vec{F} = F_1 e_1 + F_2 e_2 + F_3 e_3$, where $F_1, F_2, F_3 \in \mathscr{C}'(\mathrm{E})$.

Now, $\vec{F} = \nabla u = (D_1 u) e_1 + (D_2 u) e_2 + (D_3 u) e_3$.

$$\nabla \times \vec{F} = \big(D_2(D_3 u) - D_3(D_2 u)\big) e_1 + \big(D_3(D_1 u) - D_1(D_3 u)\big) e_2 + \big(D_1(D_2 u) - D_2(D_1 u)\big) e_3.$$

$$= [D_{23} u - D_{32} u] e_1 + [D_{31} u - D_{13} u] e_2 + [D_{12} u - D_{21} u] e_3 = 0.$$

Let $\vec{G} = G_1 e_1 + G_2 e_2 + G_3 e_3$.

Given that,

$$\vec{F} = \nabla \times \vec{G} = (D_2 G_3 - D_3 G_2) e_1 + (D_3 G_1 - D_1 G_3) e_2 + (D_1 G_2 - D_2 G_1) e_3.$$

Then, $\nabla \cdot \vec{F} = D_1(D_2 G_3 - D_3 G_2) + D_2(D_3 G_1 - D_1 G_3) + D_3(D_1 G_2 - D_2 G_1)$.

$$= D_1(D_2 G_3) - D_1(D_3 G_2) + D_2(D_3 G_1) - D_2(D_1 G_3) + D_3(D_1 G_2) - D_3(D_1 G_2).$$

Since $D_{ij} = D_{ji}$, $\nabla \cdot \vec{F} = 0$.

Here, result (a) can be stated as "Curl of gradient u is zero" and result (b) can be state as "Divergence of curl of a vector field is zero".

Theorem 6.4.7

If E is a $\mathscr{C}''$ equivalent to a convex open set, then

a) If $\nabla \times \vec{F} = 0$, then $F = \nabla u$, for some $u \in \mathscr{C}''(E)$,

b) If $\nabla \cdot \vec{F} = 0$, then $F = \nabla \times G$, for some $u \in \mathscr{C}''(E)$.

Proof

a) Let $\vec{F} = F_1 e_1 + F_2 e_2 + F_3 e_3$.

Given that $\nabla \times \vec{F} = 0$.

That implies,

$$(D_2F_3 - D_3F_2)e_1 + (D_3F_1 - D_1F_3)e_2 + (D_1F_2 - D_2F_1)e_3 = 0.$$

That is, $D_2F_3 - D_3F_2 = D_3F_1 - D_1F_3 = D_1F_2 - D_2F_1 = 0.$ .... (6.4.7.1)

Let $\lambda_{\vec{F}}$ be the 1 – form associated with $\vec{F}$.

Then, $\lambda_{\vec{F}} = F_1 dx + F_2 dy + F_3 dz$.

That is,

$$\begin{aligned} d\lambda_{\vec{F}} &= \left(\textstyle\sum_{j=1}^{3} D_jF_1 dx_j\right)\wedge dx + \left(\textstyle\sum_{j=1}^{3} D_jF_2 dx_j\right)\wedge dy + \left(\textstyle\sum_{j=1}^{3} D_jF_3 dx_j\right)\wedge dz \\ &= D_2F_1 dy\wedge dx + D_3F_1 dz\wedge dx + D_1F_2 dx\wedge dy \\ &\quad + D_3F_2 dz\wedge dy + D_1F_3 dx\wedge dz + D_2F_3 dy\wedge dz \\ &= (D_1F_2 - D_2F_1)dx\wedge dy + (D_2F_3 - D_3F_2)dy\wedge dz \\ &\quad + (D_3F_1 - D_1F_3)dz\wedge dx \end{aligned}$$

Now, by equation (6.4.7.1), we get

$$d\lambda_{\vec{F}} = 0.$$

Thus, $\lambda_{\vec{F}}$ is a closed 1 – form in E.

Since E is $\mathscr{C}''$ equivalent to a convex open set, we get that every closed form in E is exact.

Thus, $\lambda_{\vec{F}}$ is also exact in E.

Therefore, there exists a 0 – form $u \in \mathscr{C}''(E)$, such that $\lambda_{\vec{F}} = du$.

That implies, $F_1 dx + F_2 dy + F_3 dz = (D_1u)dx + (D_2u)dy + (D_3u)dz$.

That is, $F_1 = D_1u$, $F_2 = D_2u$, and $F_3 = D_3u$.

Then, $\vec{F} = F_1e_1 + F_2e_2 + F_3e_3 = (D_1u)e_1 + (D_2u)e_2 + (D_3u)e_3 = \nabla u$.

Thus, $\vec{F} = \nabla u$.

Hence part (a) is proved.

b) Given that, $\nabla \cdot \vec{F} = 0$.

Let $\vec{F} = F_1 e_1 + F_2 e_2 + F_3 e_3$, where $F_1, F_2, F_3 \in \mathscr{C}'(E)$.

Now, $\nabla \cdot \vec{F} = 0$, implies that $D_1 F_1 + D_2 F_2 + D_3 F_3 = 0$. .... (6.4.7.2)

Let $w_{\vec{F}}$ be the 2 – form associated with $\vec{F}$.

Then, $w_{\vec{F}} = F_1 dy \wedge dz + F_2 dz \wedge dx + F_3 dx \wedge dy$.

That implies,

$$dw_{\vec{F}} = \left(\sum_{j=1}^{3} D_j F_1 dx_j\right) \wedge dy \wedge dz + \left(\sum_{j=1}^{3} D_j F_2 dx_j\right) \wedge dz \wedge dx + \left(\sum_{j=1}^{3} D_j F_3 dx_j\right) \wedge dx \wedge dy$$

$$= D_1 F_1 dx \wedge dy \wedge dz + D_2 F_2 dy \wedge dz \wedge dx + D_3 F_3 dz \wedge dx \wedge dy$$

$$= (D_1 F_1 + D_2 F_2 + D_3 F_3) dx \wedge dy \wedge dz$$

Thus, by equation (6.4.7.2), $dw_{\vec{F}} = 0$.

Therefore, $w_{\vec{F}}$ is a closed 2 – form in E.

In E, every closed form is exact.

Thus, $w_{\vec{F}}$ is exact in E.

Therefore, there exists a 1 – form say $\lambda = G_1 dx + G_2 dy + G_3 dz$, where $G_1, G_2, G_3 \in \mathscr{C}'$(E), such that $w_{\vec{F}} = d\lambda$.

That is,

$$F_1 dy \wedge dz + F_2 dz \wedge dx + F_3 dx \wedge dy$$
$$= (D_2 G_1 dy + D_3 G_1 dz) \wedge dx + (D_1 G_2 dx + D_3 G_2 dz) \wedge dy + (D_1 G_3 dx + D_2 G_3 dy) \wedge dz$$
$$= (D_2 G_3 - D_3 G_2) dy \wedge dz + (D_3 G_1 - D_1 G_3) dz \wedge dx + (D_1 G_2 - D_2 G_1) dx \wedge dy$$

Comparing both sides, we get

$F_1 = D_2 G_3 - D_3 G_2$, $F_2 = D_3 G_1 - D_1 G_3$, $F_3 = D_1 G_2 - D_2 G_1$.

Then, $F_1 e_1 + F_2 e_2 + F_3 e_3 = (D_2 G_3 - D_3 G_2) e_1 + (D_3 G_1 - D_1 G_3) e_2 + (D_1 G_2 - D_2 G_1) e_3$.

$$= \nabla \times G.$$

Therefore, $F = \nabla \times G$.

Hence part (a) is proved.

Hence the theorem.

Results 6.4.8

i) $\vec{F} = \nabla u$, if and only if $\lambda_{\vec{F}} = du$.

ii) $\nabla \times \vec{F} = 0$, if and only if $d\lambda_{\vec{F}} = 0$.

iii) $\vec{F} = \nabla \times G$, if and only if $w_{\vec{F}} = d\lambda_{\vec{G}}$.

iv) $\nabla \cdot \vec{F} = 0$, if and only if $dw_{\vec{F}} = 0$.

Proof

i) Let $\vec{F} = \nabla u$. Also, let $\vec{F} = F_1 e_1 + F_2 e_2 + F_3 e_3$ and

$$\lambda_{\vec{F}} = F_1 dx + F_2 dy + F_3 dz.$$

Now, $\vec{F} = \nabla u$, if and only if, $F_1 e_1 + F_2 e_2 + F_3 e_3 = (D_1 u)e_1 + (D_2 u)e_2 + (D_3 u)e_3$.

if and only if, $F_1 = D_1 u$, $F_2 = D_2 u$, and $F_3 = D_3 u$.

if and only if, $\lambda_{\vec{F}} = (D_1 u)dx + (D_2 u)dy + (D_3 u)dz$.

If and only if, $\lambda_{\vec{F}} = du$.

Hence part (i) is proved.

ii) $\nabla \times \vec{F} = 0$,

if and only if, $(D_2F_3 - D_3F_2)e_1 + (D_3F_1 - D_1F_3)e_2 + (D_1F_2 - D_2F_1)e_3 = 0$.

if and only if, $D_2F_3 - D_3F_2 = 0, D_3F_1 - D_1F_3 = 0, D_1F_2 - D_2F_1 = 0$.

if and only if,

$(D_1F_2 - D_2F_1)dx \wedge dy + (D_2F_3 - D_3F_2)dy \wedge dz + (D_1F_3 - D_3F_1)dx \wedge dz = 0$.

if and only if, $d\lambda_{\vec{F}} = 0$.

Hence part (ii) is proved.

iii) $\vec{F} = \nabla \times G$,

if and only if, $F_1 e_1 + F_2 e_2 + F_3 e_3 = (D_2G_3 - D_3G_2)e_1 + (D_3G_1 - D_1G_3)e_2 + (D_1G_2 - D_2G_1)e_3$

if and only if, $F_1 = D_2G_3 - D_3G_2$, $F_2 = D_3G_1 - D_1G_3$, and $F_3 = D_1G_2 - D_2G_1$.

if and only if, $F_1 dy \wedge dz + F_2 dz \wedge dx + F_3 dx \wedge dy = (D_2G_3 - D_3G_2)dy \wedge dz + (D_3G_1 - D_1G_3)dz \wedge dx + (D_1G_2 - D_2G_1)dx \wedge dy$.

if and only if, $w_{\vec{F}} = d\lambda_{\vec{G}}$.

Hence part (iii) is proved.

iv) $\nabla \cdot \vec{F} = 0$,

if and only if, $D_1F_1 + D_2F_2 + D_3F_3 = 0$.

if and only if, $D_1F_1 dx\wedge dy\wedge dz + D_2F_2 dy\wedge dz\wedge dx + D_3F_3 dz\wedge dx\wedge dy = 0$.

if and only if, $dw_{\vec{F}} = 0$.

Hence part (iv) is proved.

Volume Elements 6.4.9

The 3 – form $dx\wedge dy\wedge dz$ is called the volume element in R^3. In general, $dx_1\wedge \ldots \wedge dx_k$ is called the volume element in R^k. The volume element is denoted by dV.

If $f \in \mathscr{C}'(E)$, and $\underline{\bar{\Phi}}$ is a k – surface in E, the integral $\int f(x)dx_1\wedge \ldots \wedge dx_k$ (integral over $\underline{\bar{\Phi}}$) is denoted by $\int f(x)dV$ (integral over $\underline{\bar{\Phi}}$).

When $f = 1$, the above integral gives the volume of the surface $\underline{\bar{\Phi}}$.

Theorem 6.4.10

This theorem is known as ***Green's theorem (in the plane).***

Suppose E is an open set in R^2, $\alpha, \beta \in \mathscr{C}'(E)$, and Ω is a closed subset of E, with the positively oriented boundary $\partial\Omega$. Then,

$$\int(\alpha dx + \beta dy)\ (integral\ over\ \partial\Omega) = \int \left(\frac{d\beta}{dx} - \frac{d\alpha}{dy}\right) dA(integral\ over\ \Omega).$$

Proof

Now, $\alpha dx + \beta dy$ is a 1 – form in E.

Let us take $\lambda = \alpha dx + \beta dy$.

Then, $d\lambda = D_2\alpha dy\wedge dx + D_1\beta dx\wedge dy = (D_1\beta - D_2\alpha)dx\wedge dy = \left(\frac{\partial\beta}{\partial x} - \frac{\partial\alpha}{\partial y}\right) dx\wedge dy$.

Thus, by Stoke's theorem, we have $\int\limits_{\partial\Omega} \lambda = \int\limits_{\Omega} d\lambda$.

That is,

$$\int(\alpha dx + \beta dy)\ (integral\ over\ \partial\Omega) = \int \left(\frac{d\beta}{dx} - \frac{d\alpha}{dy}\right) dA(integral\ over\ \Omega).$$

Hence the theorem.

Corollary 6.4.11

Suppose $\alpha(xy) = -y, \beta(xy) = x$. Then, using Green's theorem, we get

$\int(xdy - ydx)\ (integral\ over\ \partial\Omega) = \int(1 - (-1))\, dA(integral\ over\ \Omega)$.

That implies,

$\int dA\,(integral\ over\ \Omega) = \frac{1}{2}\int (xdy - ydx)\,(integral\ over\ \partial\Omega)$.

But, L.H.S. is the area of the surface Ω.

Therefore, $A(\Omega) = \frac{1}{2}\int (xdy - ydx)\,(integral\ over\ \partial\Omega)$.

Problem 6.4.12

Find the area of Ω, where $\Omega = (rcos\theta, rsin\theta), 0 \le r \le a, 0 \le \theta \le 2\pi$.

Solution

We know that, $\partial\Omega$ is the differential curve, which is a 1 – surface.

Now, $A(\Omega) = \frac{1}{2}\int (xdy - ydx)\,(integral\ over\ \partial\Omega)$

Thus, by Green's theorem, we have

$A(\Omega) = \frac{1}{2}\int_0^{2\pi}[acos\theta. asin\theta + asin\theta. asin\theta]d\theta = \pi a^2$.

Therefore, area of $\Omega = A(\Omega) = \pi a^2$.

Area Elements 6.4.13

Let $\emptyset$ be a 2 – surface in R^3 of class $\mathscr{C}'$, with parameter domain $D \subset R^2$. Associate with each point $(u, v) \in D$, the vector

$N(u, v) = \frac{\partial(y,z)}{\partial(u,v)}e_1 + \frac{\partial(z,x)}{\partial(u,v)}e_2 + \frac{\partial(x,y)}{\partial(u,v)}e_3$.

$\vec{N}$ is called the normal vector to the surface $\emptyset$ at (u, v).

Definition 6.4.14

If f is a continuous function on $\emptyset(D)$, the area integral of f over $\emptyset$ is defined as

$$\int_{\emptyset} f dA = \int f(\emptyset(u, v))|N(u, v)|\, dudv \text{ (integral over D)}.$$

In particular, when $f = 1$, the area integral becomes

$$\int_{\emptyset} dA = \int |N(u, v)|\, dudv \text{ (integral over D)}.$$

This gives the area of the surface $\emptyset$.

Geometric properties of $\vec{N}$ 6.4.15

Let $\emptyset = \emptyset_1 e_1 + \emptyset_2 e_2 + \emptyset_3 e_3$.

Fix a point $p_0 = (u_0, v_0) \in D$. Denote $\vec{N} = \vec{N}(p_0)$.

Let us take

$\alpha_i = (D_1\emptyset_i)p_0, i = 1,2,3.$

$\beta_i = (D_2\emptyset_i)p_0, i = 1,2,3.$

Then, $\vec{N} = \left[\frac{\partial(\emptyset_2,\emptyset_3)}{\partial(u,v)}\right]_{p_0} e_1 + \left[\frac{\partial(\emptyset_3,\emptyset_1)}{\partial(u,v)}\right]_{p_0} e_2 + \left[\frac{\partial(\emptyset_1,\emptyset_2)}{\partial(u,v)}\right]_{p_0} e_3.$

$= (\alpha_2\beta_3 - \alpha_3\beta_2)e_1 + (\alpha_3\beta_1 - \alpha_1\beta_3)e_2 + (\alpha_1\beta_2 - \alpha_2\beta_1)e_3.$

Let us define a linear transformation

$T: D \to R^3$ by $T(u,v) = \sum_{i=1}^{3}(\alpha_i u + \beta_i v)e_i$.

That is, $T(u,v) = (\alpha_1 u + \beta_1 v)e_1 + (\alpha_2 u + \beta_2 v)e_2 + (\alpha_3 u + \beta_3 v)e_3$.

The range of the affine mapping $(u,v) \to \emptyset(p_0) + T(u,v)$ is a plane π called the tangent plane to $\emptyset$ at p_0.

Property I

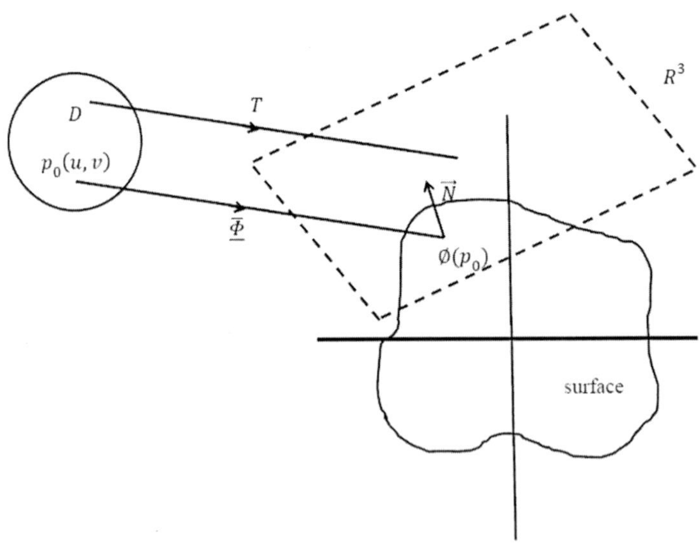

$\vec{N}$ is normal to the tangent plane π.

Proof

Consider two vectors Te_1 and Te_2 lying on π.

Now, $T(u,v) = (\alpha_1 u + \beta_1 v)e_1 + (\alpha_2 u + \beta_2 v)e_2 + (\alpha_3 u + \beta_3 v)e_3$.

Thus, $T(e_1) = T(1,0) = \alpha_1 e_1 + \alpha_2 e_2 + \alpha_3 e_3$.

$T(e_2) = T(0,1) = \beta_1 e_1 + \beta_2 e_2 + \beta_3 e_3$.

Therefore,

$$\vec{N}.\left(T(e_1)\right) = [(\alpha_2\beta_3 - \alpha_3\beta_2)e_1 + (\alpha_3\beta_1 - \alpha_1\beta_3)e_2 + (\alpha_1\beta_2 - \alpha_2\beta_1)e_3](\alpha_1 e_1 + \alpha_2 e_2 + \alpha_3 e_3)$$

$$= (\alpha_2\beta_3 - \alpha_3\beta_2)\alpha_1 + (\alpha_3\beta_1 - \alpha_1\beta_3)\alpha_2 + (\alpha_1\beta_2 - \alpha_2\beta_1)\alpha_3$$

That implies, $\vec{N}.\left(T(e_1)\right) = 0$.

Similarly, $\vec{N}.\left(T(e_2)\right) = 0$.

Thus, $\vec{N}$ is perpendicular to both $T(e_1)$ and $T(e_2)$.

Therefore, $\vec{N}$ is normal to the tangent plane π.

Because of this feature, $\vec{N}$ is called the *normal to the surface* $\emptyset$ *at* p_0.

Property II

The 3 – surface $\sigma = \left[0, Te_1, Te_2, \vec{N}\right]$ is positively oriented.

Proof

Given that, $\sigma = [0, Te_1, Te_2, N]$.

Then, we have, $\sigma(u) = \sigma(0) + Au = p_0 + Au$.

Now, $Ae_1 = p_1 - p_0, Ae_2 = p_2 - p_0, Ae_3 = p_3 - p_0$.

Thus, we have, $p_0 = 0, p_1 = Te_1, p_2 = Te_2, p_3 = N$.

Therefore, $Ae_1 = Te_1, Ae_2 = Te_2, Ae_3 = N$.

That implies, $Ae_1 = Te_1 = \alpha_1 e_1 + \alpha_2 e_2 + \alpha_3 e_3$.

$Ae_2 = Te_2 = \beta_1 e_1 + \beta_2 e_2 + \beta_3 e_3$.

$Ae_3 = (\alpha_2\beta_3 - \alpha_3\beta_2)e_1 + (\alpha_3\beta_1 - \alpha_1\beta_3)e_2 + (\alpha_1\beta_2 - \alpha_2\beta_1)e_3$.

Thus, $\begin{pmatrix} Ae_1 \\ Ae_2 \\ Ae_3 \end{pmatrix} = \begin{pmatrix} \alpha_1 & \alpha_2 & \alpha_3 \\ \beta_1 & \beta_2 & \beta_3 \\ \alpha_2\beta_3 - \alpha_3\beta_2 & \alpha_3\beta_1 - \alpha_1\beta_3 & \alpha_1\beta_2 - \alpha_2\beta_1 \end{pmatrix} \begin{pmatrix} e_1 \\ e_2 \\ e_3 \end{pmatrix}$.

Therefore, $|A| = \begin{vmatrix} \alpha_1 & \alpha_2 & \alpha_3 \\ \beta_1 & \beta_2 & \beta_3 \\ \alpha_2\beta_3 - \alpha_3\beta_2 & \alpha_3\beta_1 - \alpha_1\beta_3 & \alpha_1\beta_2 - \alpha_2\beta_1 \end{vmatrix}$

$$= (\alpha_2\beta_3 - \alpha_3\beta_2)^2 + (\alpha_3\beta_1 - \alpha_1\beta_3)^2 + (\alpha_1\beta_2 - \alpha_2\beta_1)^2$$

$$= \left|\vec{N}\right|^2 > 0.$$

Thus, the simplex $\sigma = \left[0, Te_1, Te_2, \vec{N}\right]$ is positively oriented.

Property III

Rectangular parallelepiped

$$Volume\ of\ the\ rectangular\ parallelopiped = [\overrightarrow{OA}, \overrightarrow{OB}, \overrightarrow{OC}]$$

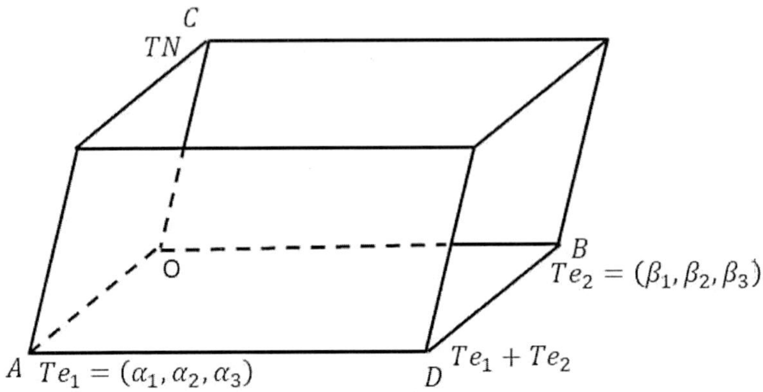

The volume of the rectangular parallelopiped, whose co – terminous edges are $[0, Te_1], [0, Te_2]$ $[0, N]$ is $|\vec{N}|^2$.

Proof

Let $OABD$ be the parallelogram whose vertices are $0, Te_1, Te_1 + Te_2, Te_2$.

Since $\vec{N}$ is perpendicular to $OADB$,

Volume of the rectangular parallelopiped = Area of $OADB \times |\vec{N}|$.

Thus, $|\vec{N}|^2$ = Area of $OADB \times |\vec{N}|$.

Therefore, Area of $OADB = |\vec{N}|$.

Problem 6.4.16

Prove that $det. \begin{bmatrix} \alpha_1 & \beta_1 & \alpha_2\beta_3 - \alpha_3\beta_2 \\ \alpha_2 & \beta_2 & \alpha_3\beta_1 - \alpha_1\beta_3 \\ \alpha_3 & \beta_3 & \alpha_1\beta_2 - \alpha_2\beta_1 \end{bmatrix} = |\vec{N}|^2$.

Solution

Now, $\begin{vmatrix} \alpha_1 & \beta_1 & \alpha_2\beta_3 - \alpha_3\beta_2 \\ \alpha_2 & \beta_2 & \alpha_3\beta_1 - \alpha_1\beta_3 \\ \alpha_3 & \beta_3 & \alpha_1\beta_2 - \alpha_2\beta_1 \end{vmatrix} = \alpha_1[\alpha_1\beta_2^2 - \alpha_2\beta_1\beta_2 - \alpha_3\beta_1\beta_3 + \alpha_1\beta_3^2]$

$$+\beta_1[\alpha_3^2\beta_1 - \alpha_1\alpha_3\beta_3 - \alpha_1\alpha_2\beta_2 - \alpha_2^2\beta_1]$$

$$+(\alpha_2\beta_3 - \alpha_3\beta_2)(\alpha_2\beta_3 - \alpha_3\beta_2).$$

$$= (\alpha_2\beta_3 - \alpha_3\beta_2)^2 + (\alpha_3\beta_1 - \alpha_1\beta_3)^2 + (\alpha_1\beta_2 - \alpha_2\beta_1)^2.$$
$$= |\vec{N}|^2.$$

Hence proved.

Results 6.4.17

i) *Integral of 1 – form in R^3*

Let γ be a $\mathscr{C}'$ curve in an open set $E \subset R^3$, whose parameter domain is $[0,1]$. γ is a 1 – surface. Let F be a vector field in E, such that

$\vec{F} = F_1 e_1 + F_2 e_2 + F_3 e_3$ and

let $\lambda_{\vec{F}} = F_1 dx + F_2 dy + F_3 dz$ be the 1 – form associated with $\vec{F}$. Then,

$$\int_\gamma \lambda_{\vec{F}} = \int \vec{F}(\gamma(u)).\vec{t}(u).|\gamma'(u)|du$$

Proof

For a given $u \in [0,1]$.

Let $\gamma'(u) = \gamma_1'(u)e_1 + \gamma_2'(u)e_2 + \gamma_3'(u)e_3$.

Thus, $\gamma'(u)$ is called the tangent vector to the curve γ at u.

We define $\vec{t} = \vec{t}(u)$ to be the unit vector in the direction of $\gamma'(u)$.

Then, $\gamma'(u) = |\gamma'(u)|\vec{t}(u)$.

Now, by taking the integral over γ, we get

$$\int_\gamma \lambda_{\vec{F}} = \int F_1 dx + F_2 dy + F_3 dz$$
$$= \int \left[F_1(\gamma(u))\gamma_1'(u)du + F_2(\gamma(u))\gamma_2'(u)du + F_3(\gamma(u))\gamma_3'(u)du\right]$$
$$= \int \textstyle\sum_{i=1}^3 F_i\,(\gamma(u))\gamma_i'(u)du$$
$$= \int \left[F_1(\gamma(u))e_1 + F_2(\gamma(u))e_2 + F_3(\gamma(u))e_3\right](\gamma_1'(u)e_1 + \gamma_2'(u)e_2 + \gamma_3'(u)e_3)du.$$
$$= \int \vec{F}(\gamma(u)).\gamma_1'(u)du.$$

Since, $\gamma'(u) = |\gamma'(u)|\vec{t}(u)$, we have

$$\int_\gamma \lambda_{\vec{F}} = \int \vec{F}(\gamma(u)).\vec{t}(u).|\gamma'(u)|du.$$

Here, $|\gamma'(u)|$ is called the element of arc length along γ. It is denoted by ds and therefore, we get, $\int_\gamma \lambda_{\vec{F}} = \int (\vec{F}.\vec{t})ds$.

Here, $\vec{F}.\vec{t}$ is called the tangential component of $\vec{F}$ along γ.

Hence proved.

ii) Integral of 2 – form in R^3

Let $\vec{F} = F_1e_1 + F_2e_2 + F_3e_3$ be a vector field in an open set $E \subset R^3$. Let $w_{\vec{F}}$ be the 2 – form associated with $\vec{F}$. Then,

$w_{\vec{F}} = F_1 dy \wedge dz + F_2 dz \wedge dx + F_3 dx \wedge dy$. Let $\emptyset$ be the 2 – surface in E of class $\mathscr{C}'$ with parameter domain D. Then,

$$\int_{\emptyset} w_{\vec{F}} = \int (\vec{F}.\vec{n})dA.$$

Proof

Now, $\int_{\emptyset} w_{\vec{F}} = \int (F_1 dy \wedge dz + F_2 dz \wedge dx + F_3 dx \wedge dy)$. (integral over $\emptyset$)

$$= \int \left[F_1(\emptyset(u,v))\frac{\partial(y,z)}{\partial(u,v)} + F_2(\emptyset(u,v))\frac{\partial(z,x)}{\partial(u,v)} + F_3(\emptyset(u,v))\frac{\partial(z,x)}{\partial(u,v)}\right] dudv.$$

(integral over D)

$$= \int (F_1e_1 + F_2e_2 + F_3e_3).\left(\frac{\partial(y,z)}{\partial(u,v)}e_1 + \frac{\partial(z,x)}{\partial(u,v)}e_2 + \frac{\partial(x,y)}{\partial(u,v)}e_3\right) dudv.$$

(integral over D)

$$= \int \vec{F}(\emptyset(u,v)).\vec{N}(u,v)dudv. \text{ (integral over D)}$$

Let $\vec{n} = \vec{n}(u,v)$ be the unit vector in the direction of $\vec{N}(u,v)$.

Then, $\vec{N} = |\vec{N}|\vec{n}$. That is, $\vec{N}(u,v) = |\vec{N}(u,v)|\vec{n}(u,v)$.

Therefore, $\int_{\emptyset} w_{\vec{F}} = \int \vec{F}(\emptyset(u,v)).\vec{n}(u,v)|\vec{N}(u,v)|dudv$. (integral over D)

Since, $\int_{\emptyset} dA = \int |\vec{N}(u,v)|dudv$ (integral over D), we have

$$\int_{\emptyset} w_{\vec{F}} = \int (\vec{F}.\vec{n})dA. \text{ (integral over } \emptyset)$$

Here, $(\vec{F}.\vec{n})$ is called the normal component of $\vec{F}$ along $\emptyset$.

Hence proved.

Stoke's formula 6.4.18

If $\vec{F}$is a vector field of class $\mathscr{C}'$ in an open set $E \subset R^3$ and if $\emptyset$ is a 2 – surface of class $\mathscr{C}''$ in E, then

$\int(\nabla \times \vec{F}).\vec{n}dA\ (integral\ over\ \emptyset) = \int(\vec{F}.\vec{t})ds.$ (integral over $\partial\emptyset$).

Proof

Let $\vec{F} = F_1e_1 + F_2e_2 + F_3e_3$, where each $F_i \in \mathscr{C}'$(E).

Then, $\nabla \times \vec{F} = (D_2F_3 - D_3F_2)e_1 + (D_3F_1 - D_1F_3)e_2 + (D_1F_2 - D_2F_1)e_3$.

Therefore, if $\vec{H}$ is a vector field in E, such that

$\vec{H} = H_1e_1 + H_2e_2 + H_3e_3 = \nabla \times \vec{F}$,

then $H_1 = D_2F_3 - D_3F_2$, $H_2 = D_3F_1 - D_1F_3$ and $H_3 = D_1F_2 - D_2F_1$.

Thus, by result 6.4.17 (ii), we have

$$\int(\nabla \times \vec{F}).\vec{n}dA\ (integral\ over\ \emptyset) = \int(\vec{H}.\vec{n})\,dA\ (integral\ over\ \emptyset)$$

$$= \int_{\emptyset} w_{\vec{H}}.$$

$= \int(H_1dy\wedge dz + H_2dz\wedge dx + H_3dx\wedge dy)$ (integral over $\emptyset$)

$$= \int[(D_2F_3 - D_3F_2)dy\wedge dz + (D_3F_1 - D_1F_3)dz\wedge dx + (D_1F_2 - D_2F_1)dx\wedge dy \text{ (integral over } \emptyset)$$

$= \int_{\emptyset} d\lambda_{\vec{F}}$, where $\lambda_{\vec{F}}$ is the 1 – form associated with $\vec{F}$.

Thus, by Stoke's theorem, we have

$$\int(\nabla \times \vec{F}).\vec{n}dA\ (integral\ over\ \emptyset) = \int_{\partial\emptyset} \lambda_{\vec{F}}.$$

That is, by result 6.4.17 (i), we have

$\int(\nabla \times \vec{F}).\vec{n}dA\ (integral\ over\ \emptyset) = \int(\vec{F}.\vec{t})ds.$ (integral over $\partial\emptyset$).

Hence proved.

Theorem 6.4.19

This theorem is known as the ***Divergence Theorem.***

If $\vec{F}$is a vector field of class $\mathscr{C}'$ in an open set $E \subset R^3$ and if Ω is a closed subset of E with positively oriented boundary Ω, then

$$\int(\nabla.\vec{F})dV\ (integral\ over\ \Omega) = \int(\vec{F}.\vec{N})dA\ (integral\ over\ \partial\Omega).$$

Proof

Let $\vec{F} = F_1e_1 + F_2e_2 + F_3e_3$, where each $F_i \in \mathscr{C}'(E)$.

Then, the 2 – form associated with $\vec{F}$ is

$$w_{\vec{F}} = F_1 dy\wedge dz + F_2 dz\wedge dx + F_3 dx\wedge dy.$$
$$= (D_1F_1 + D_2F_2 + D_3F_3)dx\wedge dy\wedge dz.$$
$$= (\nabla.\vec{F})dV.$$

Therefore, by Stoke's theorem, we have

$\int(\nabla.\vec{F})dV$ $(integral\ over\ \Omega) = \int_{\Omega} dw_{\vec{F}} = \int_{\partial\Omega} w_{\vec{F}} =$

$\int(\vec{F}.\vec{N})dA$ $(integral\ over\ \partial\Omega)$.

Hence the theorem.

Note 6.4.20

1) Let $\emptyset$ be a 2 – surface in R^3.

Thus, area of the surface $\emptyset = A(\emptyset) = \int|N(u,v)|dudv$, where

$N(u,v) = \frac{\partial(y,z)}{\partial(u,v)}e_1 + \frac{\partial(z,x)}{\partial(u,v)}e_2 + \frac{\partial(x,y)}{\partial(u,v)}e_3$ and D is the parameter domain of $\emptyset$.

2) Let $\emptyset$ be a 3 – surface (volume) in R^3.

Therefore, volume of $\emptyset = \int_{\emptyset} dV = \int dx\wedge dy\wedge dz$, (integral over $\emptyset$).

Problems 6.4.21

1) Find the volume of the solid sphere of radius 'a'.

Solution

Volume of the solid sphere is a 3 – surface in R^3.

Now, $D = [0,a] \times [0,\pi] \times [0,2\pi]$.

Here, $r = [0,a], \theta = [0,\pi], \emptyset = [0,2\pi]$.

Let $\emptyset: D \to R^3$ such that $x = rsin\theta cos\emptyset, y = rsin\theta sin\emptyset, z = rcos\theta$.

We know that,

$$V = \int_{\emptyset} dV = \int dx\wedge dy\wedge dz, \text{ (integral over } \emptyset)$$
$$= \int \frac{\partial(x,y,z)}{\partial(r,\theta,\emptyset)} dr d\theta d\emptyset = \int_0^a \int_0^\pi \int_0^{2\pi} r^2 sin\theta dr d\theta d\emptyset$$

$$= \int_0^a 2\pi \int_0^\pi r^2 sin\theta dr d\theta = \frac{2\pi a^3}{3} \int_0^\pi sin\theta d\theta = \frac{4\pi a^3}{3}.$$

Therefore, $V = \frac{4\pi a^3}{3}$.

2) Find the surface area of the sphere of radius 'a'.

Solution

The surface area of a sphere is a 2 – surface in R^3 defined as follows:

Now, $D = [0,\pi] \times [0,2\pi]$.

Here, $\theta = [0,\pi], \emptyset = [0,2\pi]$.

Let $\Psi: D \to R^3$ such that $x = asin\theta cos\emptyset, y = asin\theta sin\emptyset, z = acos\theta$.

Let us first find, $\vec{N}(\theta,\emptyset) = \frac{\partial(y,z)}{\partial(\theta,\emptyset)} e_1 + \frac{\partial(z,x)}{\partial(\theta,\emptyset)} e_2 + \frac{\partial(x,y)}{\partial(\theta,\emptyset)} e_3$.

Now, $\frac{\partial(y,z)}{\partial(\theta,\emptyset)} = \begin{vmatrix} \frac{\partial y}{\partial\theta} & \frac{\partial y}{\partial\emptyset} \\ \frac{\partial z}{\partial\theta} & \frac{\partial z}{\partial\emptyset} \end{vmatrix} = \begin{vmatrix} acos\theta sin\emptyset & asin\theta cos\emptyset \\ -asin\theta & 0 \end{vmatrix} = a^2 sin^2\theta cos\emptyset$.

$$\frac{\partial(z,x)}{\partial(\theta,\emptyset)} = \begin{vmatrix} \frac{\partial z}{\partial\theta} & \frac{\partial z}{\partial\emptyset} \\ \frac{\partial x}{\partial\theta} & \frac{\partial x}{\partial\emptyset} \end{vmatrix} = \begin{vmatrix} -asin\theta & 0 \\ acos\theta cos\emptyset & -asin\theta sin\emptyset \end{vmatrix} = a^2 sin^2\theta sin\emptyset.$$

$$\frac{\partial(x,y)}{\partial(\theta,\emptyset)} = \begin{vmatrix} \frac{\partial x}{\partial\theta} & \frac{\partial x}{\partial\emptyset} \\ \frac{\partial y}{\partial\theta} & \frac{\partial y}{\partial\emptyset} \end{vmatrix} = \begin{vmatrix} acos\theta cos\emptyset & -asin\theta sin\emptyset \\ acos\theta sin\emptyset & asin\theta cos\emptyset \end{vmatrix} = a^2 sin\theta cos\theta.$$

Thus,

$$|\vec{N}(u,v)| = \sqrt{(a^2 sin^2\theta cos\emptyset)^2 + (a^2 sin^2\theta sin\emptyset)^2 + (a^2 sin\theta cos\theta)^2}.$$

$$= \sqrt{a^4 sin^2\theta} = a^2 sin\theta.$$

Therefore, area of the surface

$$\Psi = \int |\vec{N}(u,v)| du dv \ (integral\ over\ D).$$

$$= \int_0^\pi \int_0^{2\pi} a^2 sin\theta\, d\theta\, d\emptyset = 2\pi a^2 \int_0^\pi sin\theta d\theta.$$

Thus, area of the surface $\Psi = 4\pi a^2$.

Torus 6.4.22

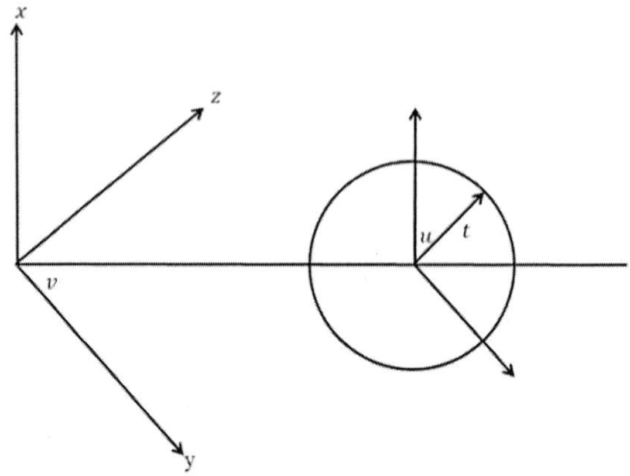

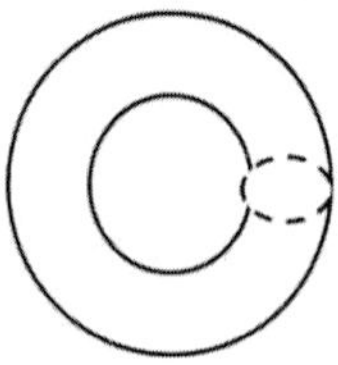

Here, $0 \le u \le 2\pi, 0 \le v \le 2\pi, 0 \le t \le a$.

$x = tcosu, y = (b + tsinu)cosv, z = (b + tsinu)sinv$.

Let $0 < a < b$.

Volume of the torus = $2\pi^2 a^2 b$.

Surface area of the torus $S = 4\pi^2 ab$.

Volume of the Torus 6.4.22.1

Let $D = [0, a] \times [0,2\pi] \times [0,2\pi]$ and $0 < a < b$.

Let $\emptyset: D \to R^3$ such that $x = tcosu, y = (b + tsinu)cosv$,

$z = (b + tsinu)sinv$.

The volume of the Torus = $\underset{\emptyset}{\int dV} = \int dx \wedge dy \wedge dz$, (integral over $\emptyset$)

$$= \int \frac{\partial(x,y,z)}{\partial(t,u,v)} dtdudv, \text{ (integral over } D)$$

$$= \int_0^a \int_0^{2\pi} \int_0^{2\pi} \frac{\partial(x,y,z)}{\partial(t,u,v)} dtdudv.$$

Now, $\frac{\partial(x,y,z)}{\partial(t,u,v)} = \begin{vmatrix} \frac{\partial x}{\partial t} & \frac{\partial x}{\partial u} & \frac{\partial x}{\partial v} \\ \frac{\partial y}{\partial t} & \frac{\partial y}{\partial u} & \frac{\partial y}{\partial v} \\ \frac{\partial z}{\partial t} & \frac{\partial z}{\partial u} & \frac{\partial z}{\partial v} \end{vmatrix}$

$$= \begin{vmatrix} cosu & -tsinu & 0 \\ sinucosv & tcosucosv & -bsinv - tsinusinv \\ sinusinv & tcosusinv & bcosv + tsinucosv \end{vmatrix}$$

$$= t(b + tsinu).$$

Therefore,

$$\int\limits_{\emptyset} dV = \int_0^a \int_0^{2\pi} \int_0^{2\pi} t(b + tsinu)dtdudv$$

$$= 2\pi \int_0^a \int_0^{2\pi} (tb + t^2 sinu)dt\, du = 2\pi \int_0^a btdt = 2\pi^2 a^2 b.$$

Thus, $\int\limits_{\emptyset} dV = 2\pi^2 a^2 b.$

Surface area of the Torus 6.4.22.2

Let $\Psi: D \to R^3$ such that $\Psi(u, v) = (x, y, z)$, where $D = [0,2\pi] \times [0,2\pi]$ and

$x = acosu, y = (b + asinu)cosv, z = (b + asinu)sinv.$

Let us first find, $\vec{N}(u, v) = \frac{\partial(y,z)}{\partial(u,v)} e_1 + \frac{\partial(z,x)}{\partial(u,v)} e_2 + \frac{\partial(x,y)}{\partial(u,v)} e_3.$

Now, $\frac{\partial(y,z)}{\partial(u,v)} = \begin{vmatrix} \frac{\partial y}{\partial u} & \frac{\partial y}{\partial v} \\ \frac{\partial z}{\partial u} & \frac{\partial z}{\partial v} \end{vmatrix} = \begin{vmatrix} acosu.cosv & -(b + asinu)sinv \\ acosu.sinv & (b + asinu)cosv \end{vmatrix}$

$$= abcosu + a^2 sinu.cosu.$$

$$\frac{\partial(z,x)}{\partial(u,v)} = \begin{vmatrix} \frac{\partial z}{\partial u} & \frac{\partial z}{\partial v} \\ \frac{\partial x}{\partial u} & \frac{\partial x}{\partial v} \end{vmatrix} = \begin{vmatrix} acosusinv & (b + asinu)cosv \\ -asinu & 0 \end{vmatrix}$$

$$= absinu.cosv + a^2 sin^2 u.cosv.$$

$$\frac{\partial(x,y)}{\partial(u,v)} = \begin{vmatrix} \frac{\partial x}{\partial u} & \frac{\partial x}{\partial v} \\ \frac{\partial y}{\partial u} & \frac{\partial y}{\partial v} \end{vmatrix} = \begin{vmatrix} -asinu & 0 \\ acosu.cosv & -(b + asinu)sinv \end{vmatrix}$$

$$= absinu.sinv + a^2 sin^2 u.sinv.$$

Thus, $\vec{N}(u, v) = (abcosu + a^2 sinu.cosu)e_1$

$$+(absinu.cosv + a^2 sin^2 u.cosv)e_2$$

$$+(absinu.sinv + a^2 sin^2 u.sinv)e_3.$$

$$= (b + asinu)[acosu.e_1 + asinu.cosv.e_2 + asinu.sinv.e_3].$$

Then,

$$|\vec{N}(u, v)| = (b + asinu)\sqrt{a^2 cos^2 u + a^2 sin^2 u.cos^2 v + a^2 sin^2 u.sin^2 v}$$

$$= a(b + asinu).$$

Therefore, area of the surface = $\int \vec{N}(u,v)dudv$ $(integral\ over\ D)$.

$$= \int_0^{2\pi}\int_0^{2\pi} a(b + asinu)du\,dv = 2\pi\int_0^{2\pi} a(b + asinu)du.$$

$$= 2\pi a(2\pi b) = 4\pi^2 ab.$$

Thus, surface area of the Torus = $4\pi^2 ab$.

Cylinder 6.4.23

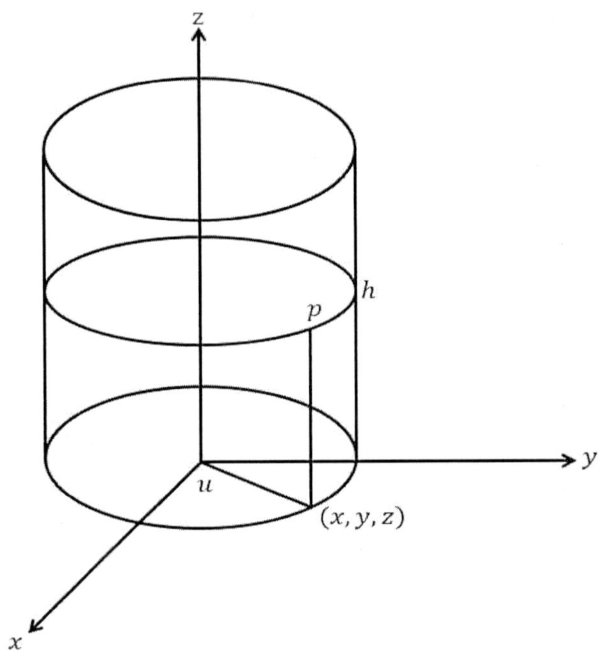

Surface area of the Cylinder 6.4.23.1

Let $\emptyset: D \to R^3$ such that $\emptyset(u,v) = (x,y,z)$, where $D = [0,2\pi] \times [0,h]$ and $x = acosu, y = asinu, z = v$.

Let us first find, $\vec{N}(u,v) = \frac{\partial(y,z)}{\partial(u,v)}e_1 + \frac{\partial(z,x)}{\partial(u,v)}e_2 + \frac{\partial(x,y)}{\partial(u,v)}e_3$.

Now, $\frac{\partial(y,z)}{\partial(u,v)} = \begin{vmatrix} \frac{\partial y}{\partial u} & \frac{\partial y}{\partial v} \\ \frac{\partial z}{\partial u} & \frac{\partial z}{\partial v} \end{vmatrix} = \begin{vmatrix} acosu & 0 \\ 0 & 1 \end{vmatrix} = acosu.$

$\frac{\partial(z,x)}{\partial(u,v)} = \begin{vmatrix} \frac{\partial z}{\partial u} & \frac{\partial z}{\partial v} \\ \frac{\partial x}{\partial u} & \frac{\partial x}{\partial v} \end{vmatrix} = \begin{vmatrix} 0 & 1 \\ -asinu & 0 \end{vmatrix} = asinu.$

$$\frac{\partial(x,y)}{\partial(u,v)} = \begin{vmatrix} \frac{\partial x}{\partial u} & \frac{\partial x}{\partial v} \\ \frac{\partial y}{\partial u} & \frac{\partial y}{\partial v} \end{vmatrix} = \begin{vmatrix} -asinu & 0 \\ acosu & 0 \end{vmatrix} = 0.$$

Thus, $\vec{N}(u,v) = a.$

Therefore, surface area of the cylinder

$$= \int \vec{N}(u,v)dudv \ (integral\ over\ D).$$

$$= \int_0^h \int_0^{2\pi} adudv = 2\pi a \int_0^h dv = 2\pi ah.$$

Thus, surface area of the cylinder = $2\pi ah$.

Unit

7

RADON MEASURES

7.1 Introduction

Recall that if X is a compact metric space, C(X), the space of continuous (real-valued) functions on X, is a Banach space with the norm

$$\|f\| = \sup_{x \in X} |f(x)| .$$

We want to identify the dual of $C(X)$ with the space of (finite) signed Borel measures on X, also known as the space of Radon measures on X.

7.2 Bounded linear functionals on L^p spaces

Definition 7.2.1

A linear functional on a normed linear space X is defined to be a mapping F of the space X into the set of real numbers such that

$F(\alpha f + \beta g) = \alpha F(f) + \beta F(g)$, where $f, g \in X$ and α, β are scalars.

Definition 7.2.2

A linear functional f is said to be bounded, if there is a constant M such that

$|F(f)| \le M\|f\|$, for all $f \in X$.

Definition 7.2.3

The smallest constant M for which the inequality $|F(f)| \le M\|f\|$, for all $f \in X$, is true is called the norm of F. Hence,

$\|F\| = \sup.\left\{\dfrac{F(f)}{\|f\|}\right\}$, as f ranges from over all nonzero elements of X.

Theorem 7.2.4

Each function g in L^q defines a linear functional F on L^p by $F(f) = \int fg$ and $\|F\| = \|g\|_q$.

Proof

Let g be a function in L^q.

Define a functional F on L^p by $F(f) = \int fg$, for all $f \in L^p$.

Claim: F is a bounded linear functional on L^p.

For $f_1, f_2 \in L^p$, and for scalars α, β, consider

$$F(\alpha f_1 + \beta f_2) = \int (\alpha f_1 + \beta f_2)g = \alpha \int f_1 g + \beta \int f_2 g = \alpha F(f_1) + \beta F(f_2).$$

Hence, F is linear on L^p.

Consider, $|F(f)| = \left|\int fg\right| < \int |fg| \leq \|f\|_p \|g\|_q$. [By Holder's inequality]

Hence, $\dfrac{|F(f)|}{\|f\|} \leq \|g\|_q$.

Since this is true for all $f \in L^p$, $\|F\| = \sup.\left\{\dfrac{|F(f)|}{\|f\|}\right\} \leq \|g\|_q$.

Hence, F is a bounded linear functional with $\|F\| \leq \|g\|_q$. .... (7.2.4.1)

To prove: $\|F\| \geq \|g\|_q$

Let $f = |g|^{q/p}\,\text{sgn}.g$, for $1 < p < \infty$, where sgn. is a function defined as

sgn. x = 1, if $x > 0$
sgn. 0 = 0, and
sgn. x = -1, if $x < 0$.

Therefore, $|f|^p = \left||g|^{q/p}\,\text{sgn}.g\right|^p = |g|^q$,

and $fg = \left(|g|^{q/p}\,\text{sgn}.g\right).g = |g|^{\frac{q}{p}+1} = |g|^q$. [Since $\dfrac{1}{p} + \dfrac{1}{q} = 1$].

Hence, $|f|^p = |g|^q = fg$ ....(7.2.4.2)

That implies, $\int |f|^p = \int fg$.

Therefore, $f \in L^p$.

Now, $\|f\|_p = \left(\int |f|^p\right)^{1/p} = \left(\int |g|^q\right)^{1/p}$ [By (7.2.4.2)]

$$= \left(\|g\|_q\right)^{q/p}.$$

Therefore, $F(f) = \int fg = \int |g|^q$ [By (2)]

$$= \left(\|g\|_q\right)^q = \left(\|g\|_q\right)\left(\|g\|_q\right)^{q-1} = \|g\|_q \left(\|g\|_q\right)^{q/p} = \|g\|_q \|f\|_p.$$

Hence, $\dfrac{|F(f)|}{\|f\|_p} = \|g\|_q$.

Therefore, $|F(f)| \geq \|g\|_q$. .... (7.2.4.3)

From (7.2.4.1) & (7.2.4.3), we get

$$\|F\| = \|g\|_q.$$

Hence the theorem.

Theorem 7.2.5

Let g be an integrable function on [0, 1], and suppose that there is a constant M such that $\left|\int fg\right| \leq M\|f\|_p$, for all bounded measurable functions f. Then, $g \in L^q$ and $\|g\|_q = M$.

Proof

Assume that $1 < p < \infty$.

Define a sequence of bounded measurable functions g_n as

$$g_n(x) = \begin{cases} g(x), & \text{if } |g(x)| \leq n \\ 0, & \text{if } |g(x)| > n \end{cases}$$

Then, $\{g_n\}$ is a sequence of bounded measurable functions.

Let $f_n = |g_n|^{q/p} \operatorname{sgn}.g_n$.

Then, $|f_n|^p = \left||g_n|^{q/p}\,\text{sgn}.g_n\right|^p = |g_n|^q$.

Therefore, $\left(\|f_n\|_p\right)^p = \int |f_n|^p = \int |g_n|^q = \left(\|g_n\|_q\right)^q$.

Hence, $\|f_n\|_p = \left(\|g_n\|_q\right)^{q/p}$. .... (7.2.5.1)

Also, $f_n g_n = \left(|g_n|^{q/p}\,\text{sgn}.g_n\right)g_n = |g_n|^{q/p}|g_n| = |g_n|^{\frac{q}{p}+1} = |g_n|^q$.

Hence, $|g_n|^q = f_n g_n = f_n g$. .... (7.2.5.2)

Therefore, $\int |g_n|^q = \int f_n g \le M\|f_n\|_p$ [By assumption]

$= M\left(\|g_n\|_q\right)^{q/p}$ [By (7.2.5.1)]

That is, $\left(\|g_n\|_q\right)^q \le M\left(\|g_n\|_q\right)^{q/p}$.

Hence, $\left(\|g_n\|_q\right)^{q-\frac{q}{p}} \le M$.

That is, $\|g_n\|_q \le M$, [since $\frac{1}{p}+\frac{1}{q}=1$, we have $q-\frac{q}{p}=1$].

Therefore, $\int |g_n|^q \le M^q$.

Since $|g_n|^q$ converges to $|g|^q$ a.e., by Fatou's lemma, we have

$$\int |g|^q \le \underline{\lim}\int |g_n|^q \le M^q.$$

Hence, $g \in L^q$ and $\|g\|_q \le M$.

Hence the theorem is proved for $1 < p < \infty$.

If $p = 1$, let $E = \{x / |g(x)| \ge M + \varepsilon\}$ and $f = (\text{sgn}.g)\chi_E$.

Then, $|f| = \chi_E$.

Therefore, $\|f\|_1 = \int |f| = \int \chi_E = mE$.

Hence, $MmE = M\|f\|_1 \ge \int fg$ [By assumption]

$\ge (M+\varepsilon)mE$.

Since ε is arbitrary, we have $mE = 0$.

Hence, $g \in L^q$ and $\|g\|_q = M$.

Therefore, we have proved the theorem for $p = 1$.

Hence the theorem.

Definition 7.2.6

A *signed Radon measure* is a signed Borel measure whose positive and negative variations are Radon. A *complex Radon measure* is a complex Borel measure whose real and imaginary parts are signed Radon measures.

7.3 Riesz Representation theorem

The following theorem is known as ***Riesz Representation theorem***.

Let F be a bounded linear functional on L^p, $1 \le p < \infty$. Then, there is a function g in L^q such that

$$F(f) = \int fg .$$

Also, $\|F\| = \|g\|_q$.

Proof

Let χ_s be the characteristic function of the interval [0, s].

Since F is a bounded linear functional, for each s, $F(\chi_s)$ is a real number.

Define $\Phi(s)$ as this number.

Hence Φ defines a function on [0,1].

Claim: Φ is absolutely continuous.

Let $\{(s_i, s_i')\}$ be any finite collection of non - overlapping subintervals of [0, 1] of total length less than δ.

$$\sum_i |\Phi(s_i') - \Phi(s_i)| = F(f),$$

where $f = \sum_i \left(\chi_{s_i'} - \chi_{s_i}\right) \text{sgn}.\left(\Phi(s_i') - \Phi(s_i)\right)$.

Hence, $(\|f\|_p)^p = \int |f|^p = \sum_i (s_i' - s_i) < \delta$.

Hence, $\sum_i |\Phi(s_i') - \Phi(s_i)| = F(f) \le \|F\| \ \|f\|_p < \|F\| \delta^{1/p}$.

Therefore, if we choose $\delta = \dfrac{\varepsilon^p}{\|F\|^p}$, then $\sum_i |\Phi(s_i') - \Phi(s_i)| < \varepsilon$.

Hence, Φ is absolutely continuous.
Therefore, by the theorem "A function *F* is an indefinite integral if and only if it is absolutely continuous", Φ is an indefinite integral.

That is, there is an integrable function *g* on [0, 1] such that $\Phi(s) = \int_0^s g$.

Hence, $F(\chi_s) = \Phi(s) = \int_0^s g = \int_0^1 g.\chi_s$.

Since every step function on [0, 1] is equal almost everywhere to a suitable linear combination $\sum c_i \chi_{s_i}$, by the linearity of *F* and the integral, we get

$$F(\psi) = \int_0^1 g\psi \text{, for each step function } \psi.$$

Let *f* be a bounded measurable function on [0, 1].
Therefore, there is a bounded sequence $\{\psi_n\}$ of step functions which converge almost everywhere to *f*.

Hence, the sequence $\left\{|f - \psi_n|^p\right\}$ is uniformly bounded and $|f - \psi_n|^p \to 0$ a.e.

Hence, by bounded convergence theorem, $\|f - \psi_n\|^p \to 0$.

Since *F* is bounded, and

$$|F(f) - F(\psi_n)| = |F(f - \psi_n)| \le \|F\| \ \|f - \psi_n\|_p.$$

Hence, $|F(f) - F(\psi_n)| \to 0$.

Therefore, $F(f) = \lim. F(\psi_n)$.

Since $g\psi_n$ is always less than $|g|$ times the uniform bound for the sequence $\{\psi_n\}$, by bounded convergence theorem, $\int fg = \lim. \int g\psi_n$.

Hence, $\int fg = \lim . F(\psi_n) = F(f)$, for each bounded measurable function *f*.

Since, $|F(f)| \leq \|F\| \|f\|_p$, we have $\left|\int fg\right| \leq \|F\| \ \|f\|_p$.

Hence, by theorem 7.3, we have $g \in L^q$ and $\|g\|_q = \|F\|$.

Claim: $F(f) = \int fg$, for each *f* in L^p.

Let *f* be an arbitrary function in L^p.

Then, for each $\varepsilon > 0$, there exists a step function ψ such that $\|f - \psi\|_p < \varepsilon$.

Since ψ is bounded, $F(\psi) = \int \psi g$.

Hence, $\left|F(f) - \int fg\right| = \left|F(f) - F(\psi) + \int \psi g - \int fg\right|$.

$$\leq |F(f-\psi)| + \left|\int (\psi - f) g\right|.$$

$$\leq \|F\| \ \|f-\psi\|_p + \|g\|_q \|f-\psi\|_p.$$

$$\leq \left(\|F\| + \|g\|_q\right) \|f-\psi\|_p.$$

$$< \left(\|F\| + \|g\|_q\right) \varepsilon.$$

Since ε is arbitrary, $F(f) = \int fg$.

Hence by theorem 7.2.4, $\|F\| = \|g\|_q$.

Therefore, we have proved, that there is a function g in L^q such that $F(f) = \int fg$ and $\|F\| = \|g\|_q$.

Hence the theorem.

Unit

8 ELEMENTS OF FOURIER ANALYSIS

8.1 Introduction

A convolution is a mathematical operation taking two functions as input, and producing a third function as output, much like addition or multiplication operations but with a more involved definition. One of the basic operations performed in image and signal processing is an operation called convolution. In image processing, many noise reduction filters utilize the convolution operation in order to perform their tasks. From a purely mathematical standpoint, convolution is an integral. In this chapter, we learn about Fourier series, Gamma functions and their properties and some of the related theorems.

8.2 The Convolutions

Definition 8.2.1

Let f and g be measurable functions on $\mathbb{R}^n$. The *convolution* of f and g is the function $f * g$ defined by

$$f * g(x) = \int f(x-y)g(y)dy .$$

8.3 The Fourier Series

Definition 8.3.1

The trigonometric polynomial is the finite sum of the form

$$f(x) = a_0 + \sum_{n=1}^{N} a_n \cos nx + b_n \sin nx,$$

where N is real, $a_0, a_1, \ldots\ldots, a_N$ and $b_0, b_1, \ldots\ldots, b_N$ are complex numbers. That is,

$$f(x) = a_0 + \sum_{n=1}^{N} a_n \left(\frac{e^{inx} + e^{-inx}}{2} \right) + \sum_{n=1}^{N} b_n \left(\frac{e^{inx} - e^{-inx}}{2i} \right).$$

Therefore, $f(x) = \sum_{n=-N}^{N} c_n e^{inx}$, for all $c_n \in C$.

It is clear that every trigonometric polynomial is periodic with period 2π.

Note 8.3.2

1) If $n = 0$, then

$$\frac{1}{2\pi}\int_{-\pi}^{\pi} e^{inx}dx = \frac{1}{2\pi}\int_{-\pi}^{\pi} dx = 1.$$

If $n = \pm1, \pm2, \ldots\ldots$, then

$$\frac{1}{2\pi}\int_{-\pi}^{\pi} e^{inx}dx = \frac{1}{2\pi}\int_{-\pi}^{\pi} (\cos nx + i\sin nx)dx.$$

$$= \frac{1}{2\pi}\left[\left(\frac{\sin nx}{n}\right)_{-\pi}^{\pi} + i\left(\frac{-\cos nx}{n}\right)_{-\pi}^{\pi}\right].$$

$$= \frac{1}{2\pi}\left[\frac{1}{n}(0-0)\right] - \frac{i}{n}[\cos n\pi - \cos n\pi] = 0.$$

Therefore, $\frac{1}{2\pi}\int_{-\pi}^{\pi} e^{inx}dx = \begin{cases} 1, & \text{if} \quad n = 0 \\ 0, & \text{if} \quad n = \pm1, \ \pm2, \ldots. \end{cases}$

2) We know that, $f(x) = \sum_{n=-N}^{N} c_n e^{inx}$, for all $c_n \in C$.

$f(x)$ is real if and only if $f(x) = \overline{f(x)}$.

if and only if $\sum_{n=-N}^{N} c_n e^{inx} = \sum_{n=-N}^{N} \overline{c_n} e^{-inx}$.

if and only if $\sum_{n=-N}^{N} c_{-n} e^{-inx} = \sum_{n=-N}^{N} \overline{c_n} e^{-inx}$.

if and only if $c_{-n} = \overline{c_n}$, for all $n = 0, 1, 2, \ldots\ldots$.

Definition 8.3.3

The trigonometric series is a series of the form $\sum_{n=-\infty}^{\infty} c_n e^{inx}$, x is real. The nth partial sum of this series is $\sum_{n=-N}^{N} c_n e^{inx}$.

Definition 8.3.4

Let f be an integrable function in $[-\pi,\pi]$. Then, $c_n = \frac{1}{2\pi}\int_{-\pi}^{\pi} f(x)e^{-inx}dx$, where n is an integer, is called the *Fourier coefficient of f* and the series $\sum_{n=-\infty}^{\infty} c_n e^{inx}$ is called the *Fourier series of f.*

Definition 8.3.5

Let $\{\phi_n\}$ be a sequence of complex functions defined on $[a, b]$, such that

$$\int_a^b \varphi_n(x)\overline{\varphi_m(x)}\, dx = 0, \text{ if } n \neq m.$$

Then, $\{\phi_n\}$ is called the sequence of orthogonal functions on $[a, b]$. If, in addition,

$$\int_a^b |\phi_n(x)|^2\, dx = 1, \text{ if } n = 1, 2, 3, \ldots.,$$

then, we say $\{\phi_n\}$ is an orthonormal system on $[a, b]$.

Example 8.3.6

Define $\varphi_n(x) = \frac{1}{\sqrt{2\pi}}e^{-inx}$, $x \in [-\pi,\pi]$.

When $n \neq m$, we have

$$\int_{-\pi}^{\pi} \varphi_n(x)\overline{\varphi_m(x)}\, dx = \int_{-\pi}^{\pi} \frac{1}{\sqrt{2\pi}}e^{-inx}\frac{1}{\sqrt{2\pi}}e^{imx}dx.$$

$$= \frac{1}{2\pi}\int_{-\pi}^{\pi} e^{i(m-n)x}dx = 0, \text{ [since } n \neq m \text{]}$$

Also, $\int_{-\pi}^{\pi} |\varphi_n(x)|^2 \, dx = \int_{-\pi}^{\pi} \varphi_n(x)\overline{\varphi_n(x)} \, dx$.

$$= \int_{-\pi}^{\pi} \frac{1}{\sqrt{2\pi}} e^{-inx} \frac{1}{\sqrt{2\pi}} e^{inx} dx.$$

$$= \frac{1}{2\pi} \int_{-\pi}^{\pi} dx = 1.$$

Therefore, $\{\phi_n\}$ is orthonormal on $[-\pi, \pi]$.

Definition 8.3.7

Let $\{\phi_n\}$ be orthonormal on $[a, b]$ and f be an integrable function $[a, b]$. Then,

$c_n = \int_a^b f(x)\overline{\varphi_n(x)} \, dx$, are called the Fourier coefficients of f with respect to $\{\phi_n\}$. We write $f(x) \approx \sum_{n=1}^{\infty} c_n \varphi_n(x)$. The series $\sum_{n=1}^{\infty} c_n \varphi_n(x)$ is called the Fourier series relative to $\{\varphi_n\}$.

Theorem 8.3.8

Let $\{\phi_n\}$ be orthonormal on $[a, b]$. Let $s_n(x) = \sum_{m=1}^{n} c_m \varphi_m(x)$ be the nth partial sum of the series f and $t_n(x) = \sum_{m=1}^{n} \gamma_m \phi_m(x)$. Then, $\int_a^b |f - s_n|^2 \, dx \le \int_a^b |f - t_n|^2 \, dx$ and equality holds if and only if $\gamma_m = c_m$, m = 1, 2, ..., n, ... That is, among all functions t_n, s_n gives the best possible mean square approximation to f.

Proof

$$\int_a^b |f-t_n|^2\,dx = \int_a^b \left(f(x)-t_n(x)\right)\left(\overline{f(x)}-\overline{t_n(x)}\right)dx.$$

$$= \int_a^b \left[f(x)\overline{f(x)} - f(x)\overline{t_n(x)} - \overline{f(x)}t_n(x) + t_n(x)\overline{t_n(x)}\right]dx.$$

$$= \int_a^b |f(x)|^2\,dx - \int_a^b f(x)\overline{t_n(x)}\,dx - \int_a^b \overline{f(x)}t_n(x)\,dx + \int_a^b |t_n(x)|^2\,dx. \quad \text{.......... (8.3.8.1)}$$

Now, $\displaystyle\int_a^b f(x)\overline{t_n(x)}\,dx = \int_a^b f(x)\sum_{m=1}^n \overline{\gamma_m}\ \overline{\varphi_m(x)}\,dx.$

$$= \sum_{m=1}^n \overline{\gamma_m}\int_a^b f(x)\overline{\phi_m(x)}\,dx = \sum_{m=1}^n \overline{\gamma_m}\,c_m\,. \quad \text{.......... (8.3.8.2)}$$

Similarly, $\displaystyle\int_a^b \overline{f(x)}\,t_n(x)\,dx = \sum_{m=1}^n \gamma_m\overline{c_m}\ .$ .... (8.3.8.3)

$$\int_a^b |t_n(x)|^2\,dx = \int_a^b t_n(x)\overline{t_n(x)}\,dx = \int_a^b \sum_{m=1}^n \gamma_m\phi_m \sum_{k=1}^n \overline{\gamma_k}\ \overline{\phi_k(x)}\,dx.$$

$$= \sum_{m=1}^n\sum_{k=1}^n \gamma_m\overline{\gamma_k}\int_a^b \phi_m(x)\overline{\phi_k(x)}\,dx.$$

$$= \sum_{m=1}^n \gamma_m\overline{\gamma_m}.1 \text{ [Since } \{\phi_n\} \text{ is orthonormal]}$$

Therefore, $\displaystyle\int_a^b |t_n(x)|^2\,dx = \sum_{m=1}^n |\gamma_m|^2\,.$ .... (8.3.8.4)

Using (8.3.8.2), (8.3.8.3) and (8.3.8.4) in (8.3.8.1), we get

$$\int_a^b |f-t_n|^2\,dx = \int_a^b |f(x)|^2\,dx - \sum_{m=1}^n \overline{\gamma_m}\,c_m - \sum_{m=1}^n \gamma_m\overline{c_m} + \sum_{m=1}^n |\gamma_m|^2\,. \quad \text{.......... (8.3.8.5)}$$

When $\gamma_m = c_m$, we get $c_n = s_n$.

Therefore, $\int_a^b |f-s_n|^2\,dx = \int_a^b |f(x)|^2\,dx - \sum_{m=1}^{n} \overline{c_m}\,c_m - \sum_{m=1}^{n} c_m\overline{c_m} + \sum_{m=1}^{n} |c_m|^2$.

$$= \int_a^b |f(x)|^2\,dx - \sum_{m=1}^{n} |c_m|^2. \qquad \text{.......... (8.3.8.6)}$$

Subtracting (8.3.8.6) from (8.3.8.5), we get

$$\int_a^b |f-t_n|^2\,dx - \int_a^b |f-s_n|^2\,dx = -\sum_{m=1}^{n} \overline{\gamma_m}\,c_m - \sum_{m=1}^{n} \gamma_m\overline{c_m} + \sum_{m=1}^{n} |\gamma_m|^2 + \sum_{m=1}^{n} |c_m|^2.$$

$$= \sum_{m=1}^{n} \left\{ \left(\gamma_m\overline{\gamma_m} - \overline{\gamma_m}\,c_m\right) + \left(c_m\overline{c_m} - \gamma_m\overline{c_m}\right) \right\}.$$

$$= \sum_{m=1}^{n} \left[\overline{\gamma_m}(\gamma_m - c_m) - \overline{c_m}(\gamma_m - c_m) \right].$$

$$= \sum_{m=1}^{n} (\gamma_m - c_m)(\overline{\gamma_m} - \overline{c_m}) = \sum_{m=1}^{n} |\gamma_m - c_m|^2 \geq 0.$$

$$\text{.......... (8.3.8.7)}$$

Therefore, $\int_a^b |f-t_n|^2\,dx \geq \int_a^b |f-s_n|^2\,dx$.

Second part:

$$\int_a^b |f-t_n|^2\,dx = \int_a^b |f-s_n|^2\,dx \Leftrightarrow \int_a^b |f-t_n|^2\,dx - \int_a^b |f-s_n|^2\,dx = 0.$$

$$\Leftrightarrow \sum_{m=1}^{n} |\gamma_m - c_m|^2 = 0.$$

$\Leftrightarrow |\gamma_m - c_m| = 0$, for $m = 1, 2, 3, \ldots\ldots, n$.

$\Leftrightarrow \gamma_m = c_m$, for $m = 1, 2, 3, \ldots\ldots, n$.

Therefore, among all functions t_n, s_n gives the best possible mean square approximation to f.

Hence the theorem.

Note 8.3.9

From equation (8.3.8.4) of the above theorem 8.3.8, we have

$$\int_a^b |t_n(x)|^2\, dx = \sum_{m=1}^{n} |\gamma_m|^2 .$$

By Taking $\gamma_m = c_m$, we get $t_n = s_n$.

Therefore, By theorem 8.3.8, equation (8.3.8.6), we get

$$\int_a^b |s_n(x)|^2\, dx = \sum_{m=1}^{n} |c_m|^2 = \int_a^b |f(x)|^2\, dx - \int_a^b |f - s_n|^2\, dx .$$

$$\leq \int_a^b |f(x)|^2\, dx .$$

Therefore, $\int_a^b |s_n(x)|^2\, dx \leq \int_a^b |f(x)|^2\, dx$.

Theorem 8.3.10

The following inequality is known as ***Bessel's inequality.***

If $\{\phi_n\}$ is orthonormal on $[a, b]$ and if $f(x) \sim \sum_{n=1}^{\infty} c_n \phi_n(x)$, then

$$\sum_{n=1}^{\infty} |c_n|^2 \leq \int_a^b |f(x)|^2\, dx .$$

In particular, $\lim_{n\to\infty} c_n = 0$.

Proof

Given that $\{\phi_n\}$ is orthonormal on $[a, b]$ and $f(x) \sim \sum_{n=1}^{\infty} c_n \phi_n(x)$.

Let us take $s_m(x) \sim \sum_{m=1}^{n} c_m \phi_m(x)$.

Then, $\int_a^b |s_m(x)|^2 = \sum_{m=1}^{n} |c_m|^2 \leq \int_a^b |f(x)|^2\, dx$. [By note 8.3.9]

It is true for every n.

Taking limit as $n \to \infty$, we get

$$\sum_{m=1}^{\infty} |c_m|^2 \leq \int_a^b |f(x)|^2 \, dx .$$

That is, $\sum_{n=1}^{\infty} |c_n|^2 \leq \int_a^b |f(x)|^2 \, dx$.

Particular part:

$$\int_a^b |f(x)|^2 \, dx < \infty .$$

Therefore, $\sum_{n=1}^{\infty} |c_n|^2 < \infty$.

$$\Rightarrow \lim_{n \to \infty} |c_n|^2 = 0 .$$

$$\Rightarrow \lim_{n \to \infty} c_n = 0 .$$

Hence proved.

Definition 8.3.11

Let f be a periodic function with period 2π which is integrable in $[-\pi, \pi]$.

Put $c_n = \frac{1}{2\pi} \int_{-\pi}^{\pi} f(x) e^{inx} dx$. Then, $\sum_{n=-\infty}^{\infty} c_n e^{inx}$ is the Fourier series of f. The Nth partial sum is $s_N(x) = s_N(f : x) = \sum_{n=-N}^{N} c_n e^{inx}$.

Now, $\int_{-\pi}^{\pi} |s_N(x)|^2 \, dx = \sum_{n=-N}^{N} |c_n|^2 \leq \int_{-\pi}^{\pi} |f(x)|^2 \, dx$.

Therefore, $\frac{1}{2\pi} \int_{-\pi}^{\pi} |s_N(x)|^2 \, dx \leq \frac{1}{2\pi} \int_{-\pi}^{\pi} |f(x)|^2 \, dx$.

Definition 8.3.12

The Dirichlet's Kernel is defined as $D_N(x) = \sum_{n=-N}^{N} e^{inx}$.

Results 8.3.13

1) $D_N(x) = \dfrac{\sin\left(N+\dfrac{1}{2}\right)x}{\sin\dfrac{x}{2}}$.

Proof

We know that, $D_N(x) = \sum\limits_{n=-N}^{N} e^{inx}$.

$$\Rightarrow (e^{ix}-1)D_N(x) = (e^{ix}-1)\sum_{n=-N}^{N} e^{inx} = \sum_{n=-N}^{N}\left(e^{i(n+1)x} - e^{inx}\right) = e^{i(N+1)x} - e^{-iNx}$$

Hence, $e^{-ix/2}(e^{ix}-1)D_N(x) = e^{-ix/2}(e^{i(N+1)x} - e^{-iNx})$.

$$\Rightarrow (e^{ix/2} - e^{-ix/2})D_N(x) = e^{i\left(N+\frac{1}{2}\right)x} - e^{-i\left(N+\frac{1}{2}\right)x}.$$

$$\Rightarrow 2i\sin\frac{x}{2}.D_N(x) = 2i\sin\left(N+\frac{1}{2}\right)x.$$

$$\Rightarrow D_N(x) = \frac{\sin\left(N+\dfrac{1}{2}\right)x}{\sin\dfrac{x}{2}}.$$

Hence proved.

2) $\dfrac{1}{2\pi}\int\limits_{-\pi}^{\pi} D_N(x)dx = 1$.

Proof

$$\frac{1}{2\pi}\int_{-\pi}^{\pi} D_N(x)dx = \frac{1}{2\pi}\int_{-\pi}^{\pi}\sum_{n=-N}^{N} e^{inx}dx = \sum_{n=-N}^{N}\frac{1}{2\pi}\int_{-\pi}^{\pi} e^{inx}dx = 1.$$

[Since $\dfrac{1}{2\pi}\int\limits_{-\pi}^{\pi} e^{inx}dx = \begin{cases} 1, & \text{if } n=0 \\ 0, & \text{if } n=\pm 1, \pm 2, \ldots \end{cases}$].

Hence proved.

3) $s_N(f:x)=\frac{1}{2\pi}\int_{-\pi}^{\pi} f(x-t)D_N(t)dt$.

Proof

$$s_N(f:x)=\sum_{n=-N}^{N} c_n e^{inx}=\sum_{n=-N}^{N} e^{inx}\frac{1}{2\pi}\int_{-\pi}^{\pi} f(t)e^{-\text{int}}dt.$$

$$=\frac{1}{2\pi}\int_{-\pi}^{\pi} f(t)\sum_{n=-N}^{N} e^{in(x-t)}dt.$$

$$=\frac{1}{2\pi}\int_{-\pi}^{\pi} f(t)D_N(x-t)dt.$$

By taking $u = x - t$, we have $du = -dt$.

When $t=-\pi$, we have $u=x+\pi$.

When $t=\pi$, we have $u=x-\pi$.

Therefore, $s_N(f:x)=\frac{1}{2\pi}\int_{x+\pi}^{x-\pi} f(x-u)D_N(u)(-du)$.

$$=\frac{1}{2\pi}\int_{x-\pi}^{x+\pi} f(x-t)D_N(t)dt=\frac{1}{2\pi}\int_{-\pi}^{\pi} f(x-t)D_N(t)dt.$$

[Since f and D_N are periodic in the period 2π]

Hence proved.

Theorem 8.3.14

If for some x, there are constants $\delta>0$ and $M<\infty$ such that $|f(x+t)-f(x)|\le M(t)$, for all $t\in(-\delta,\delta)$, then $\lim_{N\to\infty} s_N(f:x)=f(x)$.

Proof

Define, $g(t)=\frac{f(x-t)-f(t)}{\sin(t/2)}$, $0<|t|\le\pi$.

Now, $g(0) = 0$.

Also, $\frac{1}{2\pi}\int_{-\pi}^{\pi} D_N(x)dx=1$.

Therefore, $s_N(f:x)-f(x)=\frac{1}{2\pi}\int_{-\pi}^{\pi} f(x-t)D_N(t)dt - f(x)\frac{1}{2\pi}\int_{-\pi}^{\pi} D_N(t)dt$.

[By result 8.3.13, equations (8.3.13.2) and (8.3.13.3)]

$$=\frac{1}{2\pi}\int_{-\pi}^{\pi}[f(x-t)-f(x)]D_N(t)dt.$$

$$=\frac{1}{2\pi}\int_{-\pi}^{\pi} g(t)\sin(t/2)\frac{\sin\left(N+\frac{1}{2}\right)t}{\sin(t/2)}dt.$$

[By result 8.3.13, equation (8.3.13.1)]

$$=\frac{1}{2\pi}\int_{-\pi}^{\pi} g(t)[\sin Nt.\cos(t/2)+\cos Nt.\sin(t/2)]dt.$$

$$=\frac{1}{2\pi}\int_{-\pi}^{\pi}(g(t)\cos(t/2))\sin Nt.dt+\frac{1}{2\pi}\int_{-\pi}^{\pi}(g(t)\sin(t/2))\cos Nt.dt$$

.... (8.3.14.1)

Since f is bounded in $[-\pi,\pi]$, there exists $k > 0$, such that $|f(x)|\le k$, for all $x\in[-\pi,\pi]$.

Now, $|g(t)\sin(t/2)|=|f(x-t)-f(x)|\le|f(x-t)|+|f(x)|\le k+k=2k$.

Therefore, $g(t)\sin(t/2)$ is bounded in $[-\pi,\pi]$.

By hypothesis, $|t|<\delta \Rightarrow |f(x+t)-f(x)|\le M|t|$. .... (8.3.14.2)

Hence, $|g(t)\cos(t/2)|=|g(t)||\cos(t/2)|\le|g(t)|$ [Since $|\cos(t/2)|\le 1$]

$$=\frac{|f(x-t)-f(x)|}{|\sin(t/2)|}\le\frac{M|t|}{\sin|t/2|}, \text{ if } |t|<\delta \text{ [By (8.3.14.2)]}$$

$$<\frac{2M|t/2|}{\sin|t/2|}.$$

$$<\pi M. \text{ [Since, if } 0<x<\frac{\pi}{2}, \text{ then } \frac{\sin x}{x}>2/\pi\text{]}$$

Therefore, $|g(t)\cos(t/2)|<\pi M$. .... (8.3.14.3)

If $\delta\le|t|\le\pi$, then $\delta/2\le|t|/2\le\pi/2$.

Therefore, $\sin(\delta/2) \le \sin(|t|/2)$, [Since, sin is increasing in $[\delta/2, \pi/2]$.

$$\Rightarrow \frac{1}{\sin(\delta/2)} \ge \frac{1}{\sin(|t|/2)}.$$

Hence, $|g(t)\cos(t/2)| \le |g(t)| = \left|\frac{f(x-t)-f(x)}{\sin(t/2)}\right| \le \frac{|f(x-t)|+|f(x)|}{\sin(t/2)} \le \frac{2k}{\sin(\delta/2)}$.

Also, $|g(0)\cos(0/2)| = 0$.

Therefore, $g(t).\cos(t/2)$ is bounded in $[-\pi, \pi]$.

We know that, if $\{\phi_n\}$ is orthonormal on $[a, b]$, then $\lim\limits_{n\to\infty} \int_a^b f(x)\overline{\varphi_n(x)}\, dx = 0$.

Define $\varphi_n(x) = \frac{\sin nx}{\sqrt{\pi}}$ or $\frac{\cos nx}{\sqrt{\pi}}$, $x \in [-\pi, \pi]$.

Hence, $\{\varphi_n(x)\}$ is orthonormal in $[-\pi, \pi]$.

Therefore, $\lim\limits_{N\to\infty} \int_{-\pi}^{\pi} g(t)\cos(t/2)\sin Nt.dt = 0$ and

$$\lim_{N\to\infty} \int_{-\pi}^{\pi} g(t)\sin(t/2)\cos Nt.dt = 0.$$

Substituting this in (8.3.14.1), we get

$$\lim_{N\to\infty} s_N(f:x) - f(x) = 0.$$

$$\Rightarrow \lim_{N\to\infty} s_N(f:x) = f(x).$$

Hence the theorem.

Corollary 8.3.15

If $f(x) = 0$, for all x in some segment J, then $\lim\limits_{N\to\infty} s_N(f:x) = 0$, for all $x \in J$.

Proof

Let $x \in J$.

Since J is open, there exists $\delta > 0$ such that $(x-\delta, x+\delta) < J$.

By data, $f(t) = 0$, for all $t \in J$.

Therefore, $f(t) = 0$, for all $t \in (x-\delta, x+\delta)$.

Now, for all $t \in (-\delta, \delta)$, we have $x+t \in (x-\delta, x+\delta)$.

Hence, $f(x + t) = 0$ and $f(x) = 0$.

Therefore, $|f(x+t) - f(x)| = 0 \le |t|$, for all $t \in (-\delta, \delta)$.

Hence, by the previous theorem 8.3.14, we have

$$\lim_{N\to\infty} s_N(f:x) = f(x) = 0, \text{ for all } x \in J.$$

Hence proved.

Note 8.3.16

The above corollary can be formulated in a different way. That is, if $f(t)=g(t)$, for all t, in some neighbourhood of x, then $s_N(f-g:x) = 0$ as $N \to \infty$.

Proof

This can be proved by taking $f - g$ instead of f in the corollary 8.3.15.

This is called Localization theorem.

Theorem 8.3.17

If f is continuous (with period 2π) and if $\varepsilon > 0$, then there is a trigonometric polynomial P, such that $|P(x) - f(x)| < \varepsilon$, for all real x.

Theorem 8.3.18

The following theorem is known as ***Parseval's theorem.***

Suppose f and g are R-integrable function with period 2π and

$$f(x) \sim \sum_{n=-\infty}^{\infty} c_n e^{inx}, \quad g(x) \sim \sum_{n=-\infty}^{\infty} \gamma_n e^{inx}, \text{ then}$$

$$\lim_{N\to\infty} \frac{1}{2\pi} \int_{-\pi}^{\pi} |f(x) - s_N(f:x)|^2 \, dx = 0.$$

1) $\displaystyle \frac{1}{2\pi} \int_{-\pi}^{\pi} f(x)\overline{g(x)} \, dx = \sum_{n=-\infty}^{\infty} c_n \overline{\gamma_n}$.

2) $\displaystyle \frac{1}{2\pi} \int_{-\pi}^{\pi} |f(x)|^2 \, dx = \sum_{n=-\infty}^{\infty} |c_n|^2$.

Proof

We make use of, $\|h\|_2 = \left[\frac{1}{2\pi}\int_{-\pi}^{\pi}|h(x)|^2\,dx\right]^{1/2}$.

1) To prove: $\lim_{N\to\infty}\frac{1}{2\pi}\int_{-\pi}^{\pi}|f(x)-s_N(f:x)|^2\,dx = 0$.

Let $\varepsilon > 0$ be given.

Since $f \in \mathbb{R}$ and f has period 2π, by a known result, there exists a continuous 2π -periodic function *f*, such that $\|f-h\|_2 < \varepsilon$.

.... (8.3.18.1)

By the previous theorem 8.3.14, there exists a trigonometric polynomial *P*, such that $|P(x)-h(x)| < \varepsilon$, for all real *x*.

Now, $\|h-P\|_2 = \left[\frac{1}{2\pi}\int_{-\pi}^{\pi}|h(x)-P(x)|^2\,dx\right]^{1/2} < \left[\frac{1}{2\pi}\int_{-\pi}^{\pi}\varepsilon^2 dx\right]^{1/2} = \varepsilon$.

Therefore, $\|h-P\|_2 < \varepsilon$. .... (8.3.18.2)

If *P* has degree N_0, then for all $N \geq N_0$, we have

$$\|h-s_N(h)\|_2 = \left[\frac{1}{2\pi}\int_{-\pi}^{\pi}|h(x)-s_N(h)|^2\,dx\right]^{1/2} \leq \left[\frac{1}{2\pi}\int_{-\pi}^{\pi}|h(x)-P(x)|^2\,dx\right]^{1/2}$$

$$= \|h-P\|_2 < \varepsilon.$$ [By (8.3.18.2)]

Therefore, $\|h-s_N(h)\|_2 < \varepsilon$. .... (8.3.18.3)

Now, $\|s_N(h)-s_N(f)\|_2 = \|s_N(h-f)\|_2 = \left[\frac{1}{2\pi}\int_{-\pi}^{\pi}|s_N(h-f)|^2\,dx\right]^{1/2}$

$$\leq \left[\frac{1}{2\pi}\int_{-\pi}^{\pi}|h(x)-f(x)|^2\,dx\right]^{1/2} = \|h-f\|_2 < \varepsilon.$$

[By (8.3.18.1)]

Hence, $\|s_N(h)-s_N(f)\| \leq \varepsilon$. .... (8.3.18.4)

Therefore, for all $N \geq N_0$, we have

$$\|f - s_N(f)\|_2 \leq \|f - h\|_2 + \|h - s_N(h)\|_2 + \|s_N(h) - s_N(f)\|_2$$

$< \varepsilon + \varepsilon + \varepsilon = 3\varepsilon$. [By equations (8.3.18.1), (8.3.18.3) and (8.3.18.4)]

Therefore, $\lim\limits_{N\to\infty} \|f - s_N(f)\|_2 = 0$. .... (8.3.18.5)

Hence, $\lim\limits_{N\to\infty} \left[\frac{1}{2\pi}\int_{-\pi}^{\pi} |f(x) - s_N(f)|^2\, dx\right]^{1/2} = 0$.

Therefore, $\lim\limits_{N\to\infty} \left[\frac{1}{2\pi}\int_{-\pi}^{\pi} |f(x) - s_N(f)|^2\, dx\right] = 0$.

Hence part (1) is proved.

2) To prove: $\frac{1}{2\pi}\int_{-\pi}^{\pi} f(x)\overline{g(x)}\, dx = \sum\limits_{n=-\infty}^{\infty} c_n \overline{\gamma_n}$.

$$\frac{1}{2\pi}\int_{-\pi}^{\pi} s_N(f)\overline{g(x)}\, dx = \frac{1}{2\pi}\int_{-\pi}^{\pi} \sum_{n=-N}^{N} c_n e^{inx}\overline{g(x)}\, dx.$$

$$= \sum_{n=-N}^{N} c_n \frac{1}{2\pi}\int_{-\pi}^{\pi} e^{inx}\overline{g(x)}\, dx = \sum_{n=-N}^{N} c_n \frac{1}{2\pi}\int_{-\pi}^{\pi} \overline{e^{-inx} g(x)}\, dx = \sum_{n=-N}^{N} c_n \overline{\gamma_n}.$$

Therefore, $\frac{1}{2\pi}\int_{-\pi}^{\pi} s_N(f)\overline{g(x)}\, dx = \sum\limits_{n=-N}^{N} c_n \overline{\gamma_n}$. .... (8.3.18.6)

Now, $\left|\int_{-\pi}^{\pi} f(x)\overline{g(x)}\, dx - \int_{-\pi}^{\pi} s_N(f)\overline{g(x)}\, dx\right|$

$$= \left|\int_{-\pi}^{\pi} (f(x) - s_N(f))\overline{g(x)}\, dx\right| \leq \|f(x) - s_N(f)\|_2 \|\overline{g}\|_2.$$

[Since, by Schwarz inequality]

By using equation (8.3.18.5), we get

$$\lim_{N\to\infty}\left|\int_{-\pi}^{\pi} f(x)\overline{g(x)}\, dx - \int_{-\pi}^{\pi} s_N(f)\overline{g(x)}\, dx\right| = 0.$$

$$\Rightarrow \lim_{N\to\infty} \int_{-\pi}^{\pi} f(x)\overline{g(x)}\,dx = \lim_{N\to\infty} \int_{-\pi}^{\pi} s_N(f)\overline{g(x)}\,dx.$$

$$\Rightarrow \lim_{N\to\infty} \frac{1}{2\pi} \int_{-\pi}^{\pi} f(x)\overline{g(x)}\,dx = \lim_{N\to\infty} \frac{1}{2\pi} \int_{-\pi}^{\pi} s_N(f)\overline{g(x)}\,dx.$$

$$\Rightarrow \frac{1}{2\pi} \int_{-\pi}^{\pi} f(x)\overline{g(x)}\,dx = \lim_{N\to\infty} \sum_{n=-N}^{N} c_n \overline{\gamma_n} = \sum_{n=-\infty}^{\infty} c_n \overline{\gamma_n}.$$

Hence, part (2) is proved.

3) To prove: $\frac{1}{2\pi} \int_{-\pi}^{\pi} |f(x)|^2\,dx = \sum_{n=-\infty}^{\infty} |c_n|^2$.

By part (2), we have

$$\frac{1}{2\pi} \int_{-\pi}^{\pi} f(x)\overline{g(x)}\,dx = \sum_{n=-\infty}^{\infty} c_n \overline{\gamma_n}.$$

By taking $g = f$, we get

$$\frac{1}{2\pi} \int_{-\pi}^{\pi} f(x)\overline{f(x)}\,dx = \sum_{n=-\infty}^{\infty} c_n \overline{c_n}.$$

$$\Rightarrow \frac{1}{2\pi} \int_{-\pi}^{\pi} |f(x)|^2\,dx = \sum_{n=-\infty}^{\infty} |c_n|^2.$$

Hence, part (3) is proved.

Hence the theorem.

Theorem 8.3.19

Suppose the series $\sum a_n x^n$ and $\sum b_n x^n$ converge in the segment $S = (-R, R)$. Let E be the set of all $x \in S$ at which $\sum_{n=0}^{\infty} a_n x^n = \sum_{n=0}^{\infty} b_n x^n$. If E has a limit point in S, then $a_n = b_n$, for $n = 0, 1, 2, \ldots..$ and $E = S$.

Proof

Let us assume that $c_n = a_n - b_n$ and $f(x) = \sum_{n=0}^{\infty} c_n x^n, \quad x \in S$.

Therefore, $f(x) = 0$ in E.

Let A be the set of all limit points of E in S.

By hypothesis, E has a limit point in S.

Hence, $A \neq \varphi$.

Now, $A = E'$ is closed in S.

Therefore, $B = S - A$ is open in S.

Claim: A is open in S.

Let $x_0 \in A$. That implies, $x_0 \in S$.

Let $|x_0| < R$.

Therefore, by Taylor's theorem, we have

$$f(x) = \sum_{n=0}^{\infty} d_n (x - x_0)^n , \qquad \text{.......... (8.3.19.1)}$$

where $|x - x_0| < R - |x_0|$.

i) Now, we have to prove that, for all n, $d_n = 0$.

Suppose $d_n \neq 0$. Then, let k be the smallest positive integer such that $d_k \neq 0$.

Therefore, $f(x) = d_k (x - x_0)^k + d_{k+1}(x - x_0)^{k+1} + ...$

$$= (x - x_0)^k \left[d_k + d_{k+1}(x - x_0) + ... \right] = (x - x_0)^k g(x) ,$$

.... (8.3.19.2)

where $g(x) = d_k + d_{k+1}(x - x_0) + ... = \sum_{m=0}^{\infty} d_{k+m}(x - x_0)^m$.

Now, g is continuous at x_0 and $g(x_0) = d_k \neq 0$ and $\left| \frac{d_k}{2} \right| > 0$.

Therefore, there exists $\delta > 0$, such that $|x - x_0| < \delta \Rightarrow |g(x) - g(x_0)| < \frac{|d_k|}{2}$.

That implies, $|g(x_0)| - |g(x)| \leq |g(x) - g(x_0)|$.

That is, $|d_k| - |g(x)| < \frac{|d_k|}{2}$.

That implies, $|g(x)| > \frac{|d_k|}{2}$.

By equation (8.3.19.2), we have $f(x) \neq 0$ in $0 < |x - x_0| < \delta$.

Therefore, $N_{\delta}(x_0) \cap E - \{x_0\} = \varphi$.

That implies, x_0 is not a limit point of E.

Hence, x_0 does not belong to A, which is a contradiction.

Therefore, for all n, $d_n = 0$.

That implies, $f(x) = \sum_{n=0}^{\infty} d_n (x - x_0)^n = 0, \qquad |x - x_0| < R - |x_0|$.

Therefore, $f(x) = 0$ in $N_{R-|x_0|}(x_0)$.

ii) We have to prove that, $N_{R-|x_0|}(x_0) \subset A$.

Let $y \in N_{R-|x_0|}(x_0)$.

Since $N_{R-|x_0|}(x_0)$ is open, there exists $\delta > 0$ such that $N_{\delta_1}(y) \subset N_{R-|x_0|}(x_0)$.

Let $N_{\delta_2}(y)$ be any neighbourhood of y.

Let us assume that, $\delta_3 = \min.(\delta_1, \delta_2)$.

Therefore, $N_{\delta_3}(y) \subset N_{\delta_1}(y) \subset N_{R-|x_0|}(x_0) \subset E$, which implies $N_{\delta_3}(y) \cap E \neq \varphi$.

Hence, y is a limit point of E.

Therefore, $y \in E$.

That implies, $N_{R-|x_0|}(x_0) \subset A$.

Hence, A is open, which proves our claim.

Now, $S = A \cup B$ and S is connected.

Again, $A \neq 0$, and A and B are open is S.

That implies, $B = \phi$ and therefore, $S = A$.

Claim: $A \subset E$.

Let $y \in A$.

Therefore, y is a limit point of E in S.

Hence, there is a sequence $\{y_n\}$ in E, such that $y_n \to y$.

Since $y_n \in E$, $f(y_n) = 0$, for all n.

Now, since f is continuous, $y_n \to y$ implies $f(y_n) \to f(y)$.

Therefore, $f(y) = 0$ which implies $y \in E$.

That implies, $A \subset E$.

Since, $A = S$, $S \subset E$.

By definition, $E \subset S$.

Hence, $S = E$.

Therefore, $\sum a_n x^n = \sum b_n x^n$, for all $x \in S$.

That is, $a_n = b_n$, for all $n = 1, 2, 3, ...$

Hence the theorem.

8.4 Gamma Function

Definition 8.4.1

For $0 < x < \infty$, the gamma function is defined as $\Gamma(x) = \int_0^\infty t^{x-1} e^{-t} dt$.

Definition 8.4.2

A real valued function *f* defined on (*a*, *b*) is said to be convex, if $f(\lambda x + (1-\lambda) y) \le \lambda f(x) + (1-\lambda) f(y)$, for all $x, y \in (a,b)$ and $0 < \lambda < 1$.

Theorem 8.4.3

i) $\Gamma(x+1) = x\Gamma x, \quad 0 < x < \infty$

ii) $\Gamma(n+1) = n!, \quad n = 1, 2, 3, ...$

iii) $\log \Gamma$ is convex on $(0, \infty)$.

Proof

i) $\Gamma(x+1) = \int_0^\infty t^x e^{-t} dt$.

Now, by assuming, $u = t^x$ and $dv = e^{-t} dt$, we get

$$du = xt^{x-1} dt \quad \text{and} \quad v = -e^{-t}.$$

Therefore, $\Gamma(x+1) = \left[-e^{-t} t^x\right]_0^\infty + \int_0^\infty e^{-t} x t^{x-1} dt = 0 + x \int_0^\infty t^{x-1} e^{-t} dt = x\Gamma x$.

Hence the first part.

ii) By part (i), we have

$$\Gamma(n+1)=n\Gamma n=n(n-1)\Gamma(n-1)=n(n-1)(n-2)........1\Gamma(1)\,. \quad .... (8.4.3.1)$$

$$\Gamma(1)=\int_0^\infty e^{-t}dt=1.$$

Therefore, equation (8.4.3.1) becomes, $\Gamma(n+1)=n(n-1)(n-2)..........2.1=n!$

Hence part (ii) is proved.

iii) To prove that, $\log\Gamma$ is convex on $(0,\infty)$.

Let $x,y\in(0,\infty)$, $\quad 0<\lambda<1$.

To prove that, $\log\Gamma\big(\lambda x+(1-\lambda)y\big)\le\lambda\log\Gamma x+(1-\lambda)\log\Gamma y$.

Since $0<\lambda<1$, we have $\infty>\dfrac{1}{\lambda}>1$.

Now, let $p=\dfrac{1}{\lambda}$, which implies $\dfrac{1}{p}=\lambda$ and $\dfrac{1}{q}=1-\lambda$.

Hence, $\dfrac{1}{p}+\dfrac{1}{q}=1$.

Now, $$\Gamma\left(\frac{x}{p}+\frac{y}{q}\right)=\int_0^\infty t^{\frac{x}{p}+\frac{y}{q}-1}e^{-t}dt$$

$$=\int_0^\infty t^{\frac{x}{p}+\frac{y}{q}-\left(\frac{1}{p}+\frac{1}{q}\right)}e^{-t\left(\frac{1}{p}+\frac{1}{q}\right)}dt=\int_0^\infty\left(t^{\frac{1}{p}(x-1)}e^{-\frac{1}{p}t}\right)\left(t^{\frac{1}{q}(y-1)}e^{-\frac{1}{q}t}\right)dt.$$

$$\le\left(\int_0^\infty\left(t^{\frac{1}{p}(x-1)}e^{-\frac{1}{p}t}\right)^p dt\right)^{\frac{1}{p}}\left(\int_0^\infty\left(t^{\frac{1}{q}(y-1)}e^{-\frac{1}{q}t}\right)^q dt\right)^{\frac{1}{q}}.$$

$$\le\left(\int_0^\infty t^{x-1}e^{-t}dt\right)^{\frac{1}{p}}\left(\int_0^\infty t^{y-1}e^{-t}dt\right)^{\frac{1}{q}}=(\Gamma x)^{\frac{1}{p}}(\Gamma y)^{\frac{1}{q}}.$$

Taking log on both sides, we get

$$\log\left\{\Gamma\left(\frac{x}{p}+\frac{y}{q}\right)\right\}\le\frac{1}{p}\log\Gamma x+\frac{1}{q}\log\Gamma y.$$

That implies, $\log\{\Gamma(\lambda x+(1-\lambda)y)\}\le \lambda\log\Gamma x+(1-\lambda)\log\Gamma y$.

Therefore, $\log\Gamma x$ is convex.

Hence part (iii) is proved.

Hence the theorem.

Theorem 8.4.4

Let f be a positive function defined on $(0,\infty)$ and

i) $f(x+1)=xf(x)$,

ii) $f(1)=1$,

iii) $\log f$ is convex, then $f(x)=\Gamma x$ on $(0,\infty)$.

Proof

Since $\Gamma(x+1)=x\Gamma x, \quad \Gamma 1=1$.

Now, $\log\Gamma$ is convex and satisfies all the three given conditions.

In order to prove the theorem, it is enough if we prove that all the three given conditions determine a unique function.

Let $\varphi=\log f$ on $(0,\infty)$.

Now, $\varphi(x+1)=\log f(x+1)=\log xf(x)=\log x+\log f(x)$.

That is, $\varphi(x+1)=\log x+\varphi(x)$. .... (8.4.4.1)

Let n be a positive integer.

Hence, $\varphi(n+1)=\log n+\varphi(n)$.

Therefore, by equation (8.4.4.1), we have

$$\varphi(n+1)=\log n+\log(n-1)+\varphi(n)=\log n+\log(n-1)+\ldots\ldots$$
$$\ldots\ldots+\varphi(1)=\log(1.2\ldots\ldots n)+\log f(1).$$

Now, by part (ii) of the statement of the theorem, we have

$$\varphi(n+1)=\log n!+\log 1=\log n!. \qquad \ldots\ldots\ldots\ (8.4.4.2)$$

Let n be a positive integer and $0<x<1$.

We claim that, $\log n\le \dfrac{\varphi(n+1+x)-\varphi(n+1)}{x}\le \log(n+1)$.

Now, $\varphi(n+1)=\varphi\left[\dfrac{(1+x)(n+1)}{(1+x)}\right]=\varphi\left[\dfrac{n+1+x}{1+x}+\dfrac{x}{1+x}n\right]$.

Let us assume that, $\lambda = \frac{1}{1+x}$.

Then, $1-\lambda = \frac{x}{1+x}$.

Since ϕ is convex, $\varphi(n+1) \le \frac{1}{1+x}\varphi(n+1+x) + \frac{x}{1+x}\varphi(n)$.

That implies, $\varphi(n+1) + x\varphi(n+1) \le \varphi(n+1+x) + x\varphi(n)$.

That is, $x[\varphi(n+1) - \varphi(n)] \le \varphi(n+1+x) - \varphi(n+1)$.

Now, by equation (8.4.4.2), we have

$$x\log\left[\frac{n!}{(n-1)!}\right] \le \varphi(n+1+x) - \varphi(n+1).$$

That implies,

$$\log n \le \frac{\varphi(n+1+x) - \varphi(n+1)}{x}.$$

Similarly, we can prove that, $\frac{\varphi(n+1+x) - \varphi(n+1)}{x} \le \log(n+1)$.

Hence, we have $\log n \le \frac{\varphi(n+1+x) - \varphi(n+1)}{x} \le \log(n+1)$. .... (8.4.4.3)

Therefore, our claim is proved.

Now, from equation (8.4.4.1), we have

$$\varphi(n+1+x) = \log(n+x) + \varphi(n+x) = \log\big((n-1)+x\big) + \varphi\big((n-1)+x\big).$$

$$= \log(n+x) + \log\big((n-1)+x\big) + \ldots\ldots + \log(1+x) + \log x + \varphi(x).$$

That is, $\varphi(n+1+x) = \log[x(1+x)\ldots\ldots(n+x)] + \varphi(x)$. .... (8.4.4.4)

Again from equation (8.4.4.3), we get

$$x\log n \le \varphi(n+1+x) - \varphi(n+1) \le x\log(n+1).$$ .... (8.4.4.5)

That is, $0 \le \varphi(n+1+x) - \varphi(n+1) - x\log n \le x\log(n+1) - x\log n = x\log\left(1+\frac{1}{n}\right)$.

.... (8.4.4.6)

From equations (8.4.4.2) and (8.4.4.4), we get

$$0 \le \varphi(n+1+x) - \varphi(n+1) - x\log n = \log[x(1+x)\ldots\ldots(n+x)] + \varphi(x) - \log n! - \log n^x.$$

$$= \varphi(x) - \log\left(\frac{n!n^x}{x(1+x)......(n+x)}\right).$$

$$\leq x\log\left(1+\frac{1}{n}\right).$$

Now, $\lim_{n\to\infty} x\log\left(1+\frac{1}{n}\right) = 0$.

Therefore, $\lim_{n\to\infty}\left\{\varphi(x) - \log\left(\frac{n!n^x}{x(1+x)......(n+x)}\right)\right\} = 0$.

That is, $\varphi(x) = \lim_{n\to\infty} \log\left(\frac{n!n^x}{x(1+x).....(n+x)}\right)$. .... (8.4.4.7)

Since the limit of a convergent sequence is unique, $\phi(x)$ is uniquely determined.

That is, log $f(x)$ is uniquely determined.

That implies, $f(x)$ is uniquely determined by conditions (i), (ii) and (iii).

Therefore, $f(x) = \Gamma(x)$, $\quad 0 < x < \infty$.

Hence proved.

Note 8.4.5

Now, from equation (8.4.4.7) of the above theorem (8.4.4), we have

$$\emptyset(x) = \lim_{n\to\infty} log\left(\frac{n!n^x}{x(1+x)......(n+x)}\right).$$

That implies, $log\Gamma(x) = \lim_{n\to\infty} log\left(\frac{n!n^x}{x(1+x).......(n+x)}\right)$.

Therefore, $\Gamma(x) = \lim_{n\to\infty}\left(\frac{n!n^x}{x(x+1).......(x+n)}\right)$.

Definition 8.4.6

For each $x > 0$ and $y > 0$, we define the Beta function as

$$\beta(x,y) = \int_0^1 t^{x-1}(1-t)^{y-1}dt.$$

Theorem 8.4.7

$\beta(x,y) = \frac{\Gamma(x)\Gamma(y)}{\Gamma(x+y)}$.

Proof

First, let us prove that, $\beta(1, y) = \frac{1}{y}$.

Now, $\beta(x, y) = \int_0^1 t^{x-1}(1-t)^{y-1}dt$ implies

$$\beta(1, y) = \int_0^1 (1-t)^{y-1}dt = \frac{1}{y}.$$

Hence, the first claim is proved.

Second, we prove that, $\beta(x+1, y) = \frac{x}{x+y}\beta(x, y)$.

Now, $\beta(x+1, y) = \int_0^1 t^x(1-t)^{y-1}dt = \int_0^1 \frac{t^x}{(1-t)^x}(1-t)^{x+y-1}dt.$

Let us assume that, $u = \left(\frac{t}{1-t}\right)^x$ and $dv = (1-t)^{x+y-1}dt$.

That implies, $du = \frac{xt^{x-1}}{(1-t)^{x+1}}dt$ and $v = -\frac{(1-t)^{x+y}}{x+y}$.

Therefore,

$$\int_0^1 t^x(1-t)^{y-1}dt = \left[-\left(\frac{t}{1-t}\right)^x \frac{(1-t)^{x+y}}{x+y}\right]_0^1 + \int_0^1 \frac{(1-t)^{x+y}}{x+y}\frac{xt^{x-1}}{(1-t)^{x+1}}dt.$$

$$= \frac{x}{x+y}\int_0^1 t^{x-1}(1-t)^{y-1}dt = \frac{x}{x+y}\beta(x, y).$$

Hence, the second claim is proved.

Third, we prove that, for each y, $log\beta(x, y)$ is a convex function.

Let $(x_1, x_2) \in (0, \infty), 0 < \lambda < 1$.

We have to prove that,

$$log\beta(\lambda x_1 + (1-\lambda)x_2, y) \leq \lambda log\beta(x_1, y) + (1-\lambda)log\beta(x_2, y).$$

Let $\frac{1}{p} = \lambda, 1 < p < \infty$ and $\frac{1}{q} = 1 - \lambda$.

Therefore, $\frac{1}{p} + \frac{1}{q} = 1$.

Now, $\beta\left(\frac{x_1}{p} + \frac{x_2}{p}, y\right) = \int_0^1 t^{\frac{x_1}{p}+\frac{x_2}{q}-1}(1-t)^{y-1}dt.$

$$= \int_0^1 t^{\frac{x_1}{p}+\frac{x_2}{q}-\left(\frac{1}{p}+\frac{1}{q}\right)}(1-t)^{y\left(\frac{1}{p}+\frac{1}{q}\right)-\left(\frac{1}{p}+\frac{1}{q}\right)}dt.$$

$$= \int_0^1 \left[t^{\frac{1}{p}(x_1-1)}(1-t)^{\frac{1}{p}(y-1)}\right]\left[t^{\frac{1}{q}(x_2-1)}(1-t)^{\frac{1}{q}(y-1)}\right]dt.$$

Hence, by Holder's inequality, we have

$$\beta\left(\frac{x_1}{p}+\frac{x_2}{p},y\right) \le \left\{\int_0^1\left[t^{\frac{1}{p}(x_1-1)}(1-t)^{\frac{1}{p}(y-1)}\right]^p dt\right\}^{\frac{1}{p}}$$

$$\left\{\int_0^1\left[t^{\frac{1}{q}(x_2-1)}(1-t)^{\frac{1}{q}(y-1)}\right]^q dt\right\}^{\frac{1}{q}}.$$

$$= \left[\int_0^1 t^{x_1-1}(1-t)^{y-1}dt\right]\left[\int_0^1 t^{x_2-1}(1-t)^{y-1}dt\right]$$

$$= [\beta(x_1,y)]^{\lambda}[\beta(x_2,y)]^{1-\lambda}.$$

Therefore,

$$log\beta(\lambda x_1+(1-\lambda)x_2,y) \le \lambda log\beta(x_1,y)+(1-\lambda)log\beta(x_2,y).$$

Hence, for each y, $log\beta$ is a convex function.

Define $f(x) = \frac{\beta(x,y)\Gamma(x+y)}{\Gamma(y)}$.

We have to prove that, $f(x) = \Gamma(x)$on $(0,\infty)$.

In order to prove this, it is enough to prove,

i) $f(x+1) = xf(x)$,

ii) $f(1) = 1$,

iii) $\log f$ is convex.

i) $f(x+1) = \frac{\beta(x+1,y)\Gamma(x+y+1)}{\Gamma(y)} = \frac{\frac{x}{x+y}\beta(x,y).(x+y)\Gamma(x+y)}{\Gamma(y)} = xf(x).$

ii) $f(1) = \frac{\beta(1,y)\Gamma(1+y)}{\Gamma(y)} = 1.$

iii) *To prove*: $\log f$ is convex.

We know that,

$$logf = log\beta(x,y) + log\Gamma(x+y) - log\Gamma(y).$$

Let $x_1, x_2 \in (0,\infty), 0<\lambda<1$.

We have to prove that,

$$logf(\lambda x_1+(1-\lambda)x_2) \le \lambda logf(x_1)+(1-\lambda)logf(x_2).$$

That is, to prove that,

$$logf(\lambda x_1+(1-\lambda)x_2) \le \lambda[log\beta(x_1,y)+log\Gamma(x_1+y)-log\Gamma(y)]$$
$$+(1-\lambda)[log\beta(x_2,y)+log\Gamma(x_2+y)-log\Gamma(y)].$$

Now,

$$logf(\lambda x_1+(1-\lambda)x_2) \le log\beta(\lambda x_1+(1-\lambda)x_2,y)$$
$$+ log\Gamma(\lambda x_1+(1-\lambda)x_2+y) - log\Gamma(y)].$$

$$\leq \lambda log\beta(x_1, y) + (1-\lambda)log\beta(x_2, y)$$
$$+\lambda log\Gamma(x_1 + y) + (1-\lambda)log\Gamma(x_2 + y) - log\Gamma(y).$$

[Since $log\beta$ and $log\Gamma$ are convex.]

$$= \lambda\{log\beta(x_1, y) + log\Gamma(x_1 + y) - log\Gamma(y)\}$$
$$+(1-\lambda)\{log\beta(x_2, y) + log\Gamma(x_2 + y) - log\Gamma(y)\}.$$

Therefore, $\log f$ is convex.

Hence, $f(x) = \Gamma(x)$.

That is, $\Gamma(x) = \frac{\beta(x,y)\Gamma(x+y)}{\Gamma(y)}$.

That implies, $\beta(x, y) = \frac{\Gamma(x)\Gamma(y)}{\Gamma(x+y)}$.

Hence the theorem.

Note 8.4.8

Properties of β and Γ

1. To prove: $\beta(x, y) = 2\int_0^{\pi/2} sin^{2x-1}\theta. cos^{2y-1}\theta d\theta.$

Proof

We know that, $\beta(x, y) = \int_0^1 t^{x-1}(1-t)^{y-1}dt.$ .... (8.4.8.1)

Let us take $t = sin^2\theta$ and hence $1 - t = cos^2\theta.$

That implies, $dt = 2sin\theta cos\theta d\theta.$

When $t = 0, \theta = 0.$

When $t = 1, \theta = \pi/2.$

Therefore, substituting in equation (8.4.8.1), we get

$$\beta(x, y) = 2\int_0^{\pi/2} sin^{2x-1}\theta. cos^{2y-1}\theta d\theta. \qquad \text{.......... (8.4.8.2)}$$

Hence proved.

2. To prove: $\Gamma(1/2) = \sqrt{\pi}.$

Proof

Taking $x = 1/2$ *and* $y = 1/2$ in the above equation (8.4.8.2), we get

$$\beta(1/2, 1/2) = 2\int_0^{\pi/2} sin^0\theta. cos^0\theta d\theta = \pi.$$

Now, by making use of the theorem 8.4.7, we get

$$\frac{\Gamma(1/2)\Gamma(1/2)}{\Gamma(1/2+1/2)} = \pi.$$

That implies, $[\Gamma(1/2)]^2 = \pi$.

That is, $\Gamma(1/2) = \sqrt{\pi}$.

Hence proved.

3. To prove: $\int_{-\infty}^{+\infty} e^{-y^2} dy = \Gamma(1/2)$.

Proof

We know that, $\Gamma(x) = \int_0^\infty t^{x-1}e^{-t}dt$.

Let us take, $t = y^2$, which implies $dt = 2ydy$.

When $t = 0$, then $y = 0$.

When $t = \infty$, then $y = \infty$.

Therefore, $\Gamma(x) = \int_0^\infty (y^2)^{x-1}e^{-y^2}2ydy = 2\int_0^\infty y^{2x-1}e^{-y^2}dy$.

By taking $x = 1/2$ in the above equation, we get

$$\Gamma(1/2) = 2\int_0^\infty y^0 e^{-y^2}dy = \int_{-\infty}^\infty e^{-y^2}dy.$$

Hence proved.

Theorem 8.4.9

The following formula is known as ***Stirling's Formula***.

This provides a simple approximate expression for $\Gamma(x+1)$, then x is large.

The *Stirling's formula* is given by

$$\lim_{x\to\infty}\left\{\frac{\Gamma(x+1)}{\left(\frac{x}{e}\right)^x\sqrt{2\pi x}}\right\} = 1.$$

Proof

We know that, $\Gamma(x+1) = \int_0^\infty t^x e^{-t}dt$.

Let us take, $t = (1+u)x$.

That is, $u = \frac{t-x}{x}$, which implies $du = \frac{1}{x}dt$.

When $t = 0$, then $u = -1$.

When $t = \infty$, then $u = \infty$.

Therefore,

$$\Gamma(x+1) = \int_{-1}^{\infty}(1+u)^x x^x e^{-(1+u)x} x\,du = x^{x+1}e^{-x}\int_{-1}^{\infty}\left((1+u)e^{-u}\right)^x du. \qquad \text{.......... (8.4.9.1)}$$

When $-1 < u < \infty$, then $u \neq 0$ defines a function $h(u)$ as

$$(1+u)e^{-u} = e^{-\frac{u^2}{2}h(u)}. \qquad \text{.......... (8.4.9.2)}$$

Now, $h(0) = 1$.

Taking log on both sides of equation (8.4.9.2), we get

$$\log(1+u) - u = -\frac{u^2}{2}h(u).$$

That implies, $h(u) = \frac{2}{u^2}[u - log(1+u)]$. .... (8.4.9.3)

It follows that h is continuous and that $h(u)$ decreases monotonically from ∞ to 0, as u increases from -1 to ∞.

Let us take $u = s\sqrt{2/x}$ in equation (8.4.9.1), then $du = \sqrt{\frac{2}{x}}ds$.

When $u = -1$, then $s = -\sqrt{\frac{x}{2}}$.

When $u = \infty$, then $s = \infty$.

Therefore, $\Gamma(x+1) = x^{x+1}e^{-x}\int_{-\sqrt{\frac{x}{2}}}^{\infty}\left[e^{-\frac{s^2\frac{2}{x}}{2}h\left(s\sqrt{\frac{2}{x}}\right)}\right]^x\sqrt{\frac{2}{x}}ds.$

$$= x^{x+1}e^{-x}\sqrt{\frac{2}{x}}\int_{-\sqrt{\frac{x}{2}}}^{\infty}e^{-s^2h\left(s\sqrt{\frac{2}{x}}\right)}ds = x^x e^{-x}\sqrt{2x}\int_{-\infty}^{\infty}\Psi_x(s)ds.$$

.... (8.4.9.4)

where $\Psi_x(s) = \begin{cases} e^{-s^2h\left(s\sqrt{\frac{2}{x}}\right)}, if \sqrt{-\frac{x}{2}} < s < \infty \\ 0, if\ s \leq -\sqrt{\frac{x}{2}} \end{cases}$

We have to note the following facts about $\Psi_x(s)$;

i) For every s, $\Psi_x(s) \to e^{-s^2}$, as $x \to \infty$,

ii) The convergence in (i) is uniform on [-A, A] for every $A < \infty$,

iii) When $s < 0, 0 < \Psi_x(s) < e^{-s^2}$,

iv) When $s > 0$ and $x > 1, 0 < \Psi_x(s) < \Psi_1(s)$,

v) $\int_0^{\infty} \Psi_1(s)ds < \infty$.

By convergence theorem, the integral in equation (8.4.9.4) converges to $\sqrt{\pi}$ as $x \to \infty$.

Therefore, equation (8.4.9.4) becomes,

$$\lim_{x\to\infty} \Gamma(x+1) = \lim_{x\to\infty} \left(\frac{x}{e}\right)^x \sqrt{2\pi x}.$$

That is, $\lim_{x\to\infty} \left\{\frac{\Gamma(x+1)}{\left(\frac{x}{e}\right)^x \sqrt{2\pi x}}\right\} = 1.$

Hence proved.

R

REFERENCES

- Anthony W. Knapp, Basic Real Analysis, 2005, Springer, USA.
- Asuman G. Aksoy and Mohamed A. Khamsi, A Problem Book in Real Analysis, 2010, Springer, USA.
- Choudhary B, Sudarshannanda, Functional Analysis with applications, 1989, New Age publishers.
- Ethan D. Bloch, The Real Numbers and Real Analysis, 2011, Springer, USA.
- Karunakaran V, Real Analysis, 2011, Pearson Education, India.
- Kenneth A. Ross, Elementary Analysis, The theory of Calculus, Second Edition, 2013, Springer, USA.
- Knopp K, Theory and Application of Infinite Series, 1990, Dover Books on Mathematics.
- Kosaku Yosida, Functional Analysis, 2008, Springer, USA.
- Marat V. Markin, Elementary Functional Analysis, 2018, De Gruyter Textbook.
- Mariano Giaquinta and Giuseppe Modica, Mathematical Analysis: Linear and Metric structures and Continuity, 2007, Springer, USA.
- Mathew A. Pons, Real Analysis for the Undergraduate, with an invitation to Functional Analysis, 2014, Springer, USA.
- Miklos Laczkovich and Vera T. Sos, Real Analysis: Foundations and Functions of one variable, 2015, Springer, USA.
- Rajnikanth Sinha, Real and Complex Analysis, vol. 2, 2018, Springer, USA.
- Robert G Bartle and Donald R Sherbert, Introduction to Real Analysis, Fourth edition, 2014, John Wiley and Sons.
- Royden HL, Real Analysis, 1968, Macmillan Publishing, USA.
- Sudhir R. Ghorpade and Balmohan V. Limaye, A Course in Calculus and Real Analysis, 2006, Springer, USA.

- Teodora – Liliana T. Radulescu, Vicentu D. Radulescu and Titu Andreescu, Problems in Real Analysis: Advanced Calculus on the Real Axis, 2009, Springer, USA.
- Walter Rudin, Principles of Mathematical Analysis, Third Edition, 1976, McGraw – Hill, Inc.

■